Dictionary of

This book is dedicated
to the memory of
R. G. White

Dictionary of Immunology

Edited by

W. J. HERBERT
PhD, MRCVS, DVTM

P. C. WILKINSON
MD, FRSE
*Professor, Department of
Bacteriology and Immunology,
University of Glasgow*

D. I. STOTT
BSc, PhD
*Lecturer, Department of
Bacteriology and Immunology,
University of Glasgow*

THIRD EDITION

BLACKWELL
SCIENTIFIC PUBLICATIONS
OXFORD LONDON EDINBURGH
BOSTON PALO ALTO MELBOURNE

© 1971, 1977, 1985 by
Blackwell Scientific Publications
Editorial offices:
Osney Mead, Oxford, OX2 OEL
8 John Street, London, WC1N 2ES
23 Ainslie Place, Edinburgh,
  EH3 6AJ
52 Beacon Street, Boston
  Massachusetts 02108, USA
667 Lytton Avenue, Palo Alto
  California 94301, USA
107 Barry Street, Carlton
  Victoria 3053, Australia

First published 1971
Reprinted 1972
Second Edition 1977
Third Edition 1985
Spanish Edition 1974
Japanese Edition 1975
Second Japanese Edition 1979
German Edition 1980

Set, printed and bound in
Great Britain by
The Alden Press, Oxford

DISTRIBUTORS

USA
  Blackwell Mosby Book
  Distributors
  11830 Westline Industrial Drive
  St. Louis, Missouri 63141

Canada
  Blackwell Mosby Book
  Distributors
  120 Melford Drive, Scarborough
  Ontario M1B 2X4

Australia
  Blackwell Scientific Publications
  (Australia) Pty Ltd
  107 Barry Street, Carlton,
  Victoria 3053

British Library
Cataloguing in Publication Data

Dictionary of immunology.—3rd ed.
  1. Immunology—Dictionaries
  I. Herbert, W.J.   II. Wilkinson, P.C.
  III. Stott, D.I.
  574.2'9'0321   QR180.4

  ISBN 0–632–00984–5

Contributors

Heather M. Dick R. G. Sutcliffe
W. J. Herbert K. Whaley
A. McI Mowat P. C. Wilkinson
D. I. Stott

The following also assisted

I. Aitken D. N. H. Hamilton
S. Alcock E. E. E. Jarrett
J. H. Brock J. R. Kusel
M. Browning Ann Lackie
G. B. Clements I. C. McKay
W. Cushley Rona M. McKie
Serene Foster D. Parratt

We also thank contributors to the previous editions whose names are listed in those editions.

Preface to the Third Edition

The Third Edition contains about 300 new entries, many in the rapidly developing fields of cellular immunology and immunogenetics. About 100 entries have been deleted and many of the existing entries have been revised.

WJH, PCW, DIS

Preface to the Second Edition

This edition contains 230 new entries, and many of the existing entries have been extensively revised and some new tables added. To contain this expansion, over one hundred of the original definitions have been deleted, either because they were obsolete or because the authors felt that they had now entered the corpus of general biological knowledge and were only marginally immunological.

WJH, PCW

Preface

The easiest dictionaries to write are dictionaries of dead languages. Living languages develop and change so that the meaning of words often becomes the subject of furious debate. Since this is undoubtedly true for immunology, it is with considerable trepidation that we offer this Dictionary to the reader. Concepts in immunology have, in recent years, undergone and continue to undergo radical changes, such that the terminology of the science is, and must remain, fluid and adaptable. But this fluidity presents great difficulty, not only to the beginner in the science and to the expert in a related subject, but even to the established immunologist whose experience lies chiefly within a specialized field.

Our aim, therefore, in compiling this Dictionary, has been to include a range of terms wide enough to satisfy the needs of any biologist, clinician or biochemist who requires easy reference to current immunological usage. The idea of the Dictionary originated from the need for a glossary for use in undergraduate teaching. We have, therefore, tried to ensure that the definitions can all be understood by anyone with a minimum background of biological knowledge. Extensive cross-referencing has been employed both to expand individual definitions and to enable a chosen theme to be followed through the book. We should like to emphasize that the definitions given are not intended to reflect our personal views as to how the terms *should* be used but, rather, to tell the reader how they *have been* used in the literature.

We have drawn on the expertise of a number of collaborators from different disciplines for help in compiling the Dictionary. We thank those listed on p.v most profoundly for the definitions that they provided and the revision and checking of entries which they carried out. We are also grateful to many other colleagues in this and other Universities, for their criticisms and suggestions at all stages of the work. However, we as editors, take full responsibility for the final form of each entry.

Finally, we invite readers who spot any mistakes or major omissions to use the tear-out page at the end of the book to let us know about them.

WJH, PCW

Acknowledgements

We are very grateful to the following who filled in the tear-out sheet or sent us letters with corrections, amendments, suggestions or complete definitions.

M. Abo-Shehada (Bangor)
Y. Arai (Japan)
D. A. Basketter (Bedfordshire)
R. B. Burns (Edinburgh)
M. K. Erickson (Illinois)
A. J. Herbert (Suffolk)
W. Hijmans (The Netherlands)
S. N. Jenkins (Leicestershire)
C. M. Johnson-Lussenburg
  (Ottawa)
E. Kaplan (Illinois)
N. Komatsu (Japan)
H. S. Koren (North Carolina)
B. K. Locker (Illinois)

W. H. R. Lumsden
  (Edinburgh)
R. F. Macadam (Inverness)
D. J. Munro (Surrey)
U. Neumann (Hanover)
J. H. L. Playfair (London)
W. K. Podleski (Colorado)
G. I. Pozniak (Hertfordshire)
J. M. Rhodes (Copenhagen)
R. J. Russell (Dublin)
Gurkapal Singh (India)
V. Sljivik (London)
R. Tarnopolsky (Iowa)
R. Wrench (Cambridge)

and various anonymous reviewers whose suggestions we have noted and incorporated where possible.

We are also grateful to J. O. O. Bale, for his assistance in reading back the proofs.

Arrangement of entries

Preferred terms

The terms included in this Dictionary have been defined under the heading that appeared most convenient at the time of writing. The Editors wish to make it clear that, unless specially indicated, it is not their intention to show any personal preferences in this way for the use of one term rather than another. However, where *preferred term* or *obsolete term* is mentioned, this indicates the supersession of an older term either by international agreement, or by a consensus of modern usage.

Numbered sections

Some definitions have been divided into sections. When these are numbered this is intended to indicate that the word has several distinct meanings. Where such sections are distinguished by letters, the differences between them are much less important, e.g. as in the entries for vaccines. In the cross references, the section of the definition intended is indicated by a superscript numeral or letter, e.g. **sensitized cells**[1].

Cross references

Words printed in **bold type** within any definition appear elsewhere as dictionary entries in their own right. The grammatical form of each cross reference has, as far as possible, been made to conform with that of the main entry, plurals being ignored. It should be noted that, in a few cases, two words referable to different entries appear in sequence and should be distinguished; thus there is no defintion of **allogeneic lymphocytes** but only of **allogeneic** and of **lymphocyte**. Superscript numerals refer to sections of an entry; see the paragraph above.

A note on alphabetical order

In this edition, we have listed the entries in strict alphabetical order as in the example given below. Greek letters appear where

Arrangement of entries

their fully spelt-out romanized version would appear, e.g. β, as beta.
Subscript letters have been ignored in listing. Numerals are listed before letters, e.g. **C2** comes before **caecal tonsils**, for example

B
bacteriolysis
B blood group
BCG
β (beta) lysin
β_1A globulin
β_2A globulin
blast cell
blood group
B lymphocyte
B_1 lymphocyte

Abbreviations

Amer. — American spelling or usage.

cf. — compare.

e.g. — for example.

esp. — especially

Gell and Coombes — *Clinical Aspects of Immunology* (1963) 1st Edition. Oxford, Blackwell Scientific Publications.

H and E stain — haematoxylin and eosin stain.

Hist. — of historical interest only.

i.e. — that is to say.

inter alia — amongst other things.

Mol. wt. — molecular weight.

mm — millimetre.

nm — nanometre (millimicron, mμ).

N.B. — Note!

obs. — obsolete

q.v. — which see (where used, indicates important extension to definition).

® — Word known to be or thought to be a proprietary name. The inclusion of any other proprietary name without such indication is not to be taken as a representation by the editors or publisher that it is not subject to proprietary rights.

superscript numeral or letter. — *see* paragraph above headed 'Numbered sections'.

Syn. — synonym.

μm — micrometre (μ or micron).

Vet. — veterinary vaccine or usage.

viz — namely.

Other abbreviations, e.g. HSA, s_{20} etc., will be found as entries in the text of the Dictionary.

ab. Abbreviation for **antibody**.

AB blood group. *See* **ABO blood group system**.

ABC. *See* **antigen binding capacity**.

aberrant clone. *See* **forbidden clone** (*preferred term*).

ablastin. An antibody that inhibits the reproduction (by multiple fission) of *Trypanosoma (Herpetosoma) lewisi,* a parasite of the rat. This antibody appears to have no other function, e.g. it does not act as a **lysin**[1] or **opsonin**[1].

A blood group. *See* **ABO blood group system**.

ABO blood group substances. Soluble substances bearing **ABO blood group system** specificity. Present in human mucous secretions, e.g. ovarian cyst fluid, gastric juice, saliva, etc. of **secretors**. They are high molecular weight glycopeptides with a high-peptide-content backbone and oligosaccharide side chains bearing ABO **antigenic determinants** identical to those of the erythrocytes of the same individual.

ABO blood group system. One of the human **blood group** systems. It is the most important in blood transfusion serology because **natural antibodies** against ABO blood group antigens occur in serum. Humans belong to one of four groups: A, B, AB and O; the red cells of each group carry respectively the A antigen, the B antigen, both A and B antigens, or neither antigen. The antibodies in serum are specific for those ABO antigens not present on the red cells of the bearer, e.g. persons of group A have serum antibodies to B antigen, as shown in the table below. *See also* **universal donor**.

Blood group (phenotype)	Antigen on cells	Antibody in serum
A	A	anti-B
B	B	anti-A
AB	A and B	neither
O	neither	anti-A and anti-B

absorption. In immunology the term refers to the use of reagents to remove antigens or antibodies from a mixture. Used to remove unwanted possibly **cross-reacting antibodies** from an **antiserum**

to make it more specific. Accomplished by adding antigen and then removing the antigen-antibody complex formed. Cf. **adsorption**.

absorption elution test. A test employed to identify the **ABO blood group** of human blood and seminal stains. The stain is first fixed by dipping into boiling water and is then treated with antiserum to one of the blood groups and excess serum removed by washing. Subsequent heating in saline to 56°C elutes any antibody that has combined with the stain; if red cells of the appropriate group are then added to the **eluate**, they agglutinate in positive cases.

accessory cell. Non-lymphocytic cell which functions as a modulator of immune responses or of lymphocyte function or development. Usually Ia-positive (*see* **Ia antigens**). In many cases, essential for **helper T lymphocyte** activity in initiating immune responses, the interaction between accessory cells and helper T lymphocytes showing **MHC restriction**, as the two cell-types require to be **syngeneic** for **Class II antigens**. *See* also **antigen-presenting cell**. Many accessory cells resemble the **mononuclear phagocytes** in their physiological characteristics but others e.g. **dendritic cells**[2] and **Langerhans cells** are not phagocytic.

acquired immunity. **Immunity**[1] that develops as a result of exposure to a foreign substance or organism. Cf. **native immunity** and **non-specific immunity**.

acquired immunodeficiency syndrome (AIDS). Severe immunodeficiency appearing in adults, and characterized by repeated bizarre and severe infections and an otherwise rare skin tumour, Kaposi's sarcoma. Common in homosexuals and heroin addicts esp. in USA. Patients appear to have a deficiency of **helper T lymphocytes**. Probably caused by a **T cell leukaemia virus** (HTLV-3).

acquired tolerance. **Immunological tolerance** induced by injecting very small or very large doses of antigen, and persisting only so long as that antigen remains in the body; in contrast to immunological tolerance arising naturally. *See also* **adoptive tolerance**.

activated lymphocyte. Any **lymphocyte** in an active state of differentiation. The term may therefore refer either to a lymphocyte that is proliferating on meeting antigen for the first time, or to a **committed lymphocyte** that is taking part in a cell-mediated immune reaction, reacting to a **mitogen,** or developing to produce antibody.

activated macrophage. Macrophage with increased functional activity induced by a stimulating agent. The term was first used of macrophages that, following differentiation and increased DNA and protein synthesis, had become more efficient killers of bacteria (such as *Listeria monocytogenes*) than their predecessors. Activation in this system was usually **T lymphocyte**-dependent. The term activation is often also used to refer to the enhancement of other macrophage functions. It should probably only be used with a qualification defining the experimental system under study.

active immunity. Protection due to development of an **immune response** in an individual following stimulation with antigen, e.g. in a **vaccine** or during infection. Cf. **passive immunity**.

active immunization. Stimulation of an individual's **immune responses** in order to confer protection against disease. Effected by exposure to **protective antigens** either during the course of infection (which may be subclinical) or by **vaccination**. The protection effected takes a week or more to develop, but is then long lasting (*see* **immunological memory**) and rapidly revived by a **booster dose**, cf. **passive immunization**.

acute lymphoblastic leukaemia. Leukaemia in which the predominant cell-type is **lymphoblast**-like, and usually lacking **T** or **B lymphocyte** markers. Possibly a neoplasm of committed **stem cells**. In a minority of cases, the cells are identifiable as immature B or T lymphocytes.

acute myeloblastic leukaemia. Leukaemia in which the predominant cell-type is myeloblast-like (*see* **myeloid cell series**).

acute phase serum. Serum collected in the acute phase of an infectious disease. Cf. **convalescent serum**.

acute phase substances. Non-antibody substances appearing in increased quantities in plasma soon after the onset of infections or tissue damage. Many are proteins synthesized in the liver. They include **C reactive protein,** fibrinogen, certain **complement** components, α_1-antitrypsin and α_1-acid glycoprotein (orosomucoid). Functions still debatable.

ADCC. *See* **antibody-dependent cell-mediated cytotoxicity**.

Addison's disease. Adrenal cortical atrophy with hypofunction. In the so-called idiopathic form, lymphocytic infiltration of the atrophic cortex is seen, and **autoantibodies** to adrenal cortical **tissue**

adenosine deaminase deficiency

specific antigens (steroid hormone producing cells) are present in the serum in a high proportion of cases. Experimental allergic adrenalitis has been produced by injecting adrenal tissue into experimental animals.

adenosine deaminase deficiency. Enzyme deficiency found in children in close association with **severe combined immunodeficiency syndrome**. Inherited as autosomal recessive trait.

adjuvant. Substance injected with **antigens** (usually mixed with them but sometimes given prior to or following the antigen) which non-specifically enhances or modifies the **immune response** to that antigen. Thus **antibody** production or the reactions of **cell-mediated immunity** are more vigorous than would be the case were the antigen injected without adjuvant. In addition, the response may be modified qualitatively, e.g. antibodies of different immunoglobulin classes may be stimulated. *See* **aluminium adjuvants**, **complete Freund's adjuvant** and **pertussis adjuvant**.

Adjuvant 65®. A water-in-oil emulsion of antigen in arachis (peanut) oil stabilized by the addition of **Arlacel A®** and aluminium monostearate. This is accepted as a safe **water-in-oil emulsion adjuvant** for use in man as, being made from a vegetable oil, it is biologically degradable.

adjuvant disease. Clinical abnormality following injection of **complete Freund's adjuvant,** without an added antigen, into experimental animals especially rats. Characterized by inflammatory lesions in joints and periarticular tissues particularly those of the extremities and tail; hence *syn.* 'adjuvant arthritis'.

adjuvant granuloma. Granuloma[2,3] that forms at the site of injection of **adjuvants**, e.g. **complete Freund's adjuvant** granuloma and **alum granuloma**.

adjuvanticity. The ability of a substance to enhance or modify an **immune response** in a non-specific manner (*see* **adjuvant**).

adoptive immunity. **Passive immunity** transmitted, not by antibody in serum but by **lymphocytes**. *See* **cell-mediated immunity**.

adoptive tolerance. A state of **immunological tolerance** in an irradiated recipient animal to which have been transferred **lymphoid cells** obtained from a donor made tolerant to an antigen.

adoptive transfer. **Passive transfer** of immunity by transferring lymphocytes from a **primed** donor to a non-immune recipient.

adsorption.   Non-specific attachment of soluble substances, proteins, etc. to the surfaces of cells or inert particles. Useful in **serology**, e.g. an antigen may be adsorbed on to red cells and the antibody to it can then be detected by **agglutination** of the cells. Cf. **absorption**.

AET rosette test.   A test for human **T lymphocytes** using amino-ethylthiouridium bromide-treated sheep erythrocytes. These rosettes are more stable than E rosettes formed using untreated sheep erythrocytes (*see* **E-rosette forming cell**).

affinity.   A thermodynamic expression of the strength of interaction or binding between two entities, e.g. between an antigen-binding site and antigenic determinant, and thus, of the stereochemical compatibility between them. As such it is expressed as the equilibrium or **association constant** (K litres mole^{-1})for the antigen–antibody interaction but, since there is usually a heterogeneity of affinities within a population of antibody molecules of defined specificity it is, at the best, an average value referred to as the 'mean intrinsic association constant'.
  The term affinity is most accurately applied to interactions involving simple, uniform determinants, e.g. haptens, thus obviating the difficulty of considering heterogeneous determinants on the same molecule.
  Techniques for measuring affinity include **equilibrium dialysis**, fluorescence quenching and ammonium sulphate precipitation of antibody-hapten complexes.

affinity labelling.   Immunochemical method of locating the **antigen binding site**. Antibody is treated with a chemically-reactive, radioactive **hapten,** which binds specifically to the antigen binding site and, more slowly, bonds covalently to amino acid residues surrounding the antigen-binding site. The antibody is then hydrolysed and the peptide fragment that has bound to the hapten is separated and identified.

ag.   Abbreviation for **antigen**.

agammaglobulinaemia.   *See* **hypogammaglobulinaemia** (*preferred term*).

Agarose®.   Neutral polygalactoside purified from agar. Agarose gels differ from agar gels in that they show less adsorption of basic substances and less electro-osmosis. Used as a medium for **haemolytic plaque tests** and leucocyte **chemotaxis** assays.

agglutination. Clumping of **particulate antigens**, e.g. red cells, bacteria, etc. by reaction with specific antibody which forms bridges between **antigenic determinants** on contiguous particles. As agglutination is easily visible, it forms the basis of many serological tests.

agglutinin. (1) An antibody that reacts with surface antigens of particles, e.g. red cells and bacteria, to agglutinate them. *See* **agglutination**. (2) Any substance, not necessarily antibody, capable of agglutinating particles, e.g. **lectin**.

agglutinogen. Term used in blood group serology to refer to a **particulate antigen** that reacts with an **agglutinin**[1].

aggressins. Diffusible substances produced by pathogenic bacteria. These substances though not necessarily toxic themselves, interfere with normal defence mechanisms and enhance the ability of the organism to establish itself in the host's tissues.

agranulocytosis. Pathological fall in the level of circulating **neutrophil leucocytes** resulting from depression of myelopoiesis. It results in a lowered resistance to bacterial infection, and often presents as a severe pharyngitis (agranulocytic angina). Death may follow from septicaemia, meningitis, etc. or myelopoiesis may be resumed and recovery follow. Can develop without known cause or following administration of certain cytotoxic drugs, e.g. nitrogen mustards, and also as an idiosyncratic response to normally harmless doses of various chemicals or drugs, e.g. chloramphenicol.

AIDS. *See* **acquired immunodeficiency syndrome**.

albumin. *See* **serum albumin**.

albumin agglutinating antibody. Antibody capable of causing **agglutination** of red cells in presence of high concentrations of serum albumin, e.g. 30 per cent **BSA**, but not in saline alone. Many **incomplete antibodies**[1] can be detected in this way, and the method has been extensively used for their detection in blood group **serology**.

albumin gradient centrifugation. *See* **density gradient centrifugation**.

Aleutian mink disease. A 'slow' viral disease of mink, particularly those homozygous for the Aleutian gene giving light coloured fur. The disease is transmissable, suggesting that it is due to an infectious agent. There are clinical and pathological similarities to **systematic lupus erythematosus** and **polyarteritis nodosa** in man. Characterized by hepatitis, vasculitis, nephritis, hypergammaglobulinaemia and the presence of anti-nuclear antibodies (*see* **anti-nuclear factor**). It is postulated that the chief pathogenic agents are the **immune complexes** formed in the disease.

alexin. Obsolete synonym for **complement**. The term used by Bordet to describe a thermolabile material present in serum that caused the lysis of cells that had previously been sensitized by an immune serum (*see* **sensitized cells**[2]).

ALG. *See* **anti-lymphocyte globulin.**

ALL antigen. (**Acute lymphoblastic leukaemia** antigen). Surface glycoprotein present on human **pre-B** and **pre-T lymphocytes**, but not expressed on more mature forms (**thymocytes, T lymphocytes, B lymphocytes**). Present on cells of the common form of **acute lymphoblastic leukaemia**, hence name.

allelic exclusion. A somatic phenomenon found in animals heterozygous for (an) antibody **allotype(s)**. Although the animal's serum contains both allotypic forms of **antibody**, individual **B-lymphocytes** express only one allotype, not both. Different **lymphocytes** therefore express the different allotypic forms of antibody. This unusual genetic phenomenon relates to the way that antibody genes are assembled in B lymphocytes.

allergen. Antigenic substance capable of provoking an **allergic response**. In common usage the term is restricted to substances, e.g. pollens and dander, that combine with reaginic antibody (**reagin**[1]) to provoke allergic reactions in **atopic** subjects.

allergic alveolitis. *See* **farmer's lung.**

allergic encephalomyelitis. *See* **experimental allergic encephalomyelitis.**

allergic response. A specific **immune** response to antigen resulting in **allergy.**

allergic rhinitis. Exudative inflammation of the nasal passage occurring in **atopic** persons in contact with airborne **allergen** to which they are sensitive. Caused by local release of vasoactive substances in an **immediate hypersensitivity** reaction. Allergic rhinitis is a constant feature of **hay fever.**

allergic state. Clinical term for diseases in which **hypersensitivity** plays a part, especially **atopic** diseases such as **hay fever**.

allergy. Term introduced by von Pirquet in 1906 to mean altered host reactivity to an antigen. No longer holds this meaning. Current use; a synonym for **hypersensitivity** especially of **immediate hypersensitivity** type, thus with implication of immunologically induced tissue damage.

alloantigens. Different (allelic) forms of an antigen coded for at the same gene locus in all individuals of a species. E.g. **histocompatibility antigens** are coded for at the same locus but vary between individuals.

alloantiserum. An antiserum directed against antigens of another animal of the same species and raised in that species. E.g. a serum made in one **inbred strain** of a species against another inbred strain of the same species.

allogeneic (allogenic). Genetically dissimilar within the same species. *See also* **transplantation terminology**.

allogeneic disease. **Graft-versus-host reaction** in animals under immunosuppressive therapy that have been given **allogeneic** lymphocytes. *See also* **secondary disease**.

allogeneic effect. (*syn*, abnormal induction). The stimulation of antibody production to a **thymus dependent antigen** resulting from allogeneic activation of **T lymphocytes**, as in a **graft-versus-host reaction**. Probably mediated by 'non-specific' factors released from activated T lymphocytes, obviating the requirement for **helper T lymphocytes**.

allogeneic inhibition. Term descriptive of cell or tissue damage caused by contact with **lymphocytes** differing at the **major histocompatibility complex**, e.g. inhibition of growth of a parental tumour (*in vivo*) or cell line (*in vitro*) by F_1 lymphocytes. The lymphocytes do not apparently need to be **primed**.

allogeneic restriction. *See* **MHC restriction**.

allograft. Graft exchanged between two genetically dissimilar individuals of the same species, i.e. members of an outbred population, or of two different **inbred strains**. Cf **syngeneic** graft.

allotope. *See* **allotypic determinant**.

allotype. Serologically identifiable differences between **immuno-globulin** molecules that are inherited as alleles of a single genetic locus. Many allotypes have been correlated with amino acid substitutions in the **heavy** or **light chain**, e.g. **Gm** and **Km**. The **antigenic determinant** formed by these amino acids is known as the **allotope** (*see* **allotypic determinant**). Allotypes can be found in both the constant and variable regions of immunoglobulins.

allotypic determinant (*syn.* allotope). The structural region of an **antigen** which distinguishes it from another **allotype** of that antigen.

allotypic marker. *See* **allotypic determinant**.

α**(alpha) chain**. The **heavy chain** of **IgA**.

α **chain disease**. Rare **paraproteinaemia** described in subjects of eastern Mediterranean origin in which there is an infiltrative lymphoma especially of the intestine, associated with malabsorption. Abnormal **plasma cells** are present which manufacture only *a* **chains** but no **light chains**. The N-terminal sequences of these *a* chains are normal but there is a deletion extending from part of the V-region through most of the $C_{\alpha 1}$ domain so that the cysteine residue involved in cross-linking to light chains is missing (*see also* γ **chain disease** and **heavy chain disease**).

alphafetoprotein A major plasma protein of the early fetus. Also found in serum of mice and humans with primary liver cancer, teratocarcinomas and yolk sac tumours. Structurally related to serum albumin. Evidence suggests it, or an associated molecule, has immuno-suppressive properties (*see* **immunosuppression**), possibly inducing **T suppressor cells** or inhibiting **accessory cell** function.

ALS. *See* **anti-lymphocyte serum**.

altered-self hypothesis. An hypothesis proposing that **MHC restriction** (q.v.) operates through the recognition of new **antigenic determinants** formed by the interaction of a foreign **antigen** with a self-**MHC** antigen on the surface of a cell, cf. **dual recognition hypothesis**.

alternative pathway (alternate pathway). A pathway by which **complement** components C3—C9 are activated without a requirement for C1, C2 or C4. Can be activated by human **IgA** and by guinea-pig γ_1 globulin (i.e. **immunoglobulins** which do not activate the classical complement pathway), by endotoxin without antibody,

alternative pathway C3 convertase

and by polysaccharides from various fungal or bacterial sources. Sometimes called the properdin pathway since properdin (**factor P**) was the first purified component. *See also* **factor B** and **factor $\overline{\text{D}}$.**

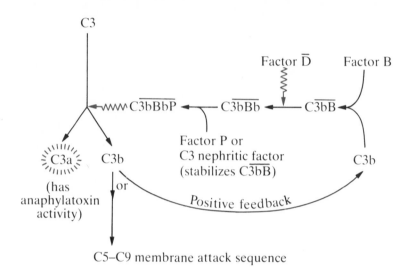

C5–C9 membrane attack sequence

ᴡᴡᴡ► = enzymic action
$\overline{\text{Cn}}$ = activated complement component

alternative pathway C3 convertase. A complex of **C3b** and **factor B** which cleaves **C3** to **C3a** and **C3b**. This is the unstable convertase ($\overline{\text{C3bB}}$); it can be stabilized by **factor P** (to give $\overline{\text{C3bBbP}}$) or **C3 nephritic factor**. Cf. **C3 convertase** ($\overline{\text{C42}}$) of the classical pathway to **complement** activation.

alum granuloma. The **granuloma**[3] formed at the site of subcutaneous or intramuscular inoculation of an **aluminium adjuvant**. Believed to be an important site of antibody production.

alum precipitate. *See* **aluminium adjuvants**.

alum precipitated toxoid. Any **toxoid** adsorbed onto an **aluminium adjuvant**. In human immunization schedules particularly, refers to **diphtheria toxoid**. *See* **adsorption**.

aluminium adjuvants. Compounds of aluminium, e.g. **aluminium hydroxide gel**, aluminium phosphate, aluminium sulphate and

10

alums such as ammonium alum $(NH_4)_2 SO_4.Al_2 (SO_4)_3$ and potassium alum, that strongly adsorb protein antigens from a solution to form a precipitate. When injected into an animal these precipitates form a depot from which the antigen is slowly released. *See also* **adjuvants, depot forming adjuvants, alum granuloma** and **adsorption**.

aluminium hydroxide gel. An **adjuvant** consisting of about 2 per cent aluminium hydroxide $Al(OH)_3$ in a highly hydrated gelatinous form that strongly adsorbs protein antigens to form a precipitate. *See also* **aluminium adjuvants**.

Am marker. An allotypic marker (*see* **allotype**) of human IgA2 existing in two forms: A2m(1) and A2m(2). In IgA2m(1) the **light chains** are linked together by a **C-terminal** disulphide bridge and are not covalently bound to the **heavy chains** owing to the absence of the corresponding cysteine residue in the α **chain**. In IgA2m(2) the cysteine residues are present in the α chain and are able to form the normal H-L disulphide bridge.

amboceptor. (1) *Hist.* Described by Ehrlich as an 'antibody' molecule that had two combining sites, one for the antigen and one for **complement**, i.e. complement was linked to the antigen by an amboceptor. (2) This term is still used colloquially to refer to the antibody employed for the **sensitization**[2] of sheep red cells for use as the **haemolytic system** in the **complement fixation test**.

aminoethylthiouridium bromide. *see* **AET rosette test**.

ampicillin hypersensitivity. An erythematous maculopapular rash occurring during, or sometimes soon after, treatment with ampicillin. This condition is not necessarily associated with **penicillin hypersensitivity** (q.v.) and characteristically shows increased incidence in **infectious mononucleosis, chronic lymphatic leukaemia** and certain other illnesses. Occurrence of the rash does not preclude re-administration of the drug. May be due to **hypersensitivity** of **type III reaction** (immune complex) type.

amplifier T lymphocyte. **T lymphocyte** which modifies a developing immune response by releasing non-specific signals to which other T lymphocytes respond. Amplifier lymphocytes may act either on **effector** or **suppressor T lymphocytes**.

amyloidosis Disease characterized by deposition of insoluble protein fibrils in a variety of tissues, often leading to failure of affected organs. Two forms of systemic amyloidosis predominate; (1) reactive amyloidosis which is characterized by fibrils derived from the acute phase protein (*see* **acute phase substances**) named serum amyloid protein A (SAA); and (ii) immunocytic amyloidosis in which the fibrils are derived from immunoglobulin **light chains**.

ANAE   alpha-naphthyl acetate esterase. *Syn* **non-specific esterase**, q.v.

anaerobic coryneform bacteria. Name given to a group of bacteria belonging to the genus *Propionibacterium* chiefly derived from human sources. Best known is *Corynebacterium parvum*. Rarely pathogenic. These organisms have immunopotentiating effects, especially as stimulants of **macrophage** function *in vitro* and *in vivo,* but also on other immune functions. They have been used in therapy of experimental and clinical tumours.

anamnestic response. (1) Response to antigenic stimulation characterized by production of large amounts of **antibody** against apparently unrelated **antigens**[1,2]. (2) Unexpectedly powerful antibody response (of **secondary immune response** type) following what is assumed to be an initial administration of antigen. *See* **heteroclitic antibody**.

anaphylactic shock.   A severe generalized form of **anaphylaxis** due to the widespread effects of **histamine** and other vasoactive substances. Mechanism identical to that of other **immediate hypersensitivity** reactions, i.e. the result of reaction of antigen with **mast cell**-bound antibody. Symptoms vary in different species. In man peripheral circulatory failure, hypotension, bronchoconstriction and urticaria are seen. In severe cases, especially following intravenous injection of antigen, rapid death may occur. In man most commonly seen following a second administration of horse serum (especially in **atopic** persons), e.g. **tetanus antitoxin** in **passive immunization**. Can be avoided by preliminary **test dosing**. Treated with adrenalin.

anaphylactoid reaction. An acute shock syndrome resembling **anaphylactic shock** but *not* caused by an immunological reaction. Substances that may produce this on inoculation are bee and snake venoms and, in the guinea pig, horse lung extracts, indian ink, gum tragacanth, acetic acid, etc. These cause the liberation of large amounts of **histamine** and other vasoactive substances. *See also* **pseudoallergic reaction**.

anaphylatoxins. A group of substances, mediators of inflammation, produced in serum during the fixation of **complement** (*see* **C3** and **C5**). Anaphylatoxins act indirectly to increase vascular permeability by causing **mast cell** degranulation and **histamine** release. Thus when injected into animals they produce symptoms similar to those of **systemic anaphylaxis**. Anaphylatoxin activity has been located in the low molecular weight fragments **C3a** and **C5a** (also C4a) that are formed upon the fixation of complement.

anaphylatoxin inactivator. An enzyme (carboxypeptidase-N) that cleaves the C-terminal arginine from **C5a** and converts it to $C5a_{desArg}$, thus causing it to lose **anaphylatoxin** activity. Present in normal human serum.

anaphylaxis. An acute **immediate hypersensitivity** (or **type 1 reaction**) following administration of antigen to a **primed** subject. The reaction is caused by release of **histamine** or other vasoactive substances when antigen combines with antibody (usually **IgE** q.v.) on the surfaces of cells. Anaphylaxis may be generalized (*see* **anaphylactic shock**) or localized to the site of injection. *See also* **passive cutaneous anaphylaxis, Prausnitz-Küstner reaction** and **local anaphylaxis**.

anavenom. Snake venom, treated with formaldehyde to render it non-toxic (*see also* **toxoid**), and used in the preparation of **anti-venom**.

anergy. Absence of reactions of **cell-mediated immunity** in a supposedly **primed** animal, e.g. in very advanced cases of *Mycobacterium tuberculosis* infection in cattle the normal **tuberculin test** skin reaction cannot be elicited.

ANF. *See* **anti-nuclear factor**.

'angry' macrophage. *See* **activated macrophage**. (*colloquial*).

antagglutinin. Substance found in the seminal plasma of mammals which inhibits spontaneous **autoagglutination**[1] of washed spermatozoa.

anthrax vaccines. (a) *Hist.* and *Vet.* Live bacilli, attenuated by growth at 42–43°C(Pasteur). (b) *Vet.* A live **attenuated vaccine** consisting of a suspension of spores derived from a non-capsulated mutant of *Bacillus anthracis* (the possession of a capsule is necessary for the organism to be virulent). **Saponin** is often added as an **adjuvant**. (c) *Human* and *Vet.* Protective antigen ('toxin'), derived from the medium in which the organism has been grown, precipitated with an **aluminium adjuvant**. Safe but does not give such strong protection as (b).

anti-antibody

anti-antibody. Antibody especially **rheumatoid factor** which is able to combine specifically with an immunoglobulin molecule that is bound to an antigen, but not with free **immunoglobulin**. It probably represents antibody against **hidden determinants** on the antibody molecule revealed by alterations in molecular shape that occur during the combination of immunoglobulin with antigen.

antibody. Protein with the molecular properties of an **immunoglobulin** q.v. and capable of specific combination with **antigen**. Carries **antigen binding sites** that link non-covalently with the corresponding **antigenic determinant**. Antibodies are produced in the body by the cells of the **lymphoid cell series**, especially **plasma cells**, in response to stimulation by antigen.

antibody absorption test. Serological test in which the **titre** of antibody in serum against a given antigen is determined before and after **absorption** with another antigen. Thus detects **cross reacting antibodies** or **cross reacting antigens**[1,2].

antibody combining site. *See* **antigen-binding site**.

antibody deficiency syndrome. **Immunodeficiency** either genetically determined or secondary to other diseases. Characterized by low serum **immunoglobulin** levels and failure to produce antibody normally on antigenic challenge. One, two or all three of the major classes of immunoglobulin (**IgG, IgA** and **IgM**) may be deficient. May exist in the presence of normal **cell-mediated immunity** as in **infantile sex linked hypogammaglobulinaemia**. In the **severe combined immunodeficiency syndrome** both humoral and cell-mediated immunity are defective. *See also* **common variable antibody deficiency**.

antibody-dependent cell-mediated cytotoxicity. Killing of certain cell-types (fibroblasts, lymphocytes, erythrocytes *inter alia* have been studied) by **K cells** which carry, bound to **Fc receptors**, antibody specific for the **target cell**[1]. Thus dependent on an immunological response to the target cells, cf, killing by **NK cells** which may not depend on an immune response.

antibody excess. Presence in a mixture of an amount of antibody sufficient to combine with all of the **antigenic determinants** in that mixture and still to leave free, uncombined antibody molecules. Under such conditions, no uncombined determinants remain available for cross-links between adjacent antigen molecules to be made (*see* **lattice hypothesis**). Therefore soluble complexes, rather than precipitates, are formed. Seen especially in **precipitin tests** of the tube or **gel diffusion** type.

antibody half life.   A measure of the average time of survival of any given **antibody** molecule after its synthesis. In practice, the time taken for the elimination of 50 per cent of a measured dose of antibody from the body of the animal. The various **immunoglobulin classes** have different half-lives, thus the half–life of antibody will vary according to immunoglobulin class.

antibody overlay.   *See* **western blotting**.

antibody units.   *See* **titre**.

anticomplementary.   Adjective used to describe an **antiserum, antigen**[1,2,3] or other substance that initiates the **complement** cascade reaction, i.e. fixes complement, in the absence of any specific union of antibody with antigen. Amongst many causes of anticomplementary activity are the presence of immunoglobulin aggregates, and other substances. Many may act by activating the **alternative pathway**. Anticomplementary substances are very important in **serology** as they interfere with the interpretation of **complement fixation tests**.

anti-D.   Antibody against the D antigen of the **Rhesus blood group system**. The commonest and most important antibody formed by the maternal tissues in **Rhesus incompatibility**. Anti-D can be given within 36 hours of parturition to prevent **isoimmunization** of the mother.

antigen.   (1) A molecule that elicits a specific **immune response** when introduced into the tissues of an animal. This may take the form either of **antibody** production together with the development of **cell-mediated immunity** (*see* **immunogen**[1]), or of specific **immunological tolerance**. If antigens are to stimulate a response they must normally be foreign to the animal to which they are administered (but *see* **autoantigen**), of a molecular weight greater than 1000 (but *see* **hapten**), and of protein or polysaccharide nature. However, the definition of an antigen is arbitrary since specific responsiveness is a property of the host tissues, not of the injected substance. Unless otherwise indicated, the word 'antigen' is used with this meaning throughout the dictionary. *See also* **particulate antigen** and **soluble antigen**. (2) The term 'antigen' is sometimes used loosely to refer to materials such as whole bacteria, when these are used to stimulate an immune response. Such organisms contain many hundreds of different antigens, and moreover it should be noted that even a single antigenic protein molecule may bear on its surface more than one different **antigenic determinant**. (3) Some workers use the term to refer to any substance that can combine with an antibody, whether or not it is capable of stimulating a specific immune response.

antigen adjuvant. *Syn*. immunological adjuvant. Both terms sometimes used to distinguish **adjuvants** used in immunology from those used in other fields, e.g. pharmacology.

antigen-antibody complex. *See* **immune complex**.

antigen binding capacity. A primary measure of the total amount of **antibody** in an **antiserum** that is available to combine with an **antigen**[1,2,3]. It is a measure of the total effective antibody, of all **immunoglobulin classes**, that is present. The antigen binding capacity of antibodies to **haptens** can be measured by **equilibrium dialysis** and to certain protein antigens, by the **Farr test**, but techniques suitable for all antigens have yet to be devised.

antigen-binding site. The sites on the antibody molecule that combine specifically with the corresponding **antigenic determinant**. Present on the **Fab fragment**. The **heavy** and **light chains** are both involved and the binding site is formed from loops formed by the **variable regions** of both chains including the **hypervariable regions**.

antigen diffusion constant. *See* **diffusion coefficient**.

antigen excess. Presence in a mixture of an amount of antigen sufficient to combine with all of the **antigen-binding sites** of the antibody molecules in the mixture and still leave free, uncombined, antigenic determinants. Thus, soluble complexes are formed. A phenomenon explained by the **lattice hypothesis**. Soluble antigen-antibody complexes formed *in vivo* in conditions of antigen excess are of considerable importance in immunopathology as such complexes give rise to **Arthus-type reactions** when injected experimentally and are found in the lesions of **serum sickness, glomerulone-phritis** and other **hypersensitivity** diseases. *See also* **antibody excess**.

antigen gain. The acquisition by cells of new **antigenic determinants** either not normally present or not normally accessible in the parent tissue. Often follows mutational change, e.g. in tumour cells, or lysogenic conversion in bacteria.

antigen-presenting cell. Non-lymphocytic cell that carries antigen and presents it to **lymphocytes** resulting in the induction of an immune response. In many cases, such induction shows **MHC-restriction** usually for **Class II antigens**, thus the antigen-presenting cell and the antigen-recognizing lymphocyte must be **syngeneic**. **Macrophages** and other types of **accessory cell** may act as antigen-presenting cells.

antigen recognition site. Site on the surface of a **lymphocyte**, which can react specifically with antigen thus initiating responses of **cell-mediated immunity** or **humoral immunity** e.g. **B lymphocyte receptors** or **T lymphocyte antigen receptors**.

antigen-specific T-cell helper factor. Soluble product of a **helper T lymphocyte** which activates other **lymphocytes** which are specific for the appropriate **antigen**[1]. The factor may itself bind antigen.

antigen-specific T-cell suppressor factor. Soluble factor produced by a **suppressor T lymphocyte** after immunization which suppresses the immune response in an antigen-specific manner. The factor may bind antigen.

antigenic competition. Phenomenon seen following challenge with an antigen in an animal responding to a different antigen. The animal fails to respond, or shows a diminished response, to the second antigen.

antigenic deletion. Loss or masking of **antigenic determinants** from cells whose parent tissue normally carries them. May result from neoplastic or other mutational change in the parent tissue and may be due to loss or repression of genetic material from the cell.

antigenic determinant. The small site on the **antigen**[1] to which **antibody** (whose production is necessarily stimulated by the whole antigen molecule) is specifically able to become attached by its **antigen-binding site**. The determinant probably forms a more or less exact three-dimensional fit with its corresponding antibody and is bound to it by close range non-covalent links. A single antigen molecule may carry several different antigenic determinants. **Haptens** attached to it will form new determinants.

antigenic diversion. Term used in tumour immunology to describe loss of **antigenic profile** of cells or tissue and replacement by that of a different normal tissue.

antigenic modulation. Disappearance of **antigenic determinants**

antigenic profile

from the surface of a living cell after their combination with specific antibody.

antigenic profile. The overall antigenic structure and arrangement of a cell or tissue.

antigenic reversion. Antigenic change in adult cells such that the **antigenic profile** reverts from the adult form to a form existing in immature or fetal cells. Such reversion may follow neoplastic change.

antigenic transformation. Any change in the **antigenic profile** of a cell, such as **antigen gain, antigenic deletion, antigenic reversion**, etc.

antigenic variation. (a) A means by which certain parasites, especially trypanosomes, plasmodia and *Borrelia,* are enabled to survive the **immune responses** of their host. When this response destroys the bulk of the parasite population a few survive. These survivors possess a cell surface of entirely different antigenic composition from that of their parents and grow into a second large parasitic population. This in turn is eliminated except for a few organisms of a third antigenic type. The cycle may be repeated many times; amongst the trypanosomes, over one hundred sequential types with no repetitions have been recorded. (b) A phenomenon associated with the influenza virus which, unlike most viruses, undergoes spontaneous variation both as a slow antigenic drift from year to year and the occasional sudden emergence of a strain with new major antigens, e.g. Asian or A2 influenza in 1957.

antigenicity. Capacity of a substance to act as an **antigen**[1] . Term often also used synonymously with **immunogenicity** q.v.

antiglobulin. An **antiserum** raised against the **globulin** portion of serum. Used in reactions such as the **antiglobulin test** and **indirect fluorescent antibody technique** q.v. It contains antibodies to **antigenic determinants** on the **immunoglobulin** molecules of the donor animal's serum. These antibodies may combine with the immunoglobulin molecules of the donor without affecting the reactivity of the latter's **antigen–binding sites**.

antiglobulin consumption test. Test in which serum, suspected of containing antibody, is incubated with cells (or particulate material derived from cells) containing the appropriate antigen. The cells are washed and incubated with **antiglobulin**. If the cells have become coated with antibody, this will take up the antiglobulin. Antiglobulin uptake is measured by testing the supernatant for free antiglobulin by adding red cells coated with **incomplete antibody**[1]. Failure to agglutinate these red cells indicates that the antiglobulin was used up in the first part of the reaction and therefore that the serum under test did contain antibody.

antiglobulin inhibition test. Inhibition of **antiglobulin test** by adding **immunoglobulin** to the antiglobulin before testing it against red cells coated with **globulin** or **incomplete antibody**. A special example of this is the **antiglobulin consumption test**.

antiglobulin test. Originally a haemagglutination test in which the addition of **anti-immunoglobulin** caused **agglutination** of red cells coated with non-agglutinating **incomplete antibody**[1]: thus demonstrating that incomplete antibody had reacted with the cells. For example, human red cells are not agglutinated by IgG antibody bound to them, but, after **washing** to remove free immunoglobulin, they are agglutinated by addition of an antiserum to human **IgG** prepared, e.g. in a rabbit. The antiglobulin test principle is also now extended to the detection of incomplete antibody that has reacted with bacteria, etc., e.g. in the diagnosis of brucellosis. *See also* **direct antiglobulin test** and **indirect antiglobulin test**.

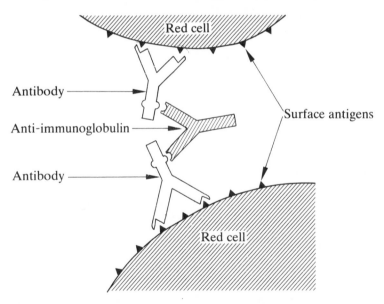

anti-I. Antibody against the I antigen, a **blood group** antigen found on most adult human erythrocytes. A **cold agglutinin** with this specificity is found as an **autoantibody** in certain cases of **cold antibody** type **haemolytic anaemia** and also in *Mycoplasma pneumoniae* infections.

anti-idiotype antibody. Antibody that binds selectively to a particular **idiotope**. Usually produced by immunizing an animal with a monoclonal immunoglobulin obtained from a member of the same species.

anti-lymphocyte globulin. The **globulin** fraction of **anti-lymphocyte serum**.

anti-lymphocyte serum. Powerful immunosuppressive agent, prepared by injecting **lymphocytes** into a different species. Can suppress all reactions of **cell-mediated immunity**, especially **graft rejection**, and also **humoral immunity** to some antigens. Major effect is the destruction of the circulatory pool of lymphocytes.

antimetabolite. A drug that interferes with the normal metabolic processes of a cell, especially those involved in mitosis. In immunology used for **immunosuppression**, examples being **azathioprine**, **mercaptopurine**, and methotrexate.

anti-nuclear factor. **Autoantibody** against constituents of cell nuclei, demonstrable by immunofluorescence and present in sera of patients with **systemic lupus erythematosus** and also sometimes in **rheumatoid arthritis**. Different anti-nuclear factors occur that react with specific nuclear components, e.g. DNA-protein, nucleic acid, histone or RNA-protein, giving typical fluorescent staining patterns. Occasionally they are tissue specific, e.g. react with only **polymorphonuclear leucocyte** nuclei (*see* **tissue specific antigen**).

antiseptic paint. Term used to describe the action of secreted **IgA** in coating mucous surfaces and preventing access of antigen.

antiserum. Serum from any animal, which contains **antibodies** against a stated **antigen**, e.g. anti-ovalbumin. *See also* **therapeutic antisera, anti-lymphocyte serum**.

anti-streptolysin-O test. Measures serum antibodies against streptolysin-O by their inhibition of the lysis of erythrocytes by streptolysin-O. These antibodies are present in sera from most healthy persons but are increased in infections due to Lancefield group A streptococci (*see* **Lancefield precipitation tests**) and in sequelae of such infections. The highest levels are seen in rheumatic fever.

antitoxin. Antibody against a bacterial toxin (usually **exotoxin**) or an **antiserum** containing such antibody.

anti-venom. *Syns.* antivenene and antivenin. A **therapeutic antiserum** containing antitoxic antibodies capable of specifically neutralizing the venom of one or more kinds of snake or poisonous arthropod.

APT. *See* **alum precipitated toxoid.**

Aquaphor®. A lanolin preparation sometimes employed as a stablizer (emulsifier) in the preparation of **water-in-oil emulsion adjuvants**.

Arlacel A®. An emulsifying agent used for stabilizing **water-in-oil emulsion adjuvants.** Essentially mannide monooleate but contains small quantities of many other compounds. Can be obtained in batches tested for non-toxicity.

armed macrophage. A **macrophage** which has received information from primed **lymphocytes.** The term includes macrophages which have not responded to the information as well as macrophages which have become **activated (macrophages)** as a result of messages from lymphocytes.

Arthus reaction. An inflammatory reaction, characterized by oedema, haemorrhage and necrosis, that follows the administration of antigen to an animal that already possesses precipitating antibody to that antigen. Classically seen as an ulcer appearing some hours after intradermal injection of antigen into a **primed** animal, i.e. later than an **immediate hypersensitivity** reaction but earlier than a reaction of **cell-mediated immunity**. Caused by formation, in the presence of **complement**, of **immune complexes** which adhere to the vascular endothelium, and become surrounded by fibrin, platelets and **neutrophil leucocytes**. The vessels become plugged with thrombi and there is exudation of fluid rich in neutrophils into the surrounding tissues. The term Arthus-type reaction has been applied to many **hypersensitivity** states in which the lesion is initiated by antigen-antibody complexes as described in the original experiments of Arthus (*see also* **type III reaction**). It is important in many clinical states, *see* **serum sickness, glomerulonephritis, farmer's lung**.

artificial antigen. *See* **synthetic antigen.**

artificially acquired immunity. Protective immunity acquired by **vaccination** or by **passive immunization**, in contrast to **naturally acquired immunity** which follows random contact with environmental antigens and organisms.

Ascoli's test. *Syn.* Ascoli thermoprecipitation reaction. A **precipitin test (ring test)** used for the diagnosis of anthrax in carcases, hides, skins, etc. by detecting antigen in saline extracts of the material. Valuable, as may be positive in putrefied material in which no culturable anthrax bacilli can be found. However, it should be noted this reaction is genus, not species, specific.

ASLT. *See* **anti-streptolysin O test**.

association constant. A measure of the extent of a reversible association between two molecular species at equilibrium. For a reaction in which n molecules of substance A combine reversibly with m molecules of substance B, i.e. $nA + mB \rightleftarrows A_nB_m$, the association constant is $[A_nB_m]/[A]^n[B]^m$ where the symbols in parentheses denote the molar concentrations (strictly, activities) at equilibrium.

asthma (bronchial asthma). A chronic disease characterized by difficulty in breathing accompanied by wheezing and over-inflation of the lungs. These clinical features are due to spasm of the bronchi and plugging of their lumina by tough mucus secreted by the bronchial glands. Some cases, classified as extrinsic asthma, are due to **type I** hypersensitivity to inhaled or ingested antigens. This is therefore an **atopic** disease, attributable to release of **histamine**, etc. by **mast cells**. Other cases accompany chronic bronchitis and may be due to **hypersensitivity** to bacteria in the bronchi (intrinsic asthma). Cardiac asthma is quite distinct consisting of pulmonary oedema due to left ventricular failure.

ataxia telangiectasia. Familial disease of children characterized by cerebellar ataxia, progressive dementia and oculocutaneous telangiectasia with recurrent infections, thymic hypoplasia and serum **immunoglobulin** deficiences. There is a high incidence of malignant tumours of **lymphoid tissue**.

atopic. Adjectival form of **atopy**.

atopic hypersensitivity. *See* **atopy**.

atopy. A constitutional or hereditary tendency to develop **immediate hypersensitivity** states, e.g. allergic **asthma** and **hay fever**, especially to **allergens** that provoke no immune reactions in normal subjects.

attenuated vaccine. A **live vaccine**[1,2] containing organisms or viruses that have been cultured or otherwise treated under conditions in which they lose virulence but retain the capacity to stimulate a protective immune response. Examples used in man include **BCG** and oral **polimyelitis vaccine**[1] (Sabin).

autoagglutination. (1) **agglutination** of a **particulate antigen** (e.g. bacteria, red cells and trypanosomes) when suspended in physiological saline alone. Important cause of error in **bacterial agglutination** tests and of false positive results in the coagulase test for pathogenicity of Staphylococci. (2) Agglutination of cells by antibody derived from the same individual.

autoantibody. **Antibody** capable of specific reaction with an **antigen** that is a normal constituent of the body of the individual in whom that antibody was formed. *In vitro* such antibodies are detected by their reaction with similar antigens obtained from other persons or from other individuals of the same species.

autoantigen (self antigen). An **antigen**[1] that is a normal constituent of the body and against which an **immune response** may be mounted by the lymphoid tissues of the same individual sometimes resulting in **autoimmune disease**.

autochthonous. Derived from self. *Syn.* **autologous**.

autofluorescence. Fluorescence of tissues due to molecules naturally present in them, i.e. unrelated to treatment of the tissue with **fluorochromes**.

autogenous vaccine. Any **vaccine** made from the actual organisms that are causing disease in an individual. These are cultured, killed and then reinoculated into that same individual. At one time used as therapy in chronic skin infections especially those due to *Staphylococcus aureus*.

autograft. Graft originated from, and applied to, the same individual, e.g. skin graft from back used for the repair of a facial burn. *See also* **transplantation terminology.**

autoimmune complement fixation reaction. Positive **complement fixation test** given by human sera with saline suspensions of liver, kidney and many other tissues. Positive in **systemic lupus erythematosus,** chronic active hepatitis and other related **autoimmune diseases**. *See also* **biological false positive reaction.**

autoimmune disease. (1) Clinical disorder resulting from an **immune response** against **autoantigen**. To fit this definition a disease should (a) show evidence of an immune response against autoantigen (b) show lesions, with the presence of **immunologically competent cells**, that are related to the distribution of such antigens, and (c) be reproducible in experimental animals following injection of the relevant antigen, and be transferable from such animals to normal animals by passive transfer of **lymphocytes** or **antibody**. (2) The term is also used loosely of diseases associated with the presence of autoantibodies even when these are not of known significance in the pathogenesis.

autoimmunity. Specific **humoral immunity (autoantibody** mediated) or **cell-mediated immunity** to constituents of the body's own tissues (**autoantigens**). If reactions between autoantibody and autoantigen result in tissue damage they may be regarded as **hypersensitivity** reactions. When such damage is sufficient to cause any clinical abnormality, an **autoimmune disease** is present.

autologous. Derived from self; used of grafts, antigens, etc.

autoradiography. Technique used to detect the presence of radioisotopes in cells and tissue sections, or in molecules (proteins, nucleic acids etc.) that have been separated by electrophoresis etc. The microscope slide, electrophoresis gel, etc. is covered with a photographic emulsion or film and exposed in the dark, usually for several days or weeks. When the photographic emulsion or film is developed the position of the radioisotope can be detected by the presence of silver grains. These may be seen as individual grains under the microscope or as blackened areas of film by the naked eye. Has also been adapted for use with sections prepared for electron microscopy. Alternatively, antigens may be detected by overlay with radio-labelled antibody followed by autoradiography. *See also* **fluorography**.

autosensitization. **Priming** by **autoantigens**.

avianized vaccine. A **vaccine** containing microorganisms (usually live) whose virulence has been attenuated by adaptation to, and passage in, chick embryos. *See* **yellow fever vaccine** and **canine distemper vaccine**[b].

avidity. An expression used to describe the strength of binding between antibody and a complex antigen. Because the antigen has a range of determinants, many of them different from each other, avidity is a composite description of the overall antibody-antigen interaction; it is, however, somewhat more complicated than a simple summation of affinities for individual determinants since, because of the effective multivalency of the antigen there is often a cooperative 'bonus' effect. The avidity is often represented by the constant K_a, which is the value of the **association constant** for the reaction $Ab + Ag = AbAg$ and which is obtained by assuming that this reaction roughly obeys the law of mass action. Avidity is, therefore, a function of the techniques used in its measurement, e.g. ammonium sulphate or anti-immunoglobulin precipitation, phage neutralization, etc. and can only be expressed in arbitrary units.

axenic. Adjective describing animals (i.e. protozoa upwards) reared in isolation from all other organisms. The absence of bacteria and larger organisms is relatively easily achieved; freedom from viruses much more difficult, especially as the latter may be incorporated in the genome. Cf. **gnotobiotic, germ free**.

azathioprine. **Immunosuppressive** anti-inflammatory drug. A purine analogue, converted to **6-mercaptopurine** *in vivo*. Used in treatment of malignant disease and in clinical transplantation. May act by depresssing **T lymphocyte** function.

azoprotein. Protein linked to any substance by an azo bond -N=N-. **Diazotization** is often used to form protein–**hapten** conjugates.

azurophil granule. **Lysosome-like granule** of the **neutrophil leucocyte**. Also known as primary granule as it first appears at the myeloblast stage, i.e. early in development (do not confuse with **primary lysosome** q.v.). Derived from the Golgi apparatus and contains acid hydrolases, cationic peptides and myeloperoxidase. Larger and denser than **specific granule** q.v.

B. Alternative complement pathway component: *see* **Factor B**.

bacille Calmette-Guérin. *See* BCG.

bacterial agglutination. The **agglutination** of bacteria by anti-body. Tests based on this are widely used in diagnostic bacteriology either for the detection of antibody (*see* **Widal reaction**) or for the identification of organisms isolated from clinical cases (*see* **slide** and **tube agglutination tests**). The *in vivo* agglutination of bacteria may also play a part in their **immune elimination**[1].

bacterial allergy. Obsolete. *Syn.* for **delayed hypersensitivity**. So named because the earliest accounts of the phenomenon were made in bacterial diseases especially tuberculosis.

bacterial hypersensitivity. *See* **bacterial allergy**.

bactericidin. Substance that kills bacteria, e.g. **antibody** and also certain non-antibody substances found in plasma.

bacterin. *Amer.* **Vaccine** consisting of suspension of bacterial cells that have been killed by chemical or physical means.

bacteriolysis. The destruction of bacteria by rupture so that the cells release their contents. Immunological agents causing this are **lysozyme**, or specific **antibody** activating **complement**, sometimes with the aid of lysozyme. Cells such as **neutrophil leucocytes** also destroy bacteria by lysis following **phagocytosis**.

bacteriophage neutralization test. *see* **phage neutralization test**.

bagassosis. Respiratory disease similar to **farmer's lung** q.v. Occurs in persons who inhale dust from mouldy overheated sugar cane bagasse. Lesions due mainly to **hypersensitivity** of **Arthus reaction** type (**type III reaction**) progressing to pulmonary fibrosis. The antigens involved are derived from thermophilic actinomycetes, antigenically related to *M.faeni* the causative agent of farmer's lung.

BALB/c mouse. An **inbred strain** of white mice. They readily develop **plasmacytomas** following intraperitoneal inoculation of mineral oil and other substances.

barrier filter. A filter placed in the eyepiece of a microscope used for the **fluorescent antibody technique**. It prevents light of the wavelength that excites the **fluorochrome** from reaching the observer's eye, thus allowing the fluorescence to be more readily seen, and prevents ultraviolet radiation from causing eye damage. *See also* **excitation filter**.

basement membrane antibody. Antibody against antigens present in basement membrane, e.g. renal glomerulus. *See* **glomerulonephritis**.

basophil degranulation test. An *in vitro* test for **immediate hypersensitivity**. Antigen is added to heparinized blood collected from the patient believed to be **sensitized**[1]. Smears are then made and the number of basophils seen in them is compared with the number in a control preparation to which antigen has not been added. An estimate of the amount of degranulation that has taken place, due to reaction of the antigen with **IgE** on the basophil cell surface, can thus be made. Alternatively, the histamine released (from basophils in lung tissue slices) can be measured spectrophotometrically.

basophil leucocyte. A **leucocyte** found in small numbers in blood and derived from bone marrow, that contains round granules of different sizes giving a basophilic reaction with normal stains. The granules are believed to contain heparin, also **histamine** and other **vasoactive amines** that may be released at sites of inflammation or in **immediate hypersensitivity** reactions. Basophil leucocytes possess **Fc receptors** for **IgE (RFcε)**. Cf. **mast cell**, which the basophil closely resembles.

Bayol 55®. A light white mineral oil used as a component of **water-in-oil emulsion adjuvants** such as **complete** and **incomplete Freund's adjuvant** for use in experimental animals. Also known as Bayol F®, and Bayol 52®. '55' refers to the viscosity at 100°F. *See also* **Drakeol 6VR®**.

Bayol F®. *See* **Bayol 55®** (*syn*).

B blood group. *See* **ABO blood group system**.

BCDF *See* **B-cell differentiation factors**

B-cell. *See* **B lymphocyte**.

B-cell differentiation factors. Factors derived from **T lymphocytes** which drive **B lymphocytes** to differentiate into antibody secreting cells. Synonymous with **T-cell replacing factor**. The terminlolgy **BSF** q.v. is now used for this group of factors.

B-cell growth factors (BCGF). Soluble factors derived from **T lymphocyes** which stimulate **B lymphocytes** to proliferate in culture. Unlike **B-cell differentiation factors**, they do not induce immunoglobulin secretion. The terminology **BSF** q.v. is now used for this group of factors, thus BCGF1, a **T lymphocyte** derived co-factor for antigen-activated B lymphocyte proliferation, is also called BSF-pl.

B-cell maturation factor. *Syn*. B-cell proliferation factor, BCPF. A factor derived from T lymphocytes that causes **immunoglobulin** secretion inducible in most clones of resting **B lymphocytes**.

BCG. Bacille Calmette–Guérin. A living attenuated bovine strain of *Mycobacterium tuberculosis* used as a **vaccine** to protect against tuberculosis (and leprosy). Prepared by two French workers (hence name) who cultivated the organism for many years on a glycerol-bile-potato medium. For usage *see* **tuberculosis immunization**.

BCGF *See* **B-cell growth factors**.

BDB. *See* **bis diazotized benzidine.**

beige mouse. A strain of mouse that is partially (but not completely) deficient in natural killer cells (**NK cells**, q.v.).

Bence-Jones protein. Protein in urine of patients with **myelomatosis**. Precipitated by heating to 60°C but redissolves on further heating to 90°C. Mol.wt. 46 000. Consists of dimerized **light chains** of **myeloma protein**.

benign monoclonal gammopathy. A **paraproteinaemia** characterized by the typical serum abnormality of this group of diseases, i.e. an electrophoretic spike of **myeloma protein**-type **immunoglobulin**, but without any of the other abnormalities associated with **myelomatosis**. Patients remain well and the prognosis is good.

bentonite. $Al_2O_3.4SiO_2.H_2O$. Native, colloidal, hydrated aluminium silicate. Particulate and insoluble. Used for **adsorption** of proteins, thus used to adsorb antigens in the **bentonite flocculation test**. Also has **adjuvant** activity.

bentonite flocculation test. Test in which particles of **bentonite** are used as carriers to adsorb antigens. On addition of specific antibody agglutination of the coated bentonite particles occurs.

berylliosis. Disease caused by contact with beryllium. Persons who inhale dust containing compounds of beryllium may develop an acute chemical pneumonia or a more chronic pulmonary granulomatous disease similar to **sarcoidosis** with **epithelioid cell** granulomata leading to pulmonary fibrosis. May also affect lymph nodes, skin, other tissues. Poorly understood but may involve **delayed hypersensitivity** to complexes of beryllium with macromolecules.

β **(beta) lysin**. Substance, first described by von Behring, present in normal sera that are active against aerobic Gram positive spore forming bacilli. Beta-lysin is a basic protein of low molecular weight released by platelets during the process of blood coagulation.

β **propiolactone**. A chemical used for the preparation of **inactivated vaccines** from pathogenic viruses. It destroys the nucleic acid core of the virus without damaging the capsids; thus the **protective antigens** are preserved.

β_1 **A globulin**. Degradation product of β_1C **globulin.** Has faster electrophoretic mobility and lower molecular weight than β_1C globulin. Degradation to β_1A is associated with loss of **C3** activity.

β_1**C globulin.** Serum **globulin** with activity as **C3** component of **complement.** Present in fresh serum; dissociates on storage into faster moving, inactive β_1**A globulin.**

β_1**E globulin.** Serum **globulin** with activity as **C4** component of **complement.**

β_1**F globulin.** Serum **globulin** with activity as **C5** component of **complement.**

β_1**H.** *See* **factor H.**

β_2**A globulin.** Obsolete *syn.* for **IgA.**

β_2**M globulin.** Obsolete *syn.* for **IgM.**

β_2 **microglobulin.** Protein of mol. wt. 11 500 daltons, containing 100 amino acids and strongly resembling in primary and secondary structure a single **homology region** of the **constant region** of immunoglobulin and therefore probably genetically related to **immunoglobulin.** Forms part of the structure of HLA antigens (*see* **HLA histocompatibility systems**).

BFPR. *See* **biological false positive reaction.**

BGG. Bovine **gamma globulin;** commonly used as an **antigen** in experimental work.

binding constant. *See* **association constant.**

binding site. Term used of **antigen-binding site** and other specified sites of attachment of macromolecules to one another.

biochemical sequestration. Inability of **hidden determinants** on a molecule or cell to stimulate an **immune response** or to combine with antibody. Following a structural change in the molecule or cell, such determinants may be revealed and become capable of **recognition.** Such changes in **autoantigens** may result in **autoantibody** production. *See* **rheumatoid factor.**

biological false positive reaction. A positive **Wassermann reaction** that is not due to infection with *Treponema pallidum* or related organisms. Due to antibodies against antigens present in many body tissues (including the heart antigen used in Wassermann tests). Such antibodies are found in many **autoimmune diseases,** e.g. **systemic lupus erythematosus.**

bird fancier's lung. Respiratory disease caused by exposure to antigens derived from the blood **plasma** of birds, especially albumin and gamma globulin. These are present in bird faeces and also in 'dust' from the skin and feathers. The disease is characterized by attacks of breathlessness due predominantly to a **hypersensitivity** reaction of **Arthus reaction** type (**type III reaction**). Diagnosed by **gel diffusion** tests in which serum is shown to contain precipitins against bird serum.

bis-diazotized benzidine. A bivalent coupling agent containing the cation $N \equiv \overset{+}{N} - \bigcirc - \bigcirc - \overset{+}{N} \equiv N$, that will link two protein molecules together. Used for **conjugation** of red blood cells with antigens for **passive agglutination tests**. *See* **diazotization**.

bi-specific antibody molecule. Antibody molecule with one **antigen-binding site** specific for one antigen, and the other antigen-binding site specific for another. A laboratory artefact, following recombination of heavy and light chains derived from two different specific antibodies.

blast cell. A cell, usually large (diameter>8μm), with ill-differentiated cytoplasm rich in RNA and actively synthesizing DNA (as shown by the rapid incorporation of tritiated thymidine). The nuclear patterns of blast cells vary and help to determine morphologically the series to which it belongs, *see* **plasmablast**, myeloblast (**myeloid cell series**), etc.

blast transformation. *See* **lymphocyte transformation**.

blockade. *See* **reticuloendothelial blockade**.

blocking antibody. (1) In **agglutination** tests, **incomplete antibody**[1] that may coat cells and prevent agglutination. It may be detected by the **antiglobulin test**. (2) In **immediate hypersensitivity**, antibody of **IgG** type that may combine preferentially with antigen (or **allergen**) thus preventing it from reacting with **IgE** type, cell-fixed **reagin**[1]. Blocking antibody is thus able to inhibit immediate hypersensitivity reactions. In **hyposensitization**, an attempt is made to encourage preferential formation of blocking antibody in **atopic** persons by repeated injection of allergen. (3) Antibody molecule which binds to a cell surface and inhibits the expression of cell mediated effector functions (*see* **blocking factor**).

blocking factor. Any factor which interferes with the expression of the immune response. Most commonly associated with inhibition of

cell mediated immunity in pregnancy and in patients with tumours or **allografts**. May be antibodies, (*see* **blocking antibody**) **immune complexes** or non-specific substances such as serum proteins.

blocking test. Any test in which the specific reaction between an antibody and antigen is blocked by prior addition to the mixture of antibody of the same specificity but with different biological activity, e.g. the addition of **incomplete antibody**[1] to a suspension of red cells may prevent (block) subsequent agglutination of those cells by **agglutinin**[1].

blood group. Classification of **isoantigens** on the surfaces of erythrocytes. The most important blood groups in man are those of the **ABO**, and **Rhesus blood group systems** q.v.

blood group substance. Soluble substance present in body fluids that bears **blood group** specificity, i.e. shares **antigenic determinants** with red cell surface **isoantigens** (*see also* **ABO blood group substances**).

B lymphocyte. A **lymphocyte** that is derived from **bone marrow** without passing through the **thymus** (cf. **T lymphocyte**). In birds B lymphocyte maturation is determined by the **bursa of Fabricius**. In mammals this organ is absent and the bursa equivalent tissue may be the bone marrow itself (probably liver and spleen in the embryo). B lymphocytes play a major role in **humoral immunity**. On stimulation by antigen they differentiate into antibody-forming **plasma cells**. In the case of **thymus dependent antigens** this process requires cooperation with T lymphocytes (cf. **thymus independent antigens**). *See* table on p.32

B lymphocyte receptor (B lymphocyte antigen receptor, B-cell receptor). A membrane-bound **immunoglobulin** molecule on the surface of **B lymphocytes**. When this binds specifically to **antigen**, the cell is stimulated to divide and differentiate into **memory cells**, **lymphoblasts** and **plasma cells** secreting **antibody** of the same **specificity** (although not necessarily the same **immunoglobulin class**) as the original **receptor**. B lymphocyte receptors are produced by the cell that bears them, as opposed to surface immunoglobulins that may be picked up by cells from the surrounding medium by their **Fc receptors**.

B lymphocyte repertoire

Differential characteristics of B and T lymphocytes

	B	T
SURFACE ANTIGENS PRESENT		
Thy 1 (θ), in mice	–	+
B lymphocyte specific antigen (in mice)	+	–
Immunoglobulin	+	–
Complement receptors	+	–
FUNCTIONAL ACTIVITIES IN VITRO		
Proliferation in response to mitogens	*See* table of **mitogens**	
Mixed leucocyte response	–	+
Respond to **thymus independent antigens**	+	–
Bind **thymus dependent antigens**	+	±
Bind thymus independent antigens	+	–
ACTIVITY IN VIVO		
Cells required to be present for antibody response to:		
thymus dependent antigens	+	+
thymus independent antigens	+	–
haptens	+	+
Carrier reactive helper activity	–	+
Anti-hapten antibody-forming cell precursor	+	–
Cell mediated immune responses	–	+
Migration of cells to lymph nodes	–	+
Lymphocyte proliferation in **thymus dependent areas**	–	+
Germinal centre formation	+	–
Plasma cell production	+	–

B lymphocyte repertoire. The number of different V_H-V_L combinations (i.e. **antigen binding sites**) that the immune system of an individual animal is potentially capable of producing. Considered to be reflected in the number of B lymphocytes with different antigen-receptors on their surface.

B lymphocyte stimulatory factors *See* **BSF, B cell differentiation factors, B cell growth factors, T cell replacing factor**.

B lymphocyte tolerance. A state of **immunological tolerance** (*q.v.*) in which only the **B lymphocytes** are unable to respond to the responsible **antigen, T lymphocytes** specific for the same antigen being unaffected.

B_1 lymphocyte. A subset of **B lymphocytes** believed to be capable of responding to **antigen** in the absence of **helper T lymphocytes**, cf. B_2 **lymphocyte**.

B_2 lymphocyte. A subset of **B lymphocytes** that requires the presence of **helper T lymphocytes** in order to be stimulated by **antigen**, cf. **B_1 lymphocyte**. The division of B lymphocytes into B_1 and B_2 cells may be complicated by the necessity of having the correct T lymphocyte subsets present to enable T-T cell interactions to take place.

BMF. *See* B-cell maturation factor

B mouse. Mouse that has been deprived of **T lymphocytes** by whole body irradiation or thymectomy plus irradiation and replacement of haemopoietic cells and **B lymphocytes** with an inoculation of bone marrow cells. Therefore it has no **cell mediated immune** responses and can only produce **humoral immune** responses to **thymus independent antigens.** *See also* **nu nu mice.**

Boivin antigen. *Syn.* **O antigen** of Gram negative bacteria. *See also* **endotoxin.**

bone marrow. The soft tissue that fills the cavities of bones. Red marrow is actively haemopoietic (i.e. blood forming) and is found in developing bone, ribs, vertebrae and parts of long bones. It contains all the cells and corpuscles (with their precursors) of the circulating blood, and also megakaryocytes, reticulum cells, **macrophages** and **plasma cells.** It contains lymphocyte **stem cells** and is the principal site of formation of **B lymphocytes** and **pre-T lymphocytes** (but not mature T lymphocytes) in the adult. In adult animals much of the red marrow is replaced by fatty tissue and becomes yellow marrow.

bone marrow derived cell. Any cell derived from bone marrow, e.g. erythrocytes, lymphocytes, granulocytes, etc.

booster dose. A dose of antigen given after the **priming dose** to stimulate accelerated production of large amounts of antibody. Especially used to refer to doses of **vaccine** given at intervals of a few months or years after a preliminary course of injections in an immunization programme.

Bordetella pertussis. The causative organism of whooping cough in children. It possesses an **endotoxin** that is an excellent **adjuvant** and particularly stimulates the production of **homocytotropic antibody.** In childhood immunization schedules, **vaccines** against whooping cough, containing killed *B.pertussis*, may be given with **diphtheria toxoid** with which they act as an **adjuvant,** *see* **triple vaccine.** A lymphocyte stimulating factor (LSF) that provokes a **lymphocytosis** has also been isolated from the organisms. Yet another factor, which may, or may not, be independent of the above, greatly increases the sensitivity of the body to **histamine.**

bovine serum albumin. Serum albumin from cattle, used as an experimental antigen and in the **albumin agglutination test** (*see* **albumin agglutinating antibody**). Also used for separation of cells by **density gradient centrifugation**.

Boyden chamber. An apparatus used in tests for **chemotaxis**. Consists of two compartments separated by a micropore filter. Cells are placed in the upper compartment and the chemotactic agent in the lower. Cells sediment onto the filter, and migrate through its pores if they are attracted by the agent. The filter is then stained and cell migration is measured.

bradykinin. A basic nonapeptide, one of the vasoactive plasma **kinins** q.v. whose action is slow compared to that of **histamine**. It is detectable in the tissues in experimental **anaphylactic shock**, indicating that the kinin system probably plays a part in the pathogenesis of **immediate hypersensitivity** lesions.

bromelin. Proteolytic enzyme used for treating red cells to render them agglutinable by **incomplete antibody**[1].

brucella vaccines. *Vet.* (a) S19 (strain 19) vaccine contains live, attenuated *Brucella abortus*. Widely used for the immunization of cattle. A disadvantage is that it stimulates long-lasting agglutinating antibodies in adults (but not calves, hence calfhood vaccination is encouraged). These complicate control of the disease by brucellosis serological tests. It is infective to man if accidentally inoculated. (b) 45/20 vaccine contains killed organisms of McEwen strain 45/20 in a **water- in-oil emulsion adjuvant**. This strain does not stimulate the production of high titres of **agglutinin**[1]. Its use does not, therefore, complicate the diagnosis of active infection.

brucellin. A material, analogous to **tuberculin**, used in **skin tests** for the diagnosis of *Brucella abortus* infection. Obtained as a filtrate from a culture of the organism. The results of the tests are of debatable value in diagnosis. A positive result indicates **delayed hypersensitivity** to brucella antigens.

Bruton type hypogammaglobulinaemia. *See* **infantile sex-linked hypogammaglobulinaemia**.

BSA. *See* **Bovine serum albumin**.

BSF B lymphocyte stimulatory factors. Nomenclature to replace **B cell differentiation factor, B-cell growth factor**, etc; BSF to be followed by a number, BSF1, BSF2...n, for different factors, and the letter p (provisional) to precede the number until the factor has been purified or its structure determined.

buffy coat. The layer of **white cells** that forms between the red cell layer and the **plasma** when unclotted blood is centrifuged.

Burkitt's lymphoma. Malignant tumour of **lymphoid tissue** especially affecting jaws, abdominal viscera. Common in, but not exclusive to, African children. Associated with hot, humid climate in circumscribed area of Africa corresponding to areas where disease-carrying mosquitoes are found. E-B virus, a herpes-type virus, has been isolated from the lymphoma cells and has also been shown to cause **infectious mononucleosis** (*glandular fever*). Antibody to E-B virus is found in the sera of patients with Burkitt's lymphoma. The disease tends to remit and to respond to chemotherapy. This may be related to an **immune response** against the tumour.

bursa of Fabricius. A sac-like lymphoepithelial structure arising as a dorsal diverticulum from the cloaca of young birds. First described in 1621 by Hieronymus Fabricius, an Italian anatomist, it is composed entirely of plicae containing numerous **primary follicles**. Lymphopoiesis takes place within these and continues until the structure involutes at about the time of sexual maturity. The bursa is associated with **humoral immunity** and **lymphocytes** processed by it are called **B lymphocytes** (q.v.). Bursectomized chickens fail to make **antibodies** to a variety of antigens and **plasma cells** and **germinal centres** are reduced or absent in their **lymphoid tissues**.

bursacyte. Lymphocyte processed by the **bursa of Fabricius** and responsible for **humoral immunity** in birds, thus a **B lymphocyte** q.v.

bursectomy. Removal or destruction of the avian **bursa of Fabricius**. When this is done surgically *in ovo* or shortly after hatching, or *in ovo* by application of testosterone or other hormones, the development of the system of cells that form **humoral antibody** is inhibited.

byssinosis. Disease of workers in vegetable fibre industry, e.g. cotton, flax, jute, hemp. Presents with chest tightness after a period of absence from work. Thus 'Monday morning tightness' and 'return to work tightness'. Suggested to be due to **hypersensitivity** to vegetable fibre dusts.

bystander lysis

bystander lysis   Non specific lysis of tissue cells during an immune response against other, specific, target structures (*see* **bystander phenomena**).

bystander phenomena   The non-specific effects (including lysis) of an immune response on tissues which are not themselves specific targets of that response, but which are susceptible to the action of non-specific factors released during the response.

C.   Symbol for **complement**.

C′ (C prime).   Obsolete symbol for **complement**. Replaced by C.

C_α; C_δ; C_ε; C_γ; $C_\varkappa$; C_λ; C_μ.   The **constant regions** of the immunoglobulin chains corresponding to the appropriate subscript Greek letter. *See* table on p109.

C_H.   The **constant region** of the **heavy chain** of immunoglobulin.

C_H1, C_H2, C_H3, C_H4.   Designations given to the **homology regions** of the **constant region** of the **heavy chain** of **immunoglobulins**. Each heavy chain is made up of a number of homology regions named (starting at the **N terminal** end) C_H1, C_H2, etc. In **IgG** C_H1 forms the constant half of the **Fab fragment** and C_H2 and C_H3 form the **Fc fragment**. IgM has a longer heavy chain with an extra homology region, C_H4.

C_L.   The **constant region** of the **light chain** of **immunoglobulin**.

C1.   The first component of **complement**. Comprises three subcomponents C1q, C1r, C1s which occur as a macromolecular complex *in vivo* in the presence of Ca^{++}ions. Heat labile. Reacts with antigen-antibody complexes to form $\overline{C1}$, the activated form, an esterase which attacks **C4** and **C2**. C1q carries the site which binds to the Fc fragment of IgG and IgM **immune complexes**. This site binds to the Fc fragment of **IgG** and **IgM** (in man). Following binding to complexes, C1r is converted to $\overline{C1r}$ which cleaves C1s to form $\overline{C1s}$. $\overline{C1s}$ carries the enzymatic site which acts on C4 and C2.

$\overline{C1}$INH.   *See* $\overline{C1}$ **inhibitor**.

$\overline{C1}$ inhibitor ($\overline{C1}$ esterase inhibitor or inactivator).   An inhibitor of $\overline{C1}$, the activated esterase formed from **C1**. An a_2 globulin normally present in serum. Deficient in **hereditary angioneurotic oedema**. Also inhibits Hageman factor fragments, **kallikrein, plasminogen activator**, plasmin.

36

C2. The second component of **complement**. A β_2 globulin with sedimentation coefficient $s_{20,w} = 6S$ (human). Split by $C\overline{1}$, and, in the presence of Mg^{++} ions, complexes with C4b to form the **C3 convertase** enzyme $C\overline{42}$. Heat labile.

C3. The third component of **complement**. Actually reacts fourth in haemolytic complement fixation sequence, thus EAC1423 (*see* **EAC**). Serum concentration much higher than that of other complement components (500–1000 µg/ml). Is also known as β_1C globulin, $s_{20,w} = 9.5S$ (human). Contains 2 polypeptide chains (α and β) linked by disulphide and non-covalent bonds. Both the **classical complement pathway C3 convertase** ($C\overline{42}$) and the **alternative pathway C3 convertase** split the α-chain to give a small fragment **C3a** and the remainder of the molecule is then known as **C3b**.

C3a. A biologically active fragment of complement component C3. It is a low molecular weight basic polypeptide (mol. wt. c. 9000 daltons) split from the **N terminal** end of the α-chain of C3 by **C3 convertase** and other tryptic enzymes. C3a is biologically active as **anaphylatoxin**. This activity is destroyed by anaphylatoxin inactivator a naturally-occurring carboxypeptidase N which digests the **C terminal** arginine from C3a.

C3b. An active fragment of complement component C3. It is produced when the α-chain of C3 is digested by **C3 convertase**, splitting off **C3a** q.v. C3b has an affinity for cell surfaces, i.e. for the **C3b receptors** present on **macrophages, neutrophil leucocytes, B lymphocytes** and possibly **T lymphocytes**, hence C3b enhances **immune adherence, phagocytosis** and acts as an **opsonin**. **Factor I** cleaves the α chain of C3b to form **iC3b**.

C3bi *Syn.* for iC3b.

C3b inactivator. (*See* **Factor I**.)

C3b receptors. Three types of receptors for C3 cleavage products are known: (a) A cell-membrane receptor (CR1) for the activated third component of complement (**C3b**). Present on human **neutrophil leucocytes, B lymphocytes, mononuclear phagocytes** and other cells such as glomerular epithelial cells and **Langerhans' cells**. The C3b receptor (CR1) mediates opsonic removal of microorganisms and **immune complexes** and bacterial killing. (b) A receptor (CR3) for

C3 convertase

inactivated C3b (**iC3b**) present on **neutrophil leucocytes, mononuclear phagocytes** and glomerular epithelial cells. (c) A receptor (CR2) for C3d, a cleavage product of C3b, present on **B lymphocytes**.

C3 convertase. Enzymes of the **complement** system that will cleave **C3** into **C3a** and **C3b**. The **classical complement pathway** C3 convertase is the bi- molecular complex C$\overline{42}$. Distinguish this from **alternative pathway C3 convertase** which is a complex of **C3b, factor B** and **factor P** (C$\overline{3bBbP}$).

C3H mice. An **inbred strain** of mice. Lymphocytes from the C3H/HeJ substrain are unresponsive to **lipopolysaccharide**.

C3 nephritic factor. An autoantibody with specificity for the **alternative pathway C3 convertase** C3bBbP. It stabilises the convertase, and renders it resistant to the decay dissociation effect of **factor H**. Thus it causes intense activation of the alternative pathway. Found in the sera of a proportion of patients with hypocomplementaemic membranoproliferative glomerulonephritis.

C3PA. (C3 proactivator). Obsolete term for **factor B**.

C3 proactivator. Obsolete term for **factor B**.

C4. The fourth component of **complement**. Actually reacts second in haemolytic complement fixation sequence, thus EAC14 (*see* **EAC**). Also known as β_1E globulin, $s_{20,w} = 10S$ (human). Substrate for C$\overline{1}$ which activates it (C$\overline{4}$) by splitting it to produce an active part C4b and a fragment, C4a. *See also* **C2**. Destroyed by **hydrazine** and other primary amines. Heat stable. Consists of 3 polypeptide chains, α, δ, γ. C4a has **anaphylatoxin** activity.

C5. The fifth component of **complement**. β_1F globulin, $s_{20,w} = 8.5S$ (human). On activation by C5 convertase (C$\overline{423}$), or by C$\overline{3b,Bb,C3b}$, the alternative pathway convertase, a small fragment, **C5a**, mol. wt. 7000–12 000 is split off. This fragment acts as an **anaphylatoxin** and has chemotactic activity for leucocytes (*see* **chemotaxis**). The remainder of the split C5 molecule, C5b, forms a complex with C6,7,8 and 9 which has an affinity for cell membranes and damages them. This is believed to be the step which mediates **immune cytolysis** and **haemolysis**.

C5a. Peptide with activity as chemotactic factor (*see* **chemotaxis**) and **anaphylatoxin**. Derived from **C5** by tryptic cleavage by C5 converTase. In man, a 74 residue, glycosylated peptide. An **anaphylatoxin inactivator** with carboxypeptidase-N activity occurs naturally in human serum and removes the C-terminal arginine from C5a to form $C5a_{des\ Arg}$. $C5a_{des\ Arg}$ lacks anaphylatoxin activity, but retains some chemotactic activity.

C6. The sixth component of **complement**. A β_2 globulin with $s_{20,w} = 6S$. A single polypeptide chain. *See also* **C5**.

C7. The seventh component of **complement**. A β_2 globulin with $s_{20,w} = 5.2S$. A single polypeptide chain. *See also* **C5**.

C8. The eighth component of **complement**. A β_1 globulin with $s_{20,w} = 8S$. Mol. wt. 150 000. Serum concentration in man 10–20 µg/ml. Consists of 3 polypeptide chains, α, β, γ.

C9. The final component of **complement**. An α_2 globulin with $s_{20,w} = 4.4S$. When C3–9 have reacted in a haemolytic sequence, the red cell membrane is damaged by bound C5b–9 and the cell undergoes lysis. Although not absolutely essential for complement-mediated lysis, C9 speeds up the low grade lytic activity of the C5b–8 complex.

caecal tonsils. Aggregations of **lymphoid tissue** with **germinal centres** found in birds in an enlarged portion of each caecal wall near the point at which the twin caeca enter the junction of the large and small intestines.

Calmette test. Obsolete **tuberculin test** in which tuberculin is instilled into the conjunctival sac. Persons or animals that are, or have been infected with *Mycobacterium tuberculosis* develop a conjunctivitis. Cf. **corneal response**.

canine distemper vaccines. (a) *Vet.* and *Hist.* **Serum virus vaccination** and **vaccine** (formalinized infected spleen) **virus** techniques were at one time extensively used. (b) *Vet.* Virus attenuated by growth in the chick embryo or in tissue culture is now employed. (c) *Vet.* A **heterologous vaccine** containing attenuated human measles virus is sometimes used to protect young puppies that have passive maternal immunity to the distemper virus, and do not respond to vaccination with the latter.

canine parvovirus vaccine. *Vet*. The first **vaccine** used against this recently discovered disease of dogs (initial cases circa 1978) was live attenuated feline enteritis vaccine. This related virus was probably the parent, by mutation, of the canine virus. The vaccination technique using a **heterologous vaccine** was thus analogous to **smallpox vaccination** using as **antigen** a virus that is a close facsimile of the infectious agent. The vaccine now used contains an attenuated form of the canine virus itself.

capping. Accumulation of clusters or patches of aggregated proteins at one site on the cell surface. Follows the aggregation of surface components of cell membranes, e.g. by the action of polyvalent ligands (*see* **patching**). When cells with such patches move, the latter are swept to the posterior area of the cell forming a cap there. Capping is an energy requiring process (cf. patching). It has been described frequently in **lymphocytes** but also takes place on many other cells.

caprinized vaccine. A vaccine containing microorganisms whose virulence has been attenuated by adaptation to, and passage in, goats. *See* **rinderpest vaccine**[b].

capsular polysaccharide. Polysaccharides present as constituents of bacterial capsules. Often antigenic. The best-studied are those of *Streptococcus pneumoniae* (pneumococcus) but many other organisms may also have polysaccharide capsules, e.g. other streptococci and members of the genus *Bacillus* (except *B.anthracis*, which has a polypeptide capsule). *See* **pneumococcus capsule swelling reaction**.

capsule swelling reaction. *See* **pneumococcus capsule swelling reaction**.

carbon clearance test. A test used to measure the activity of the **mononuclear phagocyte system** in experimental animals. A suspension of colloidal carbon particles is inoculated intravenously and blood samples collected at short intervals thereafter. The carbon present in these is estimated in a colorimeter after the red cells have been lysed with distilled water. The rate (K) of removal of the carbon from the blood by phagocytosis can then be estimated. This is the slope of the line produced by plotting the logarithms of the colorimeter readings against time. *See also* **phagocytic index**[1].

carcinoembryonic antigen. An antigen normally found only in fetal gut. Present in serum of patients with carcinoma (especially of colon and lung) but also in smokers and in subjects with inflammatory bowel disease; therefore of limited diagnostic value.

carcinomatous neuropathy. A group of neurological disorders occurring in patients with cancer but not caused by metastasis in the nervous system. In one of these diseases, sensory carcinomatous neuropathy, **autoantibodies** against RNA- protein of the cytoplasm of neurones are found in serum.

cardiolipin. Is a esterified glyceryl-phosphoryl-glyceryl-phosphoryl-glycerol. A phospholipid **hapten** purified from beef heart which is the active antigen in the **Wassermann reaction** and in other serological tests for syphilis. It may carry **antigenic determinants** similar to those of *Treponema pallidum*, the causative agent of syphilis or be similar to products of tissue necrosis formed when the spirochaete attacks human tissues.

carrier. Macromolecule to which a **hapten** is **conjugated** *in vitro*, or to which it may become attached *in vivo*, and which renders the hapten capable of stimulating an **immune response**.

carrier prophylactic. A **vaccine** adsorbed onto a 'carrier' such as **aluminium hydroxide gel**.

carrier specificity. Term used of **antibody** (or of a **cell-mediated immune** response), formed in response to injection of **hapten** conjugated to a carrier macromolecule, and which has specificity for the carrier, but not for free hapten or for hapten bound to an unrelated carrier.

cartwheel nucleus. Characteristic morphology of a **plasma cell** nucleus showing light and dark regions resembling a cartwheel under the electron microscope. The light regions, forming the spokes of the wheel, are formed by euchromatin actively engaged in transcription, whereas the dark regions are formed by the less active heterochromatin.

cascade reaction. A sequential reaction in which each event initiates the next event in the sequence. Used of enzymatic reactions such as **complement fixation**, blood coagulation, etc.

Casoni test. Intradermal **skin test** used in the diagnosis of hydatid disease (*Echinococcus granulosus* infection) in man. Sensitive but of low specificity. An extract of the tapeworm or hydatid cyst fluid is injected intradermally. This is followed by a **weal and flare response** within half an hour and by an indurated delayed (**cell-mediated immunity**) reaction after 24 hours.

CBA mouse. An **inbred strain** of mouse. Many substrains exist of which CBA/H-T6 which is homozygous for the cytological marker translocation T6, is the most important to the immunologist. *See* **T6 marker.**

CEA. *See* **carcinoembryonic antigen.**

cecropin. Member of a group of inducible, antibacterial proteins originally isolated from immunized pupae of the cecropia moth, and now known to occur in other moths and butterflies. These small, basic proteins cause rapid lysis of several species of Gram-negative and Gram-positive bacteria.

cell bound antibody (cell fixed antibody). Any **antibody** bound to the surface of a cell, i.e. **incomplete antibody**[1] bound by its **antigen- binding sites** to cell antigens, or **cytophilic antibody** or **reagin**[1] bound by other sites so that the antigen-binding sites remain free to react with antigen.

cell cooperation. *See* **T lymphocyte-B lymphocyte cooperation.**

cell-mediated immunity (CMI). **Specific immunity** which is dependent upon the presence of effector **T lymphocytes.** Cell-mediated immunity is responsible for reactions such as **allograft** rejection (*see* **graft rejection**), **delayed hypersensitivity, tuberculin test** reactions and is important in defence against viral infections (*see* **thymic hypoplasia**) and against some bacteria. Note that in these reactions, the effector cell *may* be other than a lymphocyte. Cf. **humoral immunity** and **cellular immunity**[1].

cell-mediated immunity deficiency syndromes. Syndromes characterized by failure to express reactions of **cell-mediated immunity,** i.e. to reject a skin **allograft** (*see* **graft rejection**), become sensitized to agents causing **contact hypersensitivity,** show **delayed hypersensitivity** reactions, etc. Examples include **thymic hypoplasia** and **severe combined immunodeficiency syndrome** q.v.

cellular allergy. *See* **delayed hypersensitivity, cell-mediated immunity, type IV reaction.**

cellular hypersensitivity. *See* **delayed hypersensitivity, cell-mediated immunity, type IV reaction.**

cellular immunity. (1) Term originated by Metchnikoff to refer to an increased ability of phagocytic cells to destroy or to digest parasitic organisms, and properly so used. Thus is a *syn*. for macrophage immunity. (2) Sometimes used to refer to **cell-mediated immunity** q.v.

central arteriole. Splenic vessel occupying the axis of the Malpighian follicle in the **spleen**.

central lymphoid organs. Those lymphoid organs that are essential to the ontogeny of the immune response, i.e. the **thymus** and **bursa of Fabricius**. Cf. **peripheral lymphoid organs**.

centrally acting adjuvants. **Adjuvant** substances that stimulate the **immune response** even when given at a different time or site from the antigen. They probably have a direct stimulatory effect on the cells of the immunological system. Examples are **endotoxin**, **wax D**. Cf. **depot forming adjuvants**.

centrocyte. B **lymphocyte** found in **germinal centres**. (*Also* centroblast).

CFA. *See* **complete Freund's adjuvant**.

CFT. *See* **complement fixation test**.

CFU. *See* **colony forming unit**.

C-gene. Gene coding for the **constant region** of an **immunoglobulin heavy** or **light chain**. The heavy chain C-gene is divided by **introns** into separate units (**exons**) corresponding to the **homology regions** of the heavy chain. *See* figure on p.117.

CH_{50}. In **immune haemolysis**, the dose of **complement** which is capable of lysing 50 per cent of the test suspension of **sensitized** (red) cells[2].

challenge. (1) Administration of antigen to provoke an **immunological reaction**[1]. Usually used of the second or later doses of antigen. (2) Administration of a virulent pathogen, e.g. in order to test initial immunity or the degree of protection achieved by **vaccination**.

charcoal agglutination test. A **passive agglutination test** for infection with *Trichinella* and with *Schistosoma* in which the antigen is adsorbed to cholesterol-lecithin crystals and charcoal is added to the suspension. The test is carried out on plastic cards, plasma from a finger prick blood sample is added; if this contains antibody, macroscopic **agglutination** is seen. The method has also been used for the diagnosis of other parasitic diseases.

Chediak-Higashi syndrome. Disease of children inherited as autosomal recessive, characterized by pale skin, hair and eyes due to lack of normal pigment and by increased susceptibility to severe pyogenic infection. Lymphoma may occur. There is a defect of granulopoiesis and the **neutrophil leucocytes** contain abnormally large lysosomal granules and are defective in microbicidal function. There is also a defect of **natural killer cell** function.

chemiluminescence. Emission of photons as a result of chemical reactions. In immunological contexts, measurement of chemiluminescence is a useful measure of the oxidative generation of free radicals (*see* **superoxide anion**) by **neutrophil leucocytes** and **mononuclear phagocytes** (and possibly by **NK cells**). A rapid burst of chemiluminescence can be detected following the addition to these cells of phagocytosable particles, chemotactic factors or other excitatory entities.

chemokinesis. A reaction by which the speed of locomotion and/or the frequency of random turning of cells or organisms is determined by substances in their environment. Chemokinesis does not determine the *direction* of migration of cells (cf. **chemotaxis**). **Leucocytes** show chemokinesis when exposed to certain chemical substances.

chemotaxis. Reaction by which the direction of locomotion and the orientation of cells is determined by chemical substances. The cells become oriented and move towards (positive chemotaxis) or away from (negative chemotaxis) the source of a concentration gradient of the substance. Leucocytes (**neutrophil** and **eosinophil leucocytes**, **monocytes** and **lymphocytes**) show positive chemotaxis towards many agents including **C5a, formyl peptides, leukotriene** B$_4$, **lymphokines**, bacterial substances and products of cell damage or denatured proteins.

chimera (chimaera). A fire-breathing monster of Greek mythology-with lion's head, goat's body and serpent's tail. Immunology: An animal containing a mixture of cells derived from two individuals of different genotype. Such animals occur naturally (rarely) due to the fusion of the placental blood circulatory systems of dizygotic twins in utero–has been observed in cows and humans. Chimeras can also be produced artificially, *see* **tetraparental chimera, irradiation chimera**.

chimerism. A state in which two or more genetically different populations of cells coexist. *See* **chimera** and **irradiation chimera**.

chlorodinitrobenzene. (1-chloro-2,4-dinitrobenzene). Commonly referred to as DNCB. A reagent having the same chemical effects as **dinitrofluorobenzene** but reacting more slowly. Used for studying **contact hypersensitivity (type IV reaction, or delayed hypersensitivity)**. A sensitizing dose is applied to the forearm. The test dose is applied later to the opposite forearm. This gives a nodule of the type seen in the **tuberculin test**, 48–72 hours later. Positive in most normal people, but reduced or absent in **cell-mediated immunity deficiency syndromes**.

cholera vaccine. A **vaccine** containing smooth strains of heat or formalin killed *Vibrio cholerae* Inaba and *V.cholerae* Ogawa and preferably also El Tor vibrio. Widely used to produce **active immunity** against cholera in endemic areas and in persons travelling to such areas. Immunity is shortlived (not more than 3 months).

choriocarcinoma. A rare malignant tumour originating in the trophoblast cells of the placenta, and therefore a complication of pregnancy. Of particular interest because the tumour cells are fetal and thus the tumour is an **allograft**. Possibly for this reason, spontaneous destruction of the tumour masses may very rarely occur, and the therapeutic response to **antimetabolites** (e.g. methotrexate) is much better than for most other malignant tumours. **Immunotherapy**, using the father's cells as antigen, has also been described, but drug therapy appears to be more effective.

chromium release assay. *In vitro* test in which cells are labelled with a radioisotope of chromium (^{51}Cr) and used as targets for antibody dependent or cell mediated cytotoxicity. (*See* **antibody-dependent cell-mediated cytotoxicity** and **cytotoxic T lymphocyte**.) Radiolabel is released in proportion to the number of cells killed.

chronic granulomatous disease. Inherited disease of male children characterized by recurrent suppurative inflammation of lymph nodes, pulmonary **granulomata** and visceral abscesses with anaemia, leucocytosis and raised serum **immunoglobulin** levels. The **neutrophil leucocytes** are deficient in oxidative microbicidal activity. They are able to phagocytose bacteria and viruses but are unable to destroy them after **phagocytosis**.

chronic lymphatic leukaemia. Leukaemia characterized by large numbers of circulating **lymphocytes**. In the majority of cases, these are **B lymphocytes**. The **T lymphocyte** form is rare.

chronic mucocutaneous candidiasis. A systemic disease characterized by a persistent *Candida albicans* infection affecting mainly the skin, nails and mucosae. Unresponsive to therapy with anti-*Candida* agents. Clinically of two main types: **granulomatous** and non-granulomatous. Of varied aetiology, associated with (a) iron deficiency, (b) endocrinopathies, (c) various immunological defects, i.e. lymphocyte failure to produce macrophage migration inhibition factor (*see* **macrophage migration test**), or to transform (*see* **lymphocyte transformation**) and divide in response to *Candida* antigen, etc. A few reported cases of the granulomatous form of the disease have shown short-term benefit from treatment with **transfer factor**.

chronic myeloid leukaemia. Leukaemia in which the predominant circulating cell-types are late forms of **granulocyte** development, i.e. mature granulocytes, metamyelocytes and myelocytes (*see* **myeloid cell series**).

chronic progressive vaccinia (or vaccinia gangrenosa). Rare, fatal complication of **smallpox vaccination**. Slowly spreading gangrenous vaccinial lesions of skin extend out from the original vaccination site and may become generalized. Often associated with **immunological deficiency states** especially defects of **cell-mediated immunity**.

cisternal space. The lumen of the **endoplasmic reticulum**. In **plasma cells** this contains **immunoglobulin** molecules and subunits destined for secretion.

class I antigens. **Histocompatibility antigens** composed of two non-covalently associated, glycosylated polypeptides : a heavy chain of M.Wt. 44 000 and β_2-microglobulin, M.Wt. 12 000. (Structure shown below.) β_2-microglobulin is identical in all class I antigens and is the product of a separate chromosome from that coding for the heavy chain, which is a product of the **major histocompatibility complex**. The heavy chain exhibits extensive polymorphism and is coded for by the K, D and L genes of the mouse H-2 complex and the A, B and C genes of the human HLA complex (*see* maps of the HLA and H-2 genes on pp 101 and 90). Class I antigens are expressed on the surface membranes of all nucleated cells and are recognized in the killing of **allogeneic** cells and virus infected cells by **cytotoxic T lymphocytes** (*see* **MHC restriction**).

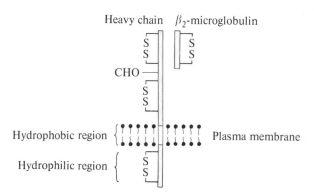

class II antigens. **Histocompatibility antigens** composed of two non-covalently associated glycosylated polypeptides : α chain, M.Wt. 32 000 and β chain, M.Wt. 28 000. (Structure shown below.) Murine H-2 **Ia antigens** and human **HLA-DR antigens** are included. Class II antigens are expressed predominantly on **B lymphocytes, macrophages** and other **accessory cells**, but are inducible on other cells including epithelium and vascular endothelium. They are involved in cell-cell recognition, especially between helper (T_H) lymphocytes, B lymphocytes and antigen-bearing macrophage/monocytes. Responses of **helper T lymphocytes** to foreign antigens require, in many cases, that the antigen be presented in association with Class II **syngeneic macrophages** or **accessory cells** (*see* **MHC restriction**). The murine Ia region includes at least 5, possibly 6 loci : Aα, Aβ, E$β_2$, Eα coding for relevant α and β chains. (*See* H-2 gene map on p90.) The J locus codes for a sub-set of antigens on suppressor (T_S) lymphocytes (*see* **I region**).

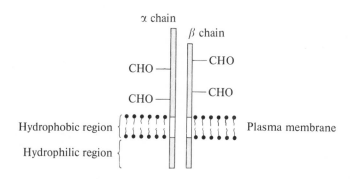

classical complement pathway. The pathway of **complement** activation that commences with activation of **C1, C4** and **C2** cf. **alternative pathway**.

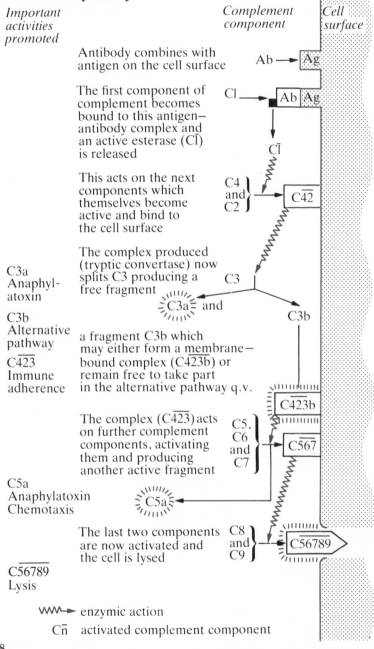

Important activities promoted		*Complement component*	*Cell surface*

Antibody combines with antigen on the cell surface — Ab → Ag

The first component of complement becomes bound to this antigen–antibody complex and an active esterase (C̄1) is released — C1 → Ab Ag → C̄1

This acts on the next components which themselves become active and bind to the cell surface — C4 and C2 → C̄42

C3a
Anaphyl-
atoxin

The complex produced (tryptic convertase) now splits C3 producing a free fragment — C3 → C3a and

C3b
Alternative pathway
C̄423
Immune adherence

a fragment C3b which may either form a membrane–bound complex (C̄423b) or remain free to take part in the alternative pathway q.v. — C3b → C̄423b

The complex (C̄423) acts on further complement components, activating them and producing another active fragment — C5, C6 and C7 → C̄567

C5a
Anaphylatoxin
Chemotaxis — C5a

C̄56789
Lysis

The last two components are now activated and the cell is lysed — C8 and C9 → C̄56789

〜〜→ enzymic action

C̄n   activated complement component

clonal abortion, clonal anergy, clonal deletion. Terms used to describe theories of the mechanism of **immunological tolerance**. They indicate, respectively, non-reactivity, early death, or complete removal of the relevant clone of immunoreactive cells.

clonal selection theory. A selective theory of antibody production proposed by Burnet. According to this theory, the normal individual carries a complement of clones of lymphoid cells capable of reacting with all possible antigenic determinants. During fetal life, those clones reactive against **autoantigens** are suppressed on contact with antigen. After birth, a change in the response to contact with antigen occurs, so that the normal response is proliferation, **antibody** production and **cell-mediated immunity**. Immunological tolerance, therefore, results from suppression of clones. Such suppressed clones against self antigens may again become active in later life leading to **autoimmune disease**.

clostridial vaccines. *Vet.* Usually **toxoids** but with addition of whole organisms in some cases, e.g. *Cl.chauvoei* and *Cl.septicum*. Adsorbed onto **aluminium adjuvant**; up to seven different toxoids can be given simultaneously to sheep. Also used incorporated into **water-in-oil emulsion adjuvant** and administered to sheep by intraperitoneal route. *See also* **tetanus toxoid**.

CMI. *See* **cell-mediated immunity**.

C$\bar{n}$. **Complement** component that has acquired biological activity. *n* refers to the number of the component. The dash over the number symbolizes activity. For example of use see **C1**.

Cna. General form of nomenclature for fragments produced from **complement** components during **complement fixation** by peptide bond cleavage, e.g. C3a from **C3**, C5a from **C5**, etc.

Cni. **Complement** component that has lost a defined biological activity (*n* refers to the number of the component).

co-agglutination. A phenomenon based on the ability of **protein A**-bearing **Staphylococcus aureus** (Cowan strain) to bind **IgG** by its **Fc fragment**, leaving the **antigen binding sites** free for attachment to antigen. If specific antibody to any particular bacterial antigen is attached to *Staph. aureus*, and a suspension of the test bacteria is then added, the latter will co-agglutinate with the antibody- coated staphylococci.

cobra venom. The venom of the Indian cobra, *Naja naja*. It contains a factor ('cobra venom factor') which is the cobra analogue of **C3b**. It therefore activates the **alternative pathway** to **complement** activation in the same way as does human C3b. Cobra venoms also contain many other biologically active factors including phospholipase A.

coeliac disease. A malabsorption syndrome with characteristic histology of the proximal small intestine, i.e. subtotal villous atrophy. Antibodies to gluten have been found in the serum of patients, and malabsorption and the morphological lesions improve when wheat and rye glutens are excluded from the diet. There is a high incidence of lymphomas, gastrointestinal malignancy, and atrophy of the spleen in adults with the disease.

coelomocyte. Generic term used in invertebrate biology for circulating and sessile leucocytes involved in internal defence mechanisms such as **phagocytosis** and **encapsulation**, in animals such as earthworms and echinoderms whose body-cavity is embryologically derived from the mesoderm (coelom). *See also* **haemocyte**.

coisogenic. *See* **congenic strain** (*syn.*).

cold agglutinin. Agglutinating antibody (*see* **agglutination**) detected at maximum titre at temperatures below 37°C. Often antibodies against antigens on the erythrocyte surface. Cf. **warm antibodies** and *see* **anti-I**.

cold antibody. Any antibody serologically detectable at a higher titre below 37°C than at 37°C. Cf. **warm antibodies** and also **cold agglutinin**.

cold ethanol fractionation. Method for separating **serum** proteins by precipitation in the cold with ethanol. By this means, several fractions are obtained, one of which (Cohn fraction II) is rich in **immunoglobulins**. The method is complicated and is only used widely for bulk separations on a commercial scale.

cold haemoglobinuria. *See* **paroxysmal cold haemoglobinuria**.

cold hypersensitivity. A propensity to develop skin lesions following application of, e.g. water ice, that can be transferred to other unaffected persons by **serum**. Therefore a putative immunological **hypersensitivity** reaction.

collagen disease. Generic term for a group of diseases of connective tissue characterized by inflammatory lesions and fibrinoid degeneration. **Hypersensitivity** or **autoimmunity** may play an important part in pathogenesis of these diseases. Examples include **systemic lupus erythematosus, polyarteritis nodosa,** dermatomyositis, scleroderma.

colony stimulating factors (CSF). Substances that, on addition to **bone marrow** or other haemopoietic tissues *in vitro*, stimulate division and maturation of **stem cells** to form colonies of progenitor cells by a sequence of proliferation and differentiation. The multipotential **stem cells** are called CFU-S (colony forming units–spleen, *see* **stem cell**). These self-replicate and also form the following progenitors of cell lines, each stimulated by separate colony stimulating factors: GM-CFC (**granulocyte-macrophage** colony forming cells), EO-CFC (**eosinophil-leucocyte-** CFC), MEG-CFC (megakaryocyte-CFC), **pre-T** and **pre-B lymphocytes,** and BFU-E (erythrocyte precursors). *See* also **interleukin 3**.

colostrum. The first milk produced by the mother *post partum*. Viscid and yellow with high protein and high **immunoglobulin** content. Source of passive **maternal immunity** in newborn of many species (not man).

combined immunodeficiency. *See* severe combined immunodeficiency syndrome.

combined prophylactic. *See* mixed vaccine.

combining site. *See* antigen-binding site.

committed cell. Cell committed to a particular differentiation pathway or line of development. In the bone marrow, committed cells arise from multipotential **stem cells** and themselves form precursor lines for the various blood cells. For details of the various committed cell pathways, *see under* **colony stimulating factors**.

common leucocyte antigen. *See* LCA.

common variable antibody deficiency. The commonest form of **antibody deficiency syndrome** in children. Levels of one or more immunoglobulins are low, but inheritance is not sex-linked, cf. **infantile sex-linked hypogammaglobulinaemia**.

comparative single intradermal tuberculin test. *Vet.* The standard test used for the detection of **tuberculin hypersensitivity**

51

in cattle in the U.K. Two **single intradermal tuberculin tests** are carried out simultaneously employing mammalian **tuberculin** for one and avian tuberculin for the other. By this means non-specific reactors that have been primed by cross-reacting saprophytic mycobacteria can be detected.

complement. An enzymatic system of serum proteins. The **classical complement pathway** is activated by many antigen-antibody reactions and is essential for antibody-mediated **immune haemolysis** and bacteriolysis and plays an important part in several other biological reactions, e.g. **phagocytosis, opsonization, chemotaxis** and **immune cytolysis.** The reaction of complement with **immune complexes** may be detected by **complement fixation tests.** Complement is made up of many components, for some of which inactivators also exist in serum and some of which are heat-labile. In the **haemolytic system**[2], the reaction on the cell surface may be represented by the symbol EAC142356789: where E is erythrocyte, A is antibody and C is complement. The numbers represent the individual components. This sequence constitutes the **classical complement pathway** (diagram on p.48). The reaction must go to completion to effect rapid lysis, but slow lysis can be effected by EAC1–8. The **alternative pathway** q.v. (diagram on p.10) by-passes C1, 4 and 2 and is activated directly by several bacterial, fungal, or plant factors without the mediation of antibody. Non-haemolytic reactions may possibly involve different sequences of complement fixation (*see* **C1–9**). It should be noted that some species, notably the pig, horse, dog and mouse, have complements that are not as haemolytically active as guinea pig or human complement (*see* **conglutinating complement absorption test**).

complement deficiency states. Hereditary deficiencies of individual components of **complement.** Patients with deficiencies of most of the complement components have now been described. The genes responsible for some of the complement components are located in the human **major histocompatibility complex** between D(R) and B (*see* fig. on p 101) (on the 6th chromosome). **C3** deficiency gives rise to a severe immunodeficiency with an increased tendency to infection. **CĪ inactivator** deficiency is associated with **hereditary angioneurotic oedema.** Complement deficiencies also occur in laboratory animals, e.g. **C6** deficient rabbits, and especially in inbred strains of mice, e.g. **C5** deficient mice.

complement deviation. Neisser-Wechsberg phenomenon. Inhibition of **complement**-induced **immune haemolysis** in presence of excess antibody (**amboceptor**[2]).

complement fixation. The activation of the **complement** system, characteristically by the interaction of antigen and antibody. The classical sequence of complement fixation is that followed in **immune haemolysis** in which complement factors **C1–C9** are activated sequentially in a **cascade reaction**, the end result being lysis of the erythrocyte at whose surface, antigen, antibody and complement have interacted. *See also* **alternative pathway.**

complement fixation inhibition test. An **inhibition test**[2] in which the presence of a substance of known structure inhibits the reaction of antibody with a complex antigen and thus the fixation of **complement**. *See also* **hapten inhibition test.**

complement fixation test. Serological test for detection of antibody which, on reacting with antigen, binds (fixes) **complement**. A two-stage test in which, firstly, antigen, complement (usually guinea pig serum complement) and the **heat inactivated** serum under test are incubated together. Secondly, when this reaction has taken place, an indicator system consisting of sheep red cells **sensitized**[2] with anti- sheep red cell antibody is added. In the presence of remaining free complement, lysis will occur. Failure of the cells to lyse indicates that the complement has been fixed in the first reaction and indicates a positive result. The test can also be used (especially in virology) to detect and identify an antigen by using a known **antiserum.**

complement fixing antibody. Antibody (usually of immuno-globulin classes **IgG** and **IgM**) which, in reacting with antigen, binds **complement**. Detectable by **complement fixation test.**

complement inhibitors. Four naturally occurring protein inhibitors of complement components are known. These are $\overline{C1}$ **inhibitor, factor I, factor H** and C4 binding protein (C4BP). In addition many substances are used *in vitro* to inhibit complement or its fractions, e.g. **hydrazine** and ammonia which inhibit **C3** and **C4**, and **heat inactivation** which destroys **C1** and **C2**. Also a purified **cobra venom** fraction or **zymosan** activate C3 via the **alternative pathway** and thus deplete the plasma of C3.

complete Freund's adjuvant. A **water-in-oil emulsion adjuvant** in which killed, dried, mycobacteria (usually *M.tuberculosis*) are suspended in the oil phase. Especially effective in stimulating **cell-mediated immunity**, and in some animals, e.g. guinea pig, potentiates production of certain **immunoglobulin classes**. Cf. **incomplete Freund's adjuvant.**

con A. *See* **concanavalin A.**

concanavalin A

concanavalin A (con A). A **lectin** derived from the jack bean *Canavalia ensiformis* which binds to glucopyranosides, mannopyranosides and fructofuranosides. Since these are common constituents of cell membrane glycoproteins, con A binds to such glycoproteins. Con A is a tetramer with four binding sites for saccharide and, therefore, acts as a polyvalent ligand to form clusters of protein on the cell membrane. It agglutinates cells of many types and acts as a **mitogen**, especially of **T lymphocytes**.

concomitant immunity. Resistance to reinfection by a parasite or the fresh establishment of a tumour by a host already infected with the parasite or bearing the tumour. The primary growth, however, is apparently unaffected by the immune response which destroys the challenge organisms or tumour cells. The term was originally used in tumour immunology but is now used widely in immunity to parasites, especially in schistosomiasis.

conditioned haemolysis test. A **passive haemolysis** test for Chagas' disease using sheep cells coated with a polysaccharide antigen obtained from *Trypanosoma cruzi*.

congenic strain. One of a number of separate strains of animals (e.g. mice) all constructed to possess identical genotypes except for a difference at a single genetic locus. Made by backcrossing an F1 to a parent strain and selecting at each generation for heterozygosity at a specified locus. A minimum of 14 backcrosses is usually made, after which intercrosses are made and homozygous congenic mice are used to initiate congenic strains. Although these strains are constructed to be genetically identical outside the single specified locus, the phenomena of mutation and genetic linkage ensure that mice within and between congenic strains will differ randomly at a minority of other loci. This complication can affect many types of genetic and immunogenetic investigations, and must be guarded against.

conglutinating complement absorption test. Test in which **complement** is absorbed out of a reaction mixture if an **immune complex** is formed therein, therefore measures antibody. The presence or absence of free uncombined complement is then tested for by an indicator reagent consisting of **sensitized**[2] red cells and **conglutinin**. In a negative test **conglutination** (aggregation) of the red cells is seen. The principle is identical to that of the **complement fixation test** but a non-haemolytic complement (usually horse serum) is used. The indicator reagent is a mixture of sheep red cells and bovine serum which contains both conglutinin and **natural antibody** to the sheep cells.

conglutination. Agglutination of **sensitized**[2] cells in the presence of (non-haemolytic) **complement** and **conglutinin**.

conglutinin. Protein present in serum of Bovidae which aggregates **complement**-bearing immune complexes (*see* **immune complex**) that possess **conglutinogen** activity (**C3b**) in the presence of divalent cations. Not an antibody and not to be confused with **immunoconglutinin** q.v.

conjugate. The product obtained by joining two or more dissimilar molecules by covalent bonds. In immunological contexts, one is usually a protein and the other either a **hapten** or else a label such as **fluorescein, ferritin,** or an enzyme (*see* **enzyme linked immunosorbent assay**).

constant region. The **C terminal** half of the **light chain** or the C-terminal portion of the **heavy chain** (containing **homology regions** C_H1, C_H2, C_H3 etc.) of an **immunoglobulin** molecule. So-called because the amino acid sequence in this region is constant from molecule to molecule except for amino acids at allotypic marker sites. *See* **Inv** and **Gm allotypes**.

consumption tests. Any serological test in which antigen or antibody is removed from the system by allowing it to react with the appropriate antibody or antigen. The amount of the reactant remaining is then titrated and compared with the amount that was present originally. For an example *see* **antiglobulin consumption test**.

contact dermatitis. Any inflammatory change in the skin due to exposure, usually repeated, to chemical substances. One form, **contact hypersensitivity** q.v., has an immunological basis.

contact hypersensitivity. **Hypersensitivity** reaction of any type provoked in the skin by contact with chemical substances which act as **antigens** or **haptens**. Many cases of **contact dermatitis** are due to hypersensitivity usually of the immediate (histamine release) or delayed (cell-mediated) types. *See* **immediate hypersensitivity** and **delayed hypersensitivity**.

contagious bovine pleuropneumonia vaccines. *Vet.* (a) Virulent organisms (*Mycoplasma mycoides*) inoculated by an abnormal, usually subcutaneous route, as infection normally only occurs by inhalation. If the tail-tip is used, violent reactions can be controlled by amputation. (b) Live organisms attenuated by repeated passage in *in vitro* culture or in embryonated eggs.

contrasuppressor T lymphocyte. **T lymphocyte** which inhibits the action of a **suppressor T cell**.

convalescent serum. A sample of serum collected from a patient about three weeks after the onset of a disease. If the **titre** of antibody against a specific microorganism is found to be significantly higher than in a serum specimen collected in the early acute phase of the illness this is considered to indicate infection with that microorganism. A significant rise is taken to be at least fourfold in virus diseases but greater than this in Gram negative bacterial infection due to the possibility of an **anamnestic response**.

conventional animals (holoxenic). All experimental animals other than those that have been reared under **gnotobiotic** or **germ free** conditions.

Coombs' test. *See* **antiglobulin test**.

cooperation. *See* **T lymphocyte-B lymphocyte cooperation**.

co-precipitation. The precipitation of soluble **immune complexes** by the addition of a second antibody or **protein A**. The second antibody may be directed against the antigen or it may be an anti-immunoglobulin. Commonly used in assays for radiolabelled antigen at very low concentration by the addition of excess antibody, which forms soluble complexes, followed by anti-immunoglobulin or protein A.

coproantibody. Antibody present in faeces.

corneal response. Opacity of the cornea that follows injection into the cornea of an antigen to which the animal has already been **primed**. Probably indicative of **cell-mediated immunity**. The opacity is due to oedema and the infiltration of lymphocytes and macrophages and it can be quantified subjectively, or by spectrophotometry, to give a measure of the cell-mediated immunity present.

corneal test. *See* **corneal response**.

Corynebacterium parvum. *See* **anaerobic coryneform bacteria**. N.B. The term *C. parvum* is an inexact one and encompasses a number of strains of related organisms with differing properties.

counter current electrophoresis. *See* **counter immunoelectrophoresis**.

counter electrophoresis. *See* **counter immunoelectrophoresis**.

counter immunoelectrophoresis (CIE). A rapid **double diffusion test** technique in which sensitivity is increased by causing the reactants to be brought together by an electric current flow. Two wells that have been cut into an agar gel are filled respectively with antigen and with antibody. The gel on the antibody side is then connected to the positive pole of a direct current supply. Negatively charged antigen travels towards the antibody well whilst the antibody is carried towards the antigen well by electroendosmosis. A precipitate forms where they meet.

counter migration electrophoresis. *See* **counter immunoelectrophoresis**.

cowpox. A virus disease first described by Jenner that causes vesicular eruptions on the teats of cows. The virus is transferable to man in whom it produces lesions similar to those that follow primary vaccination (*see* **smallpox vaccination**) and gives protection against smallpox (*see* **variola**). The virus closely resembles **vaccinia** virus except for quantitative differences in minor antigens and the fact that it produces haemorrhagic pocks on the chorio-allantoic membrane of the chick embryo.

CR1. The cell-surface receptor for **C3b**. *See* **C3b receptors**.

CR2. The cell-surface receptor for C3d, a cleavage product of **C3b**, *see* **C3b receptors**.

CR3. The cell-surface receptor for **iC3b**, the inactivated form of **C3b**, *see* **C3b receptors**.

C reactive protein. Serum protein of mol. wt. 105 000 and γ_1-electrophoretic mobility normally present in serum (concentration 0.1–8.0 mg/l) but increased in concentration in many inflammatory processes. Synthesized in the liver. Detectable by **precipitin tests** in which it reacts with a somatic C substance of *Streptococcus pneumoniae* in presence of calcium, hence name. The reactive group of C substance is phosphorylcholine, but C reactive protein also binds to other choline phosphatides and to polyanions. Following binding to ligands, C reactive protein activates the **classical pathway** of complement by binding to C1q. It can thus induce **opsonization**, e.g. of the bacterium to which it is bound.

C region. *See* **constant region**.

cross absorption. **Absorption** of antigens or antibodies using **cross reacting antibodies** or **cross reacting antigens**[1].

cross matching

cross matching. A procedure used for selecting blood for transfusion. The 'major' cross matching test consists of mixing the recipient's serum and donor's red cells; **agglutination** indicates that the recipient's serum contains antibody reactive with the donor's cells, i.e.**incompatibility**. If the test is negative, an important refinement is to wash the cells free of serum and add **antiglobulin** (Coombs') serum to detect **incomplete antibody**[1]. Various other techniques may also be used. The 'minor' cross matching test, which is of less general importance, consists of the same procedures, using the donor's serum and the recipient's red cells.

cross reacting antibody. Antibody capable of binding to an antigen which did not specifically stimulate its production. This cross reaction may not be as strong as the reaction of the antibody with its own antigen although in some cases it is stronger, *see* **heteroclitic antibody**.

cross reacting antigen. (1) Antigen capable of binding to antibody produced in response to a different antigen. May cross react due to sharing of determinants by the two antigens or because the **antigenic determinants** of each, although not identical, are closely enough related stereochemically to combine with antibody against one of them. (2) Antigen of identical structure in two strains of bacteria, so that antibody produced against one strain will react with the other.

cross sensitivity. **Hypersensitivity** to one substance produced by **priming** with another substance which bears **cross reacting antigens**[1,2].

cross tolerance. **Immunological tolerance** against an antigen or tissue produced by contact with a different antigen or tissue which bears **cross reacting antigens**[1,2].

crossed immunoelectrophoresis. A rapid and sensitive **gel diffusion** technique for the separation and semi-quantification of protein antigens. A solution containing the antigens is subjected to electrophoresis in gel so as to separate the components. A strip of the gel is then inserted into another larger sheet of a gel that contains antibodies to the antigens. Further electrophoresis is then carried out, in a direction at right angles to the first separation, so causing the antigens to enter the antibody-containing gel. Precipitation bands similar to those seen in the **Laurell rocket test** q.v. are produced.

cryoglobulin. Globulin especially **IgG** or **IgM** which precipitates spontaneously when serum is cooled below 37°C and re-dissolves on warming. Does not occur in normal serum. Cryoglobulinaemia may occur in association with **myelomatosis, macroglobulinaemia, reticulosis** and **systemic lupus erythematosus.** Characterized by peripheral vascular occlusion (Raynaud's phenomenon) and purpura of the extremities.

Cryostat®. A refrigerated chamber containing a microtome which is used to cut thin sections from quick-frozen tissues. In immunology, sections for **immunofluorescence** studies are cut in this way.

cryptodeterminant. *See* **hidden determinant.**

CSF. (1) **colony stimulating factor.** (2) cerebrospinal fluid.

C-terminal. Relating to the C-terminus, the end of a polypeptide chain with a free -COOH group. Cf. **N terminal.**

CTL. *See* **cytotoxic T lymphocyte.**

Cunningham plaque technique. Haemolytic plaque assay carried out in a monolayer of red cells formed between a slide and coverslip, without agar.

cutaneous basophil hypersensitivity (Jones-Mote reaction). A modified **delayed hypersensitivity reaction** elicited by inoculation with **tuberculin.** Demonstrable in guinea pigs, it follows the same time course as the classical delayed hypersensitivity reaction but **histamine** levels are increased at the site of inoculation, which lacks fibrin and is less indurated. 20–60% of the infiltrating inflammatory cells are **basophil leucocytes.**

cutaneous sensitization. Provocation of **hypersensitivity** by cutaneous contact with antigen.

cyclophosphamide. A potent alkylating anti-cancer drug with a place in routine chemotherapy often in combination with other drugs. Though **immunosuppressive**, it does not rival **azathioprine** (q.v.) or **cyclosporin** (q.v.) because of bone marrow depression. Experimentally it inhibits lymphocyte division and **B lymphocytes** are preferentially affected, causing depletion of thymus independent areas in lymphoid tissue.

cyclosporin A

cyclosporin A (CyA)®. A cyclic 11 amino-acid peptide with **immuno-suppressive** and antifungal properties. It has a place in clinical transplantation, particularly kidney and bone marrow grafting, having no steroidal effects and suppressing haemopoiesis less than **azathioprine**. CyA is nephrotoxic and causes hirsutism and gum hyperplasia. Experimentally it blocks lymphocyte proliferation in response to antigen and reverses the T4/T8 ratio (*see* **T-antigens**).

cytolytic T lymphocyte. *See* **cytotoxic T lymphocyte.**

cytophilic antibody. Antibody which binds to the surface of cells by the **Fc fragment**. The antibody binds to **Fc receptors** in the cell membrane. Thus the antibody is fixed to the cell but is still capable of binding to antigens in the vicinity. Important examples include **reagin**[1] or **homocytotropic antibody** q.v. and **macrophage cytophilic antibody.** *See also* **cell bound antibody.**

cytotoxic antibody. Antibody which causes damage to antigen-bearing cells especially in the presence of **complement**. Such antibodies may be cytolytic or may cause damage to the cell membrane without lysis.

cytotoxic T lymphocyte. Effector T lymphocyte **subset** (Lyt 2^+, 3^+ in mouse, $T5^+$, 8^+ in man, *see* **T-antigens**) which directly lyses **target cells**. Cytotoxic T lymphocytes kill virus-infected cells provided that the latter also carry **syngeneic Class I antigens**. *See* **MHC restriction.**

cytotoxicity tests. Tests of cell killing. For example, following incubation of cells either with specific antibody and **complement**, or with **T lymphocytes** primed against antigens on the cell surface, the cells may become damaged as a result of an immune reaction against their surface antigens. Loss of viability can then be demonstrated by a **dye exclusion test** q.v. *See also* **chromium release assay.**

17D vaccine. *See* **yellow fever vaccine.**

Dalen-Fuchs nodule. Granulomatous nodule in choroid of eye in cases of **sympathetic ophthalmia.**

D-amino acid polymers. Antigenic peptides and polypeptides synthetically prepared from D amino acids. The latter are only very rarely found in the structure of living organisms.

dander antigen. A mixture of materials continually being shed from the skin surface. Includes desquamated epithelial cells, hair fragments, microorganisms and other fragments entrained in the sebum and sweat. Sometimes implicated as a cause of **immediate hypersensitivity** reactions in **atopic** persons.

DANS. 1–dimethylaminonaphthalene–5–sulphonyl chloride. A **fluorochrome** which will combine with proteins. Used in **immunofluorescence** methods. Emits green light when irradiated with ultraviolet rays.

Danysz phenomenon. Variation of toxicity of toxin-antitoxin mixtures dependent on the way the two substances are mixed. If the whole amount of **exotoxin** is added at once to an equivalent amount of **antitoxin** (*see* **optimal proportions**), the resultant mixture is non-toxic. If the toxin is added in two halves with an interval of half an hour between each, a toxic mixture results. This is because the first half of the toxin reacts with more than its equivalent of antibody molecules so that insufficient antibody is left completely to neutralize the second half.

dead vaccine. *See* **inactivated vaccine**.

Dean and Webb titration. A test for measuring **antibody** in which constant quantities of antiserum are mixed with varying dilutions of **antigen**. The end point is the tube in which **flocculation** is first seen to occur. In this tube, antigen and antibody are present at a ratio of **optimal proportions**. Cf. **Ramon titration**.

decomplementation. Removal of haemolytic activity of **complement** from serum by **heat inactivation, cobra venom** factors, **zymosan, immune complexes**, etc. or removal of complement activity from whole animals by treatment with such agents.

delayed cell-mediated reaction. Reaction of **cell-mediated immunity**. *See also* **delayed hypersensitivity**.

delayed cutaneous reaction An erythematous, oedematous, reaction seen maximally in the skin 48 hours after application of a sensitizing agent. The reaction is mainly **lymphocyte** mediated, but requires the ability to mount an inflammatory response for full expression.

delayed hypersensitivity (delayed-type hypersensitivity, DTH). **Hypersensitivity** state mediated by **primed T lymphocytes** (never by antibody). The lesions, in which lymphocytes and **macrophages** are usually prominent, do not appear until about 24 hours after contact of a primed subject with antigen, e.g. by intradermal inoculation. Cf. **immediate hypersensitivity** and **Arthus reaction**. The ability to react in this way can be transferred to another animal with lymphocytes (from **lymph node, spleen**, etc.) only and is a manifestation of **cell-mediated immunity** q.v.

δ(delta) chain. The **heavy chain** of **IgD**.

denaturation. Alteration of the **secondary** and **tertiary structure** (coiling and folding) of a native protein, leading to an uncoiled or a more randomly coiled conformation. Occurs slowly on storage; accelerated by heating, chemical treatments, foaming, etc. The solubility of the protein is usually greatly reduced, new **antigenic determinants** may be exposed, and biological activity impaired or destroyed.

dendritic cell. (1) Follicular dendritic cell: A cell found in the **germinal centres** of the **lymph nodes** and **spleen**. Possesses long process which interdigitate between the lymphoid cells. These processes can be shown to retain antigen which reaches the germinal centre, for long periods of time.
(2) The term is now also widely used for cells of dendritic morphology found in the white pulp of the spleen and in the lymph node cortex, but not in germinal centres. These cells are **accessory cells** and are Ia-positive, but do not possess **Fc-receptors** or **C3b receptors** (cf **Langerhans cells, interdigitating cells**). Their interaction with T lymphocytes results in lymphocyte proliferation and has been shown to be important for mixed leucocyte reactions. Note that dendritic cells defined under (1) and (2) above are completely distinct.

dengue haemorrhagic shock syndrome. Complication of dengue haemorrhagic fever usually occurring during a second infection. Believed to be due to reinfection with a group B arbovirus of a serotype different from the one that caused the primary infection so that high titres of antibody that can cross-react with, but not inactivate, the infecting virus are produced. The immune complexes so formed initiate widespread **complement** activation, loss of serum enzyme inhibitors, intravascular coagulation and severe shock. The haemorrhagic shock syndrome also occurs in other virus infections, malaria and Gram negative endotoxaemia (*see* **endotoxin**) or bacteraemia.

density gradient centrifugation. A method for separating cells of different types by centrifugation through a density gradient formed from a substance to which the cells are impermeable, eg. Percoll® (colloidal silica), serum albumin, Ficoll-Hypaque®. Centrifugation may be:-
1. Isokinetic (velocity sedimentation), in which the cells separate according to size as they move through the gradient;
2. Isopyknic (equilibrium sedimentation), in which the cells sediment through the gradient until they reach a point at which their specific gravity is equal to that of the medium. The cells therefore separate

into bands of differing density. Widely used for the isolation of lymphocytes and bone marrow stem cells.

depot forming adjuvants. Substances that adsorb (*see* **adsorption**) or otherwise hold antigen, so that it remains at one site as a depot after inoculation. They probably act by releasing the antigen slowly over a long period of time and by encouraging macrophage reaction at the depot site. They are ineffective if given apart from the antigen. Examples are: **aluminium adjuvants, water-in-oil emulsion adjuvants**. However some adjuvants, e.g. **complete Freund's adjuvant**, may be mixtures of depot forming and **centrally acting adjuvants** q.v.

dermatitis herpetiformis. An intensely itchy blistering skin disease. Blisters develop at the dermoepidermal junction and **single layer immunofluorescence** demonstrates discrete granular **IgA** deposits in the papillary dermis beneath the blister and, more strikingly, around the blister. There is a close clinical relationship between dermatitis herpetiformis and adult **coeliac disease**. Cf. **pemphigoid**.

Dermatophagoides pteronyssinus. A mite present in house dust. Antigens extractable from it have been shown to be associated with **house dust allergy** in **atopic** persons and have been shown to be the most common cause of asthma in the U.K.

dermatophytid reaction. *See* **–id reaction**.

desensitization. *See* **hyposensitization**.

despecification. Treatment of heterologous **therapeutic antisera** to reduce their antigenicity, so that they are less likely to cause **hypersensitivity** reactions. Achieved by separating the **immunoglobulin** fraction which is then digested with pepsin to remove the **Fc fragment** but retain the antibody-active $F(ab')_2$ fragment, e.g. **diphtheria antitoxin**.

determinant. *See* **antigenic determinant**.

D exon. A short sequence of DNA coding for part of the third **hypervariable region** of the **heavy chain**, found on the 5' side of the **J exons** but separated from them by an **intron**. Several D (diversity) exons are associated with the μ **constant region** gene. During the differentiation of a **stem cell** to a **lymphocyte** a **V–region** gene is translocated to the position immediately 5' to one of the D exons to which it becomes attached. The combined V–D

dextrans

segment then becomes attached to a J exon to form a V–D–J sequence coding for the entire heavy chain **variable region**. *See* illustration on p.117.

dextrans. In immunological context these substances are **mitogens** for **B lymphocytes** of mice activating the cells at a primitive stage of differentiation. Chemically they are polysaccharides made up of glucose residues and some are **thymus-independent antigens**. *See also* **polyclonal activators**.

dhobi itch. Contact hypersensitivity resulting from **priming** by a laundry marking ink prepared from the nut of the ral tree of India. The reaction presented as a dermatitis on the back of the neck where the shirt collar had been marked.

diathelic immunization. Immunization[1] carried out by inoculating antigen into the mammary gland through the nipple or teat.

dialysis. The use of semipermeable membranes to separate substances of differing molecular weights in solution. **Equilibrium dialysis** (q.v.) is used for the measurement of antibody affinity.

diazotization. Introduction of the diazo group $-\overset{+}{N}\equiv N$ into a molecule, making it capable of coupling with proteins, phenols and amines. Used for example to link **haptens** with **carrier** molecules, thus:

Dick test. Test for **immunity**[1,2] to erythrogenic toxin of *Streptococcus pyogenes* and thus for immunity to scarlet fever. A small dose of toxin is injected into the skin. In persons without antibody, an area of erythema appears 6–24 hours later. In persons with antibody no reaction occurs.

diffusion coefficient (D). (diffusion constant). A coefficient expressing the diffusion rate of proteins in **gel diffusion** tests. May be used to calculate approximate molecular weight of antigens. It is the ratio of diffusion rate to concentration gradient and may be defined by the equation

$$\frac{dc}{dt} = D \frac{d^2c}{dx^2}$$

where c is the concentration at distance x along the direction of diffusion at time t.

Di George's syndrome. *See* **thymic hypoplasia** (*preferred term*).

dinitrochlorobenzene. *See* **chlorodinitrobenzene** (*preferred form*).

dinitrofluorobenzene. (2,4–dinitro–1–fluorobenzene). A reagent which introduces the 2,4–dinitrophenyl group into molecules possessing free–NH_2 groups. Used for preparing **hapten**–carrier conjugates, and also for identifying **N–terminal** amino acids. Induces **contact hypersensitivity** when applied to skin.

dinitrophenyl group (2,4–dinitrophenyl) A **hapten** which becomes attached to the –NH_2 groups of a protein when the latter is treated with **chlorodinitrobenzene, dinitrofluorobenzene**, or 2,4–dinitrobenzene sulphonic acid.

diphtheria antitoxin. Antibody against diphtheria **exotoxin** produced by **hyperimmunizing** horses with **diphtheria toxoid** and **diphtheria toxin**. Used in **passive immunization** in therapy of diphtheria or as a short-term prophylactic measure during epidemics. Now prepared from purified serum **globulin** which is digested with pepsin so that only the $F(ab')_2$ fragments of the antibody are injected. By this purification (termed **despecification**) **hypersensitivity** reactions to the foreign horse serum are reduced.

diphtheria immunization. Use of **active** (or **passive**) **immunization** in the prophylaxis or treatment of diphtheria. In prophylaxis, **diphtheria toxoid** is given in repeated doses, usually in the form of **alum precipitated toxoid** (APT) or, in adults who sometimes show reactions to APT, in the form of **toxoid-antitoxin floccules** (TAF). For passive immunization in treatment, large doses of **diphtheria antitoxin** are given.

diphtheria toxin. The **exotoxin** produced by *Corynebacterium diphtheriae*. Protein of mol. wt. 62,000. Secreted by organisms and absorbed into blood stream. Causes neuropathy and myocarditis in man. Diphtheria toxin consists of a single chain which is nicked by tryptic enzymes and reduced by thiols to form two fragments. The B fragment (Mol.wt. 40,000) is non-toxic but binds to cell membranes, thus allowing entry of the A fragment (mol.wt. 21,000) which interferes with intracellular protein synthesis. Pathogenic for guinea pigs producing necrosis at injection site, adrenal haemorrhage, pleural effusions, etc. Toxin-producing (i.e. virulent) strains of *C. diphtheriae* may be recognized by the intradermal injection of a bacterial suspension into a guinea pig using as a control a guinea pig protected with **diphtheria antitoxin.** Alternatively toxin production can be demonstrated by the **Elek plate** q.v. Diphtheria toxin is labile, breaking down to **toxoid** on storage. This process is accelerated by treatment with formalin. *See also* **L_+** and **L_0 dose of toxin,** and **Lf unit.**

diphtheria toxoid. **Toxoid** prepared by formalin treatment of the **exotoxin** of *Corynebacterium diphtheriae (see* **diphtheria toxin**). Used in **active immunization** against diphtheria most commonly in form of **triple vaccine** q.v., or **alum precipitated toxoid** (APT) or purified toxoid adsorbed onto hydrated aluminium phosphate (PTAP). The aluminium salts and *B. pertussis* in the triple vaccine act as **adjuvants.** Active immunity is produced by giving repeat injections and is now done routinely in infants. In adults who may show **hypersensitivity** to toxoids prepared with aluminium salts, **toxoid-antitoxin floccules** (TAF) are given instead.

direct antiglobulin test. An application of the **antiglobulin test** q.v. in which red cells to which antibody has become bound *in vivo* are washed (*See* **washing**) and tested with an **antiglobulin** (Coombs') serum. **Agglutination** indicates that the red cells are coated with an **incomplete antibody**[1] that has reacted with them *in vivo*. The two most important conditions giving a positive test are **erythroblastosis fetalis,** in which the infant's red cells are coated with maternal antibody, and autoimmune **haemolytic anaemia,** which is attributable to **autoantibody** to the red cells. Cf. **indirect antiglobulin test.**

direct Coombs' test. *See* **direct antiglobulin test.**

direct immunofluorescence. *See* **single layer immunofluorescence technique.**

direct reaction (or 'direct hypersensitivity reaction'). A skin reaction following the intradermal inoculation of live or dead **lymphocytes** (which may be **unprimed,** e.g. thymocytes) into an animal that has been **primed** (by skin graft, etc.) against the tissues of the donor of the lymphocytes. It corresponds to a delayed type, cell-mediated **hypersensitivity (type IV)** reaction such as the **tuberculin test**, being a reaction against antigens on the surfaces of the lymphocytes, and contrasts with the reaction seen if primed lymphocytes are inoculated as in the **normal lymphocyte transfer reaction**, i.e. a **graft–versus–host reaction**.

disodium cromoglycate. A drug of considerable prophylactic value in certain illnesses due to **immediate hypersensitivity (type I reactions)** notably allergic asthma. Usually administered by inhalation but can also be given orally and topically to eyes and nose. Its action is unknown although several mechanisms, viz. stabilization of **mast cell** membranes, bridging of **IgE** molecules (and exclusion of antigen bridging) on mast cells, or enzyme-substrate chelation, have been suggested.

distemper vaccine. *See* **canine distemper vaccines**.

distribution ratio. The ratio of the total quantity of an immunoglobulin in the plasma to that in the whole body.

disulphide bond. The –S–S– structure as present in the amino acid cystine and responsible for inter-chain and intra-chain linkages in many proteins, including **immunoglobulins**. The linkage can be broken by chemical reduction or oxidation. *See* 2–**mercaptoethanol**.

DNCB (dinitrochlorobenzene). *See* **chlorodinitrobenzene** (*preferred form*).

DNFB. *See* **dinitrofluorobenzene**.

DNP. *See* **dinitrophenyl group**.

domain. *See* **immunoglobulin domain**.

Donath-Landsteiner antibody. Haemolytic **antibody** in **paroxysmal cold haemoglobinuria**. Binds at low temperature to the P blood group **antigens** on the patient's own cells or on other, normal, erythrocytes and causes haemolysis on warming the cells.

double diffusion test. A **gel diffusion** test in which solutions of antigen and of antibody diffuse towards one another to form lines of precipitation. Used to analyse purity of antigens and antibodies in solutions and to analyse the antigenic relationships of different substances with one another. *See* **Ouchterlony test, Oakley-Fulthorpe test, reaction of identity, reaction of partial identity, reaction of non identity, spur**.

double emulsion adjuvant

double emulsion adjuvant. *See* water–in–oil–in–water emulsion adjuvant.

double intradermal tuberculin test. *Vet.* A very sensitive tuberculin test used in cattle in which a second intradermal injection of **tuberculin** is given at the same site 48 hours after the first. Diagnosis is based on the increase in skinfold thickness as measured 24 hours later. Now rarely used. Also called the **Stormont test**. Do not confuse with the **comparative single intradermal tuberculin test** q.v.

double layer fluorescent antibody technique. **Immunofluorescence** technique in which **antigen** in tissue sections or smears is located with a first layer of unlabelled **antibody** or antibody–containing serum, followed by a second layer of **fluorochrome** labelled **antiglobulin**, reactive against the antibody in the first layer. More sensitive than the **single layer immunofluorescence technique** and more convenient in the investigation of **autoimmune diseases** where the first layer is often serum from a patient which it would be impracticable to label with a fluorochrome. *See* illustration on p.122.

doubling dilution. Method of preparing **serial dilutions** for use in serological tests. To dilute a serum for titration, one volume of it is added to one volume of saline in a tube. The contents are mixed and one volume is taken and added to one volume of saline in a second tube. The procedure is repeated to the end of a row of tubes so that the dilution of serum in each tube is double that in the previous one, i.e. 1 in 2, 1 in 4, 1 in 8, 1 in 16, etc.

Drakeol 6VR®. A highly purified light white mineral oil used in preparing **water–in–oil emulsion adjuvants** for therapeutic use. 'VR' = virus research, and '6' = 60 second Saybolt viscosity at 100°F.

drug allergy. **Hypersensitivity** to drugs. May be of any type (*See* **type I, II, III and IV reactions**), systemic, or local depending on route of administration. Skin lesions are frequently seen (**contact dermatitis, eczema, urticaria**, etc.). Many drugs act as **antigens** or **haptens** and hypersensitivity reactions to a huge list of them have been reported. For examples *see* **penicilin hypersensitivity, Sedormid purpura**.

DTH (delayed–type hypersensitivity) *See* **delayed hypersensitivity.**

DTH T cell. *See* T_{DTH} **lymphocyte.**

dual recognition hypothesis. An hypothesis proposing that **MHC restriction** (q.v.) is due to the presence on the surface of **T lymphocytes** of two **receptors**, one having **specificity** for foreign **antigen**, the other having specificity for a self-**MHC** antigen, cf **altered-self hypothesis**.

Duncan's syndrome. An X chromosome linked lymphoproliferative condition in man, with uncontrolled proliferation of **B lymphocytes** producing tumours and rupture of the spleen. Due to immune response defect transmitted by X chromosome so that individual cannot resist Epstein-Barr virus infection (*see* **infectious mononucleosis**) in normal way.

dye exclusion test. *In vitro* test for viability of cells. Living cells exclude dyes such as trypan blue or eosin, whereas dead cells take them up and become stained. *See also* **cytotoxicity tests** and cf. **dye test**.

dye test. Serological test for infection with *Toxoplasma*. The serum of an infected person inhibits the uptake of methylene blue by living toxoplasma organisms obtained from the peritoneal cavity of an infected mouse, i.e. the organisms are unstained if the serum contains antibody, cf. **dye exclusion test**.

dysimmunoglobulinaemia. The term dysimmunoglobulinaemia (or dysgammaglobulinaemia) is vague and unsatisfactory. It has been used in the following contexts: (a) **antibody deficiency syndrome** and recurrent infections in patients with normal or raised levels of **immunoglobulins**. Such patients produce what seem to be normal immunoglobulin molecules in normal amounts but their antibody response to antigenic challenge is poor. (b) selective immunoglobulin deficiencies, e.g. low **IgG** with raised **IgM** or **Wiskott-Aldrich syndrome** *inter alia*.

E*. Symbol used in **complement** studies to indicate the functional lesion, at the site of **complement fixation**, on the cell membrane of an erythrocyte, i.e. between the completion of complement fixation and lysis of the cell.

EA. Erythrocyte with antibody bound to its surface membrane, as in EA rosetting, a method for measuring the activity of **Fc receptors**.

EAC. Abbreviation used in **complement** studies where E is erythrocyte (usually a sheep red blood cell), A is anti-sheep red blood cell antibody bound to the surface membrane and C is complement. The sequence of fixation of individual complement components may then follow thus, EAC1423, etc.

EAC rosette forming cell

EAC rosette forming cell. A **lymphoid cell** that forms rosettes with sheep erythrocytes in the presence of anti-sheep red blood cell antibody (A) and **complement** (C). Rosetting takes place by binding of the red cells to **C3b receptors**. EAC rosette formation has been used as a **B lymphocyte** marker in man and most mammals. Phagocytic cells possess **C3b receptors** and can therefore also form EAC rosettes.

EAE. *See* **experimental allergic encephalomyelitis.**

EBNA. (Epstein-Barr virus nuclear antigen). An antigen found in the nuclei of **B lymphocytes** or tumour cells from patients with **infectious mononucleosis, Burkitt's lymphoma,** naso-pharyngeal carcinoma and **X-linked lymphoproliferative syndrome,** diseases associated with Epstein-Barr virus. EBNA is considered to be coded by the genome of Epstein-Barr virus.

ECF-A (eosinophil chemotactic factor of anaphylaxis). Chemotactic factor (*see* **chemotaxis**) for **eosinophil leucocytes** that is released from **mast cells** when **IgE** antibody bound to them reacts with antigen.

eczema. Itching, inflammatory, non-contagious skin eruption usually irregular in distribution and character so that papules, vesicles and pustules may be present together with oedema, scaling or exudation. May occur in **atopic** persons (atopic dermatitis) or may frequently follow ingestion or local applications of haptenic drugs (*see* **hapten**) so that many cases are probably manifestations of **hypersensitivity** of various types. Common in children under 2 years who may later develop **asthma.**

eczema vaccinatum. Generalized vaccinia following **smallpox vaccination** in a subject suffering from **eczema** in which vaccine virus superinfects the diseased areas of skin. Also known as Kaposi's varicelliform eruption (but this latter may also be due to herpes simplex virus).

ED50. The fifty per cent effective dose. Used, especially in 50 per cent **haemolysis,** as a more accurately determinable figure than a 100 per cent endpoint.

educated T lymphocyte. A **T lymphocyte** used in **T lymphocyte-B lymphocyte cooperation** experiments. **T lymphocytes** and anti-gen are administered simultaneously to lethally irradiated recipients whose spleens are removed 6–7 days later. The **spleen** of the irradiated recipient is thus envisaged as the 'school' where the lymphocyte learns for the first time about the antigen.

effector lymphocyte. **Lymphocyte** which has been activated (*see* **activated lymphocyte**) either specifically or non-specifically and which has a direct functional role in the immune response. eg. **cytotoxic T-cell, NK cell, helper T-cell, suppressor T-cell, plasma cell.**

Ehrlich phenomenon. *(Hist)* The observation that the difference between the L_0 and L_+ doses of diphtheria toxin, i.e. between the dose causing minimal reaction and that causing death, is not one minimal lethal dose (MLD) as would be expected but varies from 10 to 100 MLD or more in different preparations.

Ehrlich's side chain theory. An early **selective theory of antibody production** proposed by Paul Ehrlich in 1900. He suggested that cells carried **receptor** groups with 'haptophore' side chains on their surfaces. On contact with antigen the side chains combined with it and the receptors were then thrown off the cell to be replaced by new ones. Antibody consisted of such receptors that had been thrown off into the circulation.

electroimmunodiffusion. *See* **Laurell rocket test**. Electroimmunodiffusion is the term used by the originators of this test.

Elek plate. **Gel diffusion** test for demonstrating toxigenicity of *Corynebacterium diphtheriae*. A strip of filter paper soaked in **diphtheria antitoxin** is placed on an agar plate over a streak of a test strain of *C.diphtheriae* which has been inoculated to cross the strip at right angles. As toxin is formed by the growing organisms, it diffuses through the agar and reacts with the antitoxin to form a line of precipitate which approximately bisects the right angle formed between antitoxin strip and bacterial growth.

elicited macrophage. Macrophage present at a site as a result of an eliciting stimulus. Contrast with the **resident macrophage**.

ELISA. *See* **enzyme–linked immunosorbent assay**.

ellipsoids. Fusiform structures that surround the capillaries at the terminations of the penicillar arterioles of the **spleen** where these enter the red pulp. They consist of a sheath of high (or cuboidal) endothelial cells. It is at this sheath that the most active **phagocytosis** of carbon particles, etc. in the blood stream takes place; **macrophages** containing the carbon are seen ringing the ellipsoids. Ellipsoids are prominent in the spleens of birds, pigs, horses and cats, but are difficult to distinguish in man and are absent in rodents.

eluate. Strictly, material obtained by the washing of substances, mixtures, ion-exchange resins, etc. In immunology, it often means material derived by physical or chemical means from, e.g. an **immune complex**. Thus, pure anti-red cell antibody can be obtained from serum by allowing it first to react with red cells, and then heating the cells to 56°C to dissociate the antibody from them, when it appears in the 'eluate'.

emperipolesis. The apparent penetration of lymphocytes into (and their continuous movement within) other cells as monitored by time-lapse cinephotography. It is now doubtful whether it actually occurs.

encapsulation. Leucocyte response to foreign objects too large to be phagocytosed. In invertebrates such as molluscs, annelids and arthropods, this is the typical response. The object is walled-off by a many-layered capsule of flattened leucocytes (**haemocytes** or **coelomocytes**); in arthropods this may also be associated with production of melanin around the object. Similar responses are also seen in vertebrate tissues, e.g. to foreign bodies or to metazoan parasites. These objects become surrounded by **macrophages** and other leucocytes, which form a **granuloma** and later by fibroblasts. The end result is a fibrous capsule.

encephalitogenic factors. Substances present in extracts of brain which, when injected together with **complete Freund's adjuvant,** are capable of eliciting **experimental allergic encephalomyelitis** in experimental animals. A basic protein resembling histone, associated with myelin, is probably the most important of these.

end cell. A cell that is the end product of maturation and is no longer capable of maturing further, e.g. the mature **plasma cell** is an end cell in the **lymphoid cell series**.

end point. The highest dilution to which an antiserum or antibody solution can be carried, yet still show a detectable reaction with antigen, thus giving the **titre** q.v.

endophthalmitis phacoanaphylactica. Complication of removal of cataracts in man. Lens protein may escape and stimulate a reaction of **autoimmunity** leading to inflammation of the affected eye.

endoplasmic reticulum. A cytoplasmic structure consisting of paired (parallel) membranes attached to the nuclear membrane. Present in many cells but only visible under the electron microscope. It is highly developed in protein-secreting cells where it is called rough-surfaced endoplasmic reticulum because of the numerous ribosomes attached to it. Prominent in **plasma cells** which secrete **immunoglobulin**.

endotoxin. Classically, a bacteriologist's term for toxins that are only released on the death of the cell, as opposed to the diffusible **exotoxins** (q.v.) that are produced by living bacteria. Nowadays, however, the term is used almost exclusively as a synonym for the **lipopolysaccharides**[2] q.v. of Gram negative bacteria. It should be noted, however, that the term is descriptive only and that no one substance 'endotoxin' exists.

endotoxin shock. Syndrome following administration of **lipopolysaccharide**[2] (endotoxin) in man or experimental animals, or following infection with endotoxin-producing bacteria. Mice and rabbits are killed by small doses of endotoxin ($30\mu g/Kg$) and $0.02\mu g/Kg$ is sufficient to cause fever in man (*see* **TAB vaccine**). Characterized by prostration and hypotension, fever and leucopenia. A local or general **Shwartzman reaction** with renal cortical necrosis is seen in severe cases.

enhancement. *See* **immunological enhancement**.

enzyme labelling. Method for tracing antibodies or antigens in tissue sections by binding them chemically to an enzyme and then, by using a stain specific for that enzyme, locating the antibody or antigen. Peroxidase-labelling is an example of such a method. Principle similar to that used in **immunofluorescence** and **autoradiography**.

enzyme-linked immunosorbent assay (ELISA). An immunoassay in which antibody or antigen are detected by the binding of an enzyme coupled to either anti-Ig or antibody specific for the antigen. The principle of the technique is similar to that of the **sandwich** and **double-layer** variations of the **indirect fluorescent antibody technique** (see illustration on p122) except that the **fluorochrome** is replaced by an enzyme. In the sandwich technique, antibody is bound to the surface of plastic test tubes, wells or beads followed by the test sample containing antigen, then the detecting enzyme-antibody conjugate. In the double-layer technique, antigen is bound to the plastic surface followed by the test sample containing antibody, then the enzyme-anti-Ig conjugate. Incubation of the complexes with a suitable substrate results in a coloured product which may be measured spectrophotometrically. Commonly used enzymes are horse radish peroxidase and alkaline phosphatase.

eosinophil leucocyte. A **polymorphonuclear leucocyte** with large eosinophilic granules in its cytoplasm. Present in normal blood (up to 6 per cent of total white cells, i.e. 40–440/mm³ in man) and especially numerous in the horse. The granules are rich in cationic proteins which are secreted on appropriate stimulation. Eosinophils are prominent in the lesions of **immediate hypersensitivity** and in metazoan parasitic infections. Developmental pathway is quite separate from that of the **neutrophil leucocyte.**

eosinophilia. Increase in numbers of **eosinophil leucocytes** q.v. especially in blood, above physiological levels. Particularly associated with **immediate hypersensitivity** reactions and responses to nematode worm infestations.

epithelioid cell. A morphologically compressed **macrophage** with pale pink cytoplasm, indistinct cell membrane and large pale oval nucleus (H & E stain) found in **granulomata**[2,3] such as those that occur in tuberculosis.

epitope. An **antigenic determinant.** *See also* **epitype.** Cf **paratope.**

epitype. A family of related **epitopes** q.v.

equilibrium dialysis. A technique used to study the primary interaction of a **hapten** and **antibody** to it. A container is divided into two parts by a cellophane dialysis membrane impermeable to the antibody but not to the hapten. The antibody is placed on one side of this and the hapten on the other. When equilibrium has been reached, the hapten has passed through the membrane so that equal numbers of free hapten molecules are present on each side. Also, on the antibody side additional hapten is present which is bound to the antibody. By using a radioactively labelled hapten and determining the ratio of bound to free hapten the average intrinsic **association constant** of the hapten-antibody interaction can be determined.

equivalence. *See* **optimal proportions.**

E-rosette forming cell. A lymphoid cell that forms spontaneous rosettes with sheep erythrocytes. E-rosette formation is presently accepted as a **T lymphocyte** marker in man and most mammals. The E-rosette method can be improved by pretreating the erythrocytes with aminoethyl thiouridium chloride (Not to be confused with **EAC rosette forming cells**).

erythroblastosis fetalis. A disease of the human fetus resulting from maternal-fetal blood group **incompatibility**. During pregnancy (especially during labour) fetal erythrocytes escape into the maternal blood stream and may cause the mother to develop antibody to **isoantigens** (commonly **Rhesus antigens**) not present on her own red cells but inherited by the fetus from the father. During a subsequent pregnancy, the antibody, if of **IgG** type, passes through the placenta into the fetal circulation. Haemolytic anaemia may then occur if the erythrocytes of this, subsequent, fetus also exhibit the corresponding antigen. Clinical manifestations include stillbirth, generalized oedema (hydrops fetalis), anaemia, jaundice, kernicterus. May be prevented by giving mother **anti-D** within 36 hours after parturition.

erythrocyte agglutination test. *See* **haemagglutination test**[1].

euglobulin. (1) Obsolete term used to describe the **globulin** fraction of proteins precipitated from serum by 14.2% sodium sulphate at room temperature or 33% saturated ammonium sulphate at 4°C, usually after removal of fibrinogen by prior precipitation with 20–25% saturated ammonium sulphate. Cf. **pseudoglobulin**. (2) The fraction of serum proteins precipitated at very low ionic strength. Typically the serum is dialysed to equilibrium against distilled water or, preferably, a low ionic strength buffer such as 2mM. sodium phosphate pH 6.0. The pH of the buffer affects the composition of the precipitate formed, which contains **IgM**, plasminogen and **complement** components.

exchange transfusion. Technique by which the whole blood volume of the patient is replaced by donor blood. Used in the treatment of babies and foals with **haemolytic disease of the newborn**.

excitation filter. Primary filter used in fluorescence microscopy which allows only light of the specific excitation wavelengths to reach the specimen. Commonly used excitation filters allow only the passage of ultraviolet and/or blue light.

exoantigen. *See* **released antigen**.

exon. A continuous sequence of DNA within a gene that codes for an amino acid sequence within the gene product bounded on either side by non-coding regions (**introns**). **Immunoglobulin** genes are composed of exons coding for the **leader peptide, variable region** and **light chain constant region** or, in the case of the **heavy chain** gene, a separate exon for the **hinge region** and each **homology region**. *See* figure on p.117.

exotoxin. Term used of extracellular bacterial toxins that diffuse from living bacterial cells and cause toxic effects in sites that may be remote from the locus of bacterial growth. The classical descriptive terms exotoxin and endotoxin are, however, inadequate since toxigenesis and toxin release are dependent on the stage of growth of the bacterial cells and many toxins do not fit into either category. The classical exotoxins are **diphtheria toxin** q.v., **tetanus toxin** q.v. and other clostridial toxins. These can be chemically treated to form **toxoids** q.v. and thus be used in immunization.

experimental allergic encephalomyelitis. Autoimmune disease[1] produced in various species of animal by injections of preparations of brain or spinal cord, usually incorporated in **complete Freund's adjuvant.** Ten days or so after injection an acute encephalomyelitis develops that is characterized by focal perivascular infiltrations with lymphocytes and macrophages, and usually demyelination. Resembles human demyelinating encephalomyelitis, particularly **post rabies vaccination encephalomyelitis.** Serum antibody does not correlate closely with the disease, but **delayed hypersensitivy** may be of importance. *See also* **encephalitogenic factors.**

experimental allergic neuritis. Peripheral neuritis produced in experimental animals by injection of extracts of peripheral nerve in **complete Freund's adjuvant.** An **autoimmune disease**[1].

experimental allergic orchitis. An **autoimmune disease**[1]. Orchitis produced in experimental animals by injection of **allogeneic** or **isogeneic** testicular tissue in **complete Freund's adjuvant.**

experimental allergic thyroiditis. Autoimmune disease[1] of the thyroid produced by injecting thyroid extract or thyroglobulin in **complete Freund's adjuvant** into experimental animals. Resembles **Hashimoto's thyroiditis** in man.

extrinsic allergic alveolitis. Alternative descriptive name for **farmer's lung**-type diseases q.v.

F_1. Belonging to the first generation.

F_1 hybrid. Heterozygote belonging to the first generation derived from crossing genetically dissimilar parents.

F_1 hybrid disease. **Graft–versus–host reaction** that follows the injection of parental **immunologically competent** lymphoid cells (e.g. from spleen, thoracic duct, lymph, etc.) into the **F_1 hybrid**, in a situation where each parent is homozygous but is derived from genetically different inbred strains. It occurs because the hybrid is tolerant to the **histocompatibility antigens** of *both* parents, and cannot reject (*see* **immunological rejection**) any of their cells injected into it. The parental cells, however, react to the antigens derived from the other parent. The severity of the disease depends upon the degree of genetic disparity between parents.

Fab fragment. Fragment obtained by **papain hydrolysis** of **immunoglobulin** molecules. The Fab fragment (mol. wt. 45 000 approx.) consists of one **light chain** linked to the **N-terminal** half of the contiguous **heavy chain**, i.e. the **Fd fragment** (*See* illustration on p108). Two Fab fragments are obtained from each **7S antibody** molecule. Each contains one **antigen-binding site** and so can combine with antigen as a **univalent antibody** but cannot form precipitates (*see* **lattice hypothesis**).

$F(ab')_2$ fragment. Fragment obtained by **pepsin digestion** of **immunoglobulin** molecules (mol. wt. 90 000 approx.). The $F(ab')_2$ fragment consists of that part of the immunoglobulin molecule which is on the **N-terminal** side of the site of pepsin digestion (*see* illustration on p108) and therefore contains both **Fab fragments** plus a short section (the **hinge region**) of the **Fc fragment**. It has two **antigen-binding** sites, behaves as divalent antibody but does not contain the sites for **complement fixation**, placental transmission, etc. which are found on the Fc fragment.

Facb (fragment antigen and complement binding). Residue of **IgG** molecule remaining after **pFc′** fragment has been removed from the **Fc fragment** portion by action of the enzyme **plasmin**. Includes all of the molecule except the C_H3 domain.

factor B (C3 proactivator). A component of the **alternative pathway** to **complement** activation. Once complexed with **C3b** it is cleaved by **factor $\bar{D}$** to form the **alternative pathway C3 convertase** (C3bB). Thus C3b formed by either the classical or alternative pathways to complement activation can trigger the alternative pathway and initiate a positive feedback amplification mechanism.

factor D. Inactive precursor of **factor $\bar{D}$**.

factor $\bar{D}$. A serine esterase of the **alternative pathway** to **complement** activation. It cleaves **factor B** when the latter is complexed with **C3b** to form C3bB.

factor H(β_1H). A glycoprotein that binds to **C3b** and can impair binding of **factor B** to C3b, accelerate dissociation of Bb from C3b and facilitate conversion of C3b to iC3b by **factor I**. Thus acts as **alternative pathway complement inhibitor**.

factor I (C3b inactivator). A plasma enzyme which cleaves C3b to form **iC3b**. The latter cannot react with **C3b receptors** (CR1) or participate in immune cytolysis or **alternative pathway** activation. Requires **factor H** as cofactor for its activity on fluid-phase **C3b**.

factor P (properdin). A non-**immunoglobulin, gammaglobulin** component of the **alternative pathway** to **complement** activation which is converted from an inactive to an activated form during the activation of this pathway. It complexes with **C3b** and stabilizes the **alternative pathway C3 convertase** ($\overline{C3bB}$), the properdin stabilized form of the enzyme being designated $\overline{C3bBbP}$. Consists of 3 or 4 polypeptide chains.

Fahey and McKelvey quantitative gel diffusion test. A single **radial diffusion test** q.v.

farmer's lung. Disease mainly of farm-workers due in most instances to **hypersensitivity** to spores of a thermophilic bacterium, *Micropolyspora faeni,* an organism which occurs in dust of mouldy hay. Characterized by attacks of breathlessness a few hours after inhalation of the dust, which results in diffuse interstitial pneumonitis with heavy cellular infiltration of the alveolar walls, mainly by **monocytes** and **lymphocytes**. May result in pulmonary fibrosis. Precipitating antibodies are present in the serum of some patients. The disease is probably an example of **Arthus (type III)** reaction hypersensitivity although **delayed (type IV) hypersensitivity** may play a part.

Farr test. A **radioimmunoassay** technique for measuring **antibody** in absolute amounts. Based on the capacity of antibody to combine with **antigen** rather than on secondary properties such as precipitation, etc. therefore measures antibody of all **immunoglobulin** classes and subclasses. Can only be used to measure antibody against antigens which are soluble in ammonium sulphate (e.g. albumin) or haptens (*see* **salt precipitation**). The antibody is allowed to react with radiolabelled antigen or hapten *in vitro* and then precipitated with 40 per cent saturated ammonium sulphate. Any antigen or hapten that has been bound is precipitated with the antibody and can be measured there whilst the unbound antigen remains in the supernate.

FCA. *See* **complete Freund's adjuvant**.

Fc fragment. The crystallizable fragment obtained by **papain hydrolysis** of **immunoglobulin** molecules. The Fc fragment of human **IgG** has a mol. wt. of 50 000 and consists of the **C terminal** half of two **heavy chains** linked by **disulphide bonds**. It has no activity as antibody but carries sites for fixation of **complement** and placental transmission. It also carries some of the **Gm allotype** markers as well as IgG specific and IgG **immunoglobulin subclass** specific **antigenic determinants**. It incorporates most of the carbohydrate moiety of the immunoglobulin molecule. The Fc fragments of other immunoglobulins differ in molecular weight, **primary structure** and antigenic composition from that of IgG (*see* illustration, p.108).

Fc′ fragment. A fragment produced in addition to the Fc fragment, in small amounts after papain hydrolysis of an immunoglobulin molecule. It is a non-covalently bonded dimer of the $C_\gamma 3$ homology region but without the terminal 13 amino acids, i.e. it is composed of the two $C_H 3$ domains. The mol. wt. of the dimer is 24 000 (human IgG). Present in normal urine in small quantities.

Fc piece. Synonym for **Fc fragment**.

Fc receptor. **Receptor,** found on the plasma membrane of various cells, that binds the **Fc fragment** of **immunoglobulin. Neutrophils, mononuclear phagocytes, eosinophils, B lymphocytes,** certain **T lymphocytes** and **accessory cells** have Fc receptors for **IgG.** In the case of mouse **macrophages,** Fc receptors for different IgG subclasses have been purified. **Mast cells** and **basophil leucocytes** have IgE Fc receptors. See **RFc** γ, μ, α, ε.

Fd fragment. The portion of the **heavy chain** of an **immunoglobulin** molecule which lies to the **N terminal** side of the site of **papain hydrolysis** (cf. **Fc fragment** and *see* illustration on p108). The N terminal half is variable and the **C terminal** half is constant. The variable portion is associated with the **antigen-binding** site.

Fd piece. Synonym for **Fd fragment**.

Fernandez reaction. The early stage of the lepromin reaction (*see* **lepromin test**) in which induration appears 24–48 hours after injection of a bacillus-containing suspension (prepared from lepromatous patient's tissues) into patients with tuberculoid leprosy. Less reliable than the **Mitsuda reaction** q.v. for classifying patients.

ferritin. An iron-containing protein whose physiological role is to store iron until it is required for haemoglobin synthesis. Present in large amounts in the horse spleen which is commonly used as a source. Highly electron dense and is therefore used to label antibodies or antigens in order to locate them under the electron microscope, *see* **ferritin labelling, immunoferritin technique.** Ferritin is itself a good **antigen**[1].

ferritin labelling. The attachment of **ferritin** to **antibody** molecules in order that they may be visualized under the electron microscope. A ferritin-XC (or TC) mono-ureido substituted compound is first formed by allowing ferritin to react with meta-xylylene diisocyanate (XC) or toluene-2, 4-diisocyanate (TC). The compound is then allowed to react with antibody **globulin**. *See also* **immunoferritin technique.**

Feulgen reaction. A histochemical staining reaction specific for DNA.

FIA (Freund's incomplete adjuvant). *See* **water–in–oil emulsion adjuvant.**

Ficoll-Hypaque®. A mixture of a polysaccharide (Ficoll®) and a high density, radio-opaque organic molecule (Hypaque® or Isopaque®) used in **density gradient centrifugation** q.v.

fimbrial antigens. **Antigens** associated with the submicroscopic hair-like outgrowths called fimbriae (or pilae) found on Gram-negative bacteria.

final serum dilution. Term used in **serology** to indicate that the **end point** of a titration has been quoted as the exact dilution of the test serum arrived at after addition of all necessary reagents to it. Commonly quoted in, e.g. **complement fixation tests** where to each tube of a **doubling dilution** series of the serum are added antigen, complement and **haemolytic system**[1] thereby further diluting the serum. Cf. **initial serum dilution.**

first set rejection. The **immunological rejection** of an organ or tissue that has been grafted onto a previously **unprimed** host. Cf. **second set rejection.**

FITC. Fluorescein isothiocyanate. A reactive **fluorescein** derivative which combines with proteins in alkaline solution. Used for preparing **fluorescein-labelled antibody**, etc. for **immuno-fluorescence** q.v.

fixed drug eruptions. Local manifestations of **hypersensitivity** to a drug (*see* **drug allergy**) which appear on the same area of the body surface whenever the drug is taken, and by whatever route this occurs.

flagellar antigens. Antigens of the flagella of motile strains of bacteria. Also known as **H antigens**[1].

flagellin. Protein, forming major constituent of flagella of motile bacteria. Used as experimental **antigen**[1]. The monomeric form is a **thymus dependent antigen** whereas polymerised flagellin is thymus independent.

Flemming's tingible corpuscle. *See* **tingible body**.

flocculation. Formation of 'floccules' or downy masses of precipitate in a **precipitin test** or of agglutinated bacteria in an **agglutination test** for the **H antigens**[1] of *Salmonella* species.

flocculation test. **Precipitin test** in which the precipitate appears as floccules, especially **exotoxin**–antitoxin systems.

fluid mosaic model. A model of membrane structure in which the cell membranes (including membranes of intracellular organelles as well as the plasma membrane), are assumed to consist of a fluid bilayer of lipid molecules in which the membrane proteins and glycoproteins float. The lipids are arrayed with their polar heads forming the two outer surfaces of the bilayer and their hydrophobic side chains stacked in its interior. These lipids are in a liquid-crystal-line state such that individual molecules can diffuse laterally in the plane of the bilayer or rotate on their long axes. However, there is considerable resistance to 'flip-flop' rotation of lipid (or protein) from one side of the bilayer to the other. Proteins are assumed to float in the lipid bilayer with a predominantly hydrophobic region within the bilayer in contact with the lipid hydrophobic regions and with predominantly hydrophilic regions projecting out, either into the cell cytoplasm, or into the external environment, e.g. membrane-bound immunoglobulin (*see* **receptor**) has such a hydrophobic region at the C-termini of its **heavy chains**. This is lacking in secreted immuno-globulin. Most protein-linked sugar groups are external to the bilayer. The proteins also have considerable lateral mobility in the plane of the bilayer and can thus become redistributed, e.g. they may become clustered by ligands such as bivalent antibody or antigens (*see* **patching**).

fluorescein. A yellow dye with an intense green fluorescence. Reactive derivatives of it are used for labelling proteins for **immuno-fluorescence** tests. *See* **FITC, fluorochrome**.

fluorescein labelled antibody. Antibody to which **fluorescein** has been covalently linked (*see* **covalent bonding**) usually in the form of an isothiocyanate (*see* **FITC**) or isocyanate. Used in **immunofluorescence** tests.

fluorescent antibody technique. Immunofluorescence technique in which antibody conjugated to a **fluorochrome** is used to locate antigen in tissue sections or smears by the **single layer immunofluorescence** and **double layer fluorescent antibody techniques,** or, using a first layer of antigen, to locate antibody against that antigen in sections (**sandwich technique**). *See also* illustrations on pp.122 and 202.

fluorescent treponemal antibody test. *See* **FTA-ABS test.**

fluorochrome. A substance which emits visible light of a characteristic wavelength when irradiated with a shorter wavelength. Fluorochromes are used as labels for other molecules since they can be observed in trace amounts. *See* **fluorescein, rhodamine, DANS.**

fluorodinitrobenzene. *See* **dinitrofluorobenzene** (*preferred form*).

fluorography. Technique used to detect radiolabelled molecules, especially proteins, after separation by electrophoresis in gels. The gel is impregnated with a substance (fluor), eg. diphenyl oxazole, that emits photons on exposure to radiation, dried and placed in contact with an X-ray film in the dark. Alternatively, for high energy isotopes, a plastic screen coated with the fluor may be used. After exposure for a period of a few hours to several days the X-ray film is developed and blackening is observed in regions corresponding to the radiolabelled proteins. Commonly used for the detection of **antigens** by overlay with radio-labelled **antibody.** More sensitive than **autoradiography.**

fog fever. *Vet.* (1) Classically, a sudden onset of acute dyspnoea appearing in cattle about a week after they have been moved to a new pasture (particularly to the young grass that grows up after a hayfield has been cut, called the aftermath or 'fog'). Death may follow within 24 hours. At autopsy the lungs are oedematous and there is extensive emphysema. The disease may be a manifestation of **atopy** following priming (*see* **primed**) by pollen, grass protein, fungal spores, etc. There are also indications that it may be an intoxication due to ingestion of L-tryptophan and its conversion to 3-methylindole by a lactobacillus and not immunological in origin. (2)In housed cattle, a disease rather similar to (1) is seen, the aetiology of which is allied to that of **farmer's lung**. It is associated with the feeding of hay contaminated with the spores of *Micropolyspora faeni* (which are presumably inhaled by the cattle) and the affected animals possess precipitating antibodies to this organism.

follicle. Spherical accumulation of lymphocytes in lymphoid tissue. See **lymph node, spleen, primary follicle, secondary follicle, germinal centre**.

follicular dendritic cell. *See* **dendritic cell.**

follicular hyperplasia. Local or generalized enlargement of **lymph nodes** with increase in size and number of the **follicles** which typically contain active **germinal centres**. This is a simple reactive change in the lymph nodes, usually following infection and is distinguishable from the lymphomas.

food allergy. Hypersensitivity (often **type I reaction**) to constituents of food. Ingestion of food containing **allergens** may be followed immediately by distress, buccal oedema, diarrhoea and vomiting or later by generalized manifestations such as **urticaria** or **eczema.** Many foods, especially fish, nuts or eggs, may cause such symptoms, children being particularly susceptible to eggs. Detected by **skin tests** using an extract containing the appropriate antigen (allergen)or RAST testing. Tests are of limited usefulness. It is now believed that many food hypersensitivities are due not to type I reactions but to **type III hypersensitivity.** *See also* **disodium cromoglycate.**

forbidden clone. Hypothetical clone of **immunologically competent cells** with specificity for **autoantigens** which, according to the **clonal selection theory,** have been suppressed in fetal life and which may regain activity in adult life and cause **autoimmune disease**.

formol gel test. Obsolete empirical test for rise in serum **globulin**. A drop of formalin is added to the serum which gels if the globulin level is high. Positive in Kala-azar (leishmaniasis) **myelomatosis,** etc.

formol toxoid. Any **toxoid** (but especially **diphtheria toxoid**) that has been prepared by formalin treatment of **exotoxin**. Diphtheria formol toxoid was formerly employed as a **vaccine** without the addition of **adjuvants**. It has now largely been replaced in immunization by vaccines containing **aluminium adjuvants (alum precipitated toxoid, PTAP,** etc.) or by **triple vaccine.**

formyl peptides. Synthetic formyl peptides (type example; formyl-Met-Leu-Phe) are strong chemotactic factors (*see* **chemotaxis**) for **neutrophil leukocytes** and **mononuclear phagocytes**. These cells possess specific **receptors** for them. May be analogues of chemotactic peptides released from pathogenic bacteria.

Forssman antibody. Antibody against **Forssman antigen**. Usually detected by sheep erythrocyte **agglutination** test. May occur as **natural antibody** in human serum.

Forssman antigen. A glycolipid **heterophil antigen** present on tissue cells of many species, eg. horse, sheep, mouse, dog and cat. Absent in man, rabbit, rat, pig and cow.

F:P ratio. Calculated molecular ratio of **fluorochrome** to protein of a fluorochrome labelled antibody.

fractional catabolic rate. The percentage of total plasma immunoglobulin catabolised per day. Estimated from the **plasma half-life** or alternatively from the rate of excretion of products of catabolised immunoglobulin in the urine.

framework region. The sequence of amino acids in a **light** or **heavy chain variable region** other than the **hypervariable regions**. The framework region exhibits less variability than the hypervariable regions and is responsible for the basic secondary and tertiary structure of the variable region domain (*see* **immunoglobulin domain**). It is believed to contribute less than the hypervariable regions to the structure of the **antigen-binding site**.

freemartin. The female of twin bovine calves where the other twin is male and the two placentae have become fused *in utero*. Thus the twins have exchanged cells before immunological maturity and are **chimeras** that do not reject grafts made from each other. In this situation the female calf is sterile due, amongst other things, to the influence of male hormones and can be recognized by physical examination.

Frei test. **Skin test** of **tuberculin test** type used as an indicator of **delayed hypersensitivity** in patients with lymphogranuloma venereum (LGV). A suspension of LGV virus injected intradermally gives an indurated erythematous papule 4 days later. A positive result is occasionally given in cases of psittacosis.

Freund's adjuvant. *See* **complete Freund's adjuvant** and **incomplete Freund's adjuvant**.

FTA-ABS test. A specific test for syphilis depending on the detection of antibodies to *Treponema pallidum* in a patient's serum. The serum is first treated with an extract of Reiter's treponemes (a non-pathogenic species) to absorb out group antibodies. It is then applied to killed *T.pallidum* organisms fixed to a slide. After washing, any antibody that has reacted with the organisms is demonstrated by the use of a **fluorescein**-labelled **anti** (human) **globulin** serum. This test is more specific and more sensitive than the FTA 200 test which it has replaced.

FTS. *See* **serum thymic factor**.

functional antigen. *See* **protective antigens**.

functional immunity. *See* **protective immunity**.

γ (gamma) chain. The **heavy chain** of **IgG**.

γ chain disease. A rare **paraproteinaemia** in man associated with **lymphoma** in which abnormal monoclonal γ chains are found in the plasma and urine in the absence of **light chains**. The γ chains contain a deletion in which most of the **variable region** and all of the C_H1 are deleted although some of the **N-terminal** amino acids are still present. The **hinge region** is also sometimes missing. *See also* **heavy chain disease**.

γA globulin. Obsolete *syn.* for **IgA**.

γ₁A globulin. Obsolete *syn.* for **IgA**.

γD globulin. Obsolete *syn.* for **IgD**.

γE globulin. Obsolete *syn.* for **IgE**.

γG globulin. Obsolete *syn.* for **IgG**.

gamma (γ) globulin. The serum **globulin** fraction that on electrophoresis shows the lowest anodic mobility at neutral pH. Largely composed of **antibody** globulins (**immunoglobulins**). *See also* **γ₁ globulin**, **γ₂ globulin**.

γ₁ (gamma one) globulin

γ₁ **(gamma one) globulin**. The **gamma globulin** fraction of serum which migrates to the anode on electrophoresis faster than γ₂ **globulin** q.v. but slower than the β globulins. Contains a mixture of all five **immunoglobulins**.

γ₂ **globulin**. The **gamma globulin** fraction of **serum** which migrates most slowly towards the anode on electrophoresis (cf. γ₁ **globulin**). Due to electro-endosmosis, mobility often appears to be cathodic. Consists largely of **IgG**.

γ_m. The membrane form of γ **chain**. See also **tail peptide**.

γ **macroglobulin**. Obsolete term, *see* **IgM**.

γ**M globulin**. Obsolete *syn.* for **IgM**.

γ₁**M globulin**. Obsolete term, *see* **IgM**.

γ_s. The secreted form of γ chain, i.e. that found in serum **IgG**, cf γ_m.

gammopathy. Vague term used to refer to disorders of **immuno-globulin** synthesis, e.g. **myelomatosis, paraproteinaemia**, etc.

gas gangrene antitoxin. **Antiserum** containing antibodies against the major **exotoxins** of *Clostridium perfringens (welchii) Clostridium oedematiens* and *Clostridium septicum* the agents of gas gangrene. Used in combination with surgical treatment and antibiotics for prophylaxis in cases of wounds in which gas gangrene is likely to occur and in treatment of established infections.

GCFT. *See* **gonococcal complement fixation test**.

gel diffusion test. **Precipitin test** in which antigen and antibody are placed in a gel of agar or similar substance and allowed to diffuse towards one another to form a precipitate. *See* **double diffusion test, single diffusion test, reaction of identity, Oudin test, Ouchterlony test**.

generalized vaccinia. *See* **chronic progressive vaccinia**.

germ free. Reared in the complete absence of bacteria and larger organisms. Freedom from all viruses is more difficult to achieve. Cf. **gnotobiotic, axenic**.

germinal centre. A spherical aggregation of **lymphocytes** and **lymphoblasts** of the **B lymphocyte** line (they do not develop following **bursectomy**) together with follicular **dendritic cells** and **tingible body**-containing **macrophages**. They develop within the **primary follicles** of **lymphoid tissues** in response to antigenic stimulation. Also occasionally seen in many other organs in pathological conditions. Function disputed. May be concerned with the development of the immune response and have been postulated to play a role in its homeostasis. A role in **immunological memory** has also been suggested. *See* illustrations on pp. 141 and 206.

germinal follicle. *See* **germinal centre**.

globule leucocyte. A cell often found in the intestinal wall of animals undergoing a **self cure reaction** after infestation with helminths. It is believed to represent a **mast cell** that is in the process of discharging its content of **vasoactive amines**.

globulin. Any **serum** protein whose anodic mobility on electrophoresis is less than that of albumin. Includes α, β and γ globulins; the latter fraction includes the **immunoglobulins**. Term originally used to define those serum proteins which were precipitated in distilled water and, later, those precipitated by salts such as ammonium or sodium sulphate. These definitions are less accurate than the electrophoretic definition. Cf. **serum albumin**.

glomerulonephritis. A term applied, with various qualifying prefixes, to a group of kidney diseases, in all of which the major lesion is in the glomeruli. In most types of glomerulonephritis, **IgG** is demonstrable in the glomerular capillary walls, and in experimental animals the glomerular capillaries are specially susceptible to depositions of circulating soluble **immune complexes,** with consequent injury (as in **serum sickness**). Glomerulonephritis has also been produced experimentally by injection of **heteroantibody** to capillary basement membrane, and by **immunization**[1] with basement membrane. *See also* **streptococcal nephritis**.

glycolipid. A fat or wax whose molecules contain sugar residues. Common constituent of cell membranes. *See* **wax D**.

Gm allotype (Gm group). An **allotypic** antigenic determinant on the human γ-**chain (IgG)**. First discovered by observation of varying reactions of **rheumatoid factor** of anti-IgG specificity with IgG from different normal human sera. 25 Gm allotypes are known, viz. Gm(1), Gm(2), etc. Many Gm allotypes have been shown to be confined to a particular IgG **subclass**. An older, more complicated, notation consisted of a number denoting the subclass and a letter(s) specifying the allotype, e.g. G1m(a), G3m(g), etc. Since many of the allotypes are found in more than one subclass this notation is not particularly helpful. Many of the Gm allotypes have been correlated with single or multiple amino acid substitutions at various positions in the **heavy chain constant region**. They can occur in any of the three constant **region domains**.

Gm marker. An allotypic marker of human **IgG**. *See* **Gm allotype**.

gnotobiotic. Descriptive of an environment in which all of the living organisms present are known, e.g. both a **germ free** mouse, and a mouse contaminated with a single known organism, may be described as gnotobiotic.

gonococcal complement fixation test. A **complement fixation test** for the diagnosis of gonorrhoea using an extract of *Neisseria gonorrheae* as antigen. Of no value for diagnosis of early acute cases as these present before a serum antibody response has developed, but may be of value in diagnosis of late sequelae in untreated cases.

Goodpasture syndrome. Haemoptysis (coughing up blood) associated with proliferative glomerulitis. The glomerular basement membrane is thickened and **IgG** and **complement** have been shown to be deposited there.

graft rejection. Destruction of tissue grafted into a genetically dissimilar recipient due to a **specific immune** reaction against it by the recipient.

graft-versus-host reaction. Reaction of a graft rich in **immunologically competent** cells, against the tissues of a genetically non-identical recipient. The recipient must be unable to reject the graft either because of its immaturity (newborn animals), or genetic constitution (*see* F_1**hybrid disease** and **runt disease**), or because it has been subjected to whole body irradiation (*see* **allogeneic disease**) or **immunosuppression**. The **spleen, lymph nodes,** thoracic duct lymph and to a lesser extent the **bone marrow, thymus** and peripheral blood are particularly rich in cells capable of provoking a graft-versus-host reaction.

granulocyte. A **polymorphonuclear leucocyte** ('polymorph') of the blood. Three types of granulocyte can be differentiated by the morphology and staining properties of the cytoplasmic granules (which give them their name); thus neutrophil, eosinophil and basophil granulocytes (*see* under the synonyms **neutrophil leucocyte, eosinophil leucocyte** and **basophil leucocyte**). The functions of these three types are quite different. For their precursors *see* **myeloid cell series**.

granuloma. (1) The word means, literally, a tumour composed of granulation tissue. It is not a tumour, being made up of proliferating fibroblasts and capillaries formed in the replacement of lost tissue, e.g. in an open wound, until epithelium covers the surface. (2) The term is more frequently used to refer to a localized collection of **macrophages** that by their accumulation and consequent mutual compression assume an appearance that simulates a focus of epithelial cells. Hence these compressed macrophages are often called **epithelioid cells** q.v. The cells often fuse forming giant cells and, if the stimulus to granuloma formation is sufficiently toxic, some of the cells may die. Examples of granulomata of this type are seen in tuberculosis and alimentary Crohn's disease. (3) Granulomata of type 2 above, that form in response to foreign bodies and chronic infections, often show special features. Thus foreign body granulomata have a very high proportion of giant cells, and syphilitic granulomata are heavily infiltrated by lymphocytes and plasma cells. *See also* **adjuvant granuloma**.

Griffith's typing. A method for the subdivision of Lancefield group A (*see* **Lancefield precipitation tests**) streptococci (*Streptococcus pyogenes*) by **agglutination** tests. The cell surface type-specific antigens involved are the streptococcal M and T proteins.

group agglutination. Agglutination of bacteria by antibody against group-specific, as opposed to species-specific, antigens.

Gumboro disease. *See* **infectious bursal agent**.

gut associated lymphoid tissue. **Lymphoid tissue** closely associated with the gut, e.g. **tonsils, Peyer's patches** and appendix in man, **sacculus rotundus** in the rabbit, **bursa of Fabricius** in the chicken, etc.

GVH. See **graft-versus-host response**.

H-2D. A genetic locus in the H-2 major histocompatibility complex of mouse. H-2D products are **class I antigens**. There are numerous alleles at *H-2D*, e.g. *H-2D^b* (abbreviated: D^b), *H-2D^q(D^q)*, etc. Designations of loci and alleles are written in italics, designation of their products are written in Roman print, (e.g.: the *H-2D^b* allele encodes the H-2D^b antigen). *See also* **H-2K** and fig. on p.90.

H-2 histocompatibility system. The major histocompatibility system in the mouse, H-2 genes determine the major histocompatibility antigens on somatic cells surfaces and also the immune responses of the animal (**Ir genes**). The antigens borne by a given

H2-I region

strain of mice, i.e. its H-2 type, are controlled by the arrangement of alleles within this locus and it is likely that grafts between different H-2 types will suffer immunological rejection (*see also* **HLA histocompatibility system**). Thus the H-2 locus was for many years primarily of interest as a genetic and tissue typing marker and is still important in this respect. Genes controlling the immune response (Ir genes) are situated within this locus and segregate in a like manner. Thus the H-2 type may determine not only the cell surface antigen but also the immune responsiveness of the animal. Another set of genes, the Ia (immune associated) genes control a different set of antigens (**Ia antigens**) present on **B** but not on **T lymphocytes**. *See* diagram below for arrangement of major loci and definitions (**H-2D, H-2K** etc) for details of major loci. *See* **Class I** and **Class II antigens**.

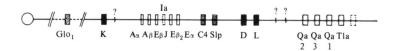

Glo₁   K   Aα Aβ Eβ J Eβ₂ Eα C4 Slp   D L   Qa Qa Qa Tla
                                                            2   3   1

■ Class I loci   : 40–45K, associated with β_2m

▯ Class II loci : $\left. \begin{array}{l} \alpha \text{ chain 32K} \\ \beta \text{ chain 28K} \end{array} \right\}$ as dimers

▤ Class III loci : complement C4 and Slp protein

▯ Qa loci   : Class I-like molecules

? Possible locus for class I molecule

Glo₁   : Red cell enzyme markers

Murine H2 :chromosome 17

H2-I region. *see* **I region, Ir gene, class II antigens**.

H-2K. A genetic locus in the H-2 major histocompatibility complex of mouse. H-2K products are **class I antigens**. There are numerous alleles at *H-2K*, e.g. H-2K^b (abbreviated: K^b), *H-2K*^{q}(K^q) etc. *See also* **H-2D**.

H-2L. **Class I** murine **histocompatibility antigen**, coded for by locus closely linked to **H-2D**. Detectable on spleen cells, and can be recognised as target determinant for **graft rejection** or in **cytotoxic killing assay.** Serological cross reactivity occurs with *H-2D* and *K* products.

H-2 restriction. **MHC restriction** (q.v.) applied to the mouse H-2 histocompatibility system.

haemadsorption inhibition test. A test for detecting, in tissue culture, antibody to a **haemagglutinating** virus which does not produce a cytopathogenic effect. When the cells are infected with virus, haemagglutinin is produced at their surface and on addition of an erythrocyte suspension clumps of red cells adhere (haemadsorb) to the infected tissue culture cells. The presence of antibody to the virus is demonstrated by its ability to inhibit this effect.

haemagglutination. **Agglutination** of erythrocytes.

haemagglutination inhibition test. Test in which antibody or antigen is detected by inhibition of erythrocyte **agglutination**. E.g. Myxoviruses and other viruses agglutinate erythrocytes. Antibody against these viruses can be detected by its capacity to inhibit this agglutination.

haemagglutination test. (1) **Agglutination** test in which antibody reacts with antigen on the surface of erythrocytes. *See also* **passive agglutination test.** (2) In virology, a test used to detect and to quantify a haemagglutinating virus (*see* **haemagglutinin**). No antibody is involved. Cf. **haemagglutination inhibition test.**

haemagglutinin. (1) **Agglutinin**[1] of red blood cells. (2) Non-antibody substance, e.g. a **lectin** or a surface component of a virus particle that has the ability to agglutinate erythrocytes. With some viruses, the haemagglutinin is a small, non-infectious particle which is a product of infection.

haematoxyphil bodies. Irregular aggregates of altered nuclear material which stain with haematoxylin and are found in the fibrinoid lesions of **systemic lupus erythematosus**. They may result from the combination of **anti-nuclear factor** with the nuclei of damaged cells.

haemocyanin. The oxygen-carrying blood pigment of invertebrates; often used as an experimental **antigen**[1] in mammals, *see* **KLHC**.

haemocyte. Generic term used in invertebrate biology for leucocytes, both circulating and sessile, associated with the mechanisms of internal defence such as **phagocytosis** and **encapsulation** in animals such as arthropods and molluscs, which have a large 'open' blood system (haemocoele). *See also* **coelomocyte.**

haemocytoblast. *syn.* for **stem cell** in bone marrow and other haemopoietic tissues.

haemolysin

haemolysin. (1) Antibody capable of lysing erythrocytes in presence of **complement**. (2) Term also used of other substances, e.g. bacterial toxins, which cause haemolysis. *See* **Streptolysin O**.

haemolysis. Lysis (bursting of cell membrane and cell death) of erythrocytes.

haemolytic anaemia. Anaemia due to an abnormal increase in the rate of destruction of circulating erythrocytes. Can result from metabolic abnormalities of the erythrocytes, from the development of antibodies to the erythrocytes, or from abnormalities of the **mononuclear phagocyte system**. Haemolytic anaemia due to **isoantibodies** occurs in **erythroblastosis fetalis** and can also result from mismatched blood or plasma transfusion. Autoimmune haemolytic anaemia results from the development of **autoantibody** to erythrocytes; it may develop as a primary disease, or as a complication of various conditions, including lymphoid neoplasms, primary atypical pneumonia, etc. The destruction of erythrocytes in haemolytic anaemia may be due to intravascular **haemolysis** or to **phagocytosis** by **mononuclear phagocytes** in the liver and spleen. In bacterial (and possibly in some protozoal) infections, antigen from the organism may coat the host's erythrocytes so that the subsequent antibody response destroys them as well as the bacteria.

haemolytic disease of the newborn. **Haemolytic anaemia** in the fetus or newborn resulting from an access of maternal anti-red cell antibody. In man, occurs due to antibody (usually **Rhesus antibody**) crossing the placenta, *see* **erythroblastosis fetalis**. In the horse and the pig, follows the neonatal ingestion of **colostrum**, as, in these species, antibody does not cross the placenta. In man, giving **anti-D** to the mother soon after parturition prevents haemolytic disease in a subsequent pregnancy.

haemolytic plaque assay. A method used to detect and enumerate **antibody** producing cells. Cells obtained from e.g. the spleen of an animal that has been **immunized**[1] against sheep erythrocytes, are mixed into molten **agarose**® containing sheep erythrocytes. The agarose is poured into a Petri dish, allowed to set and then incubated at 37°C. Later, **complement** is poured into the dish, and any cells that have secreted antibody are revealed by the appearance of a zone of **haemolysis** round each of them. The agarose layer can be dried and stained so that the cells may be identified. The technique described reveals IgM secreting cells forming *direct plaques*. By the addition of an anti-IgG serum before the complement, *indirect plaques* due to **IgG** secreting cells can be revealed. Cells producing antibodies to antigens other than erythrocytes can be detected by coating the erythrocytes with the antigen as in **passive haemolysis**. *See also* **Cunningham plaque technique, reverse plaque assay**.

haemolytic system. (1) The mixture of sheep erythrocytes and specific antibody to them that is used as an indicator of the presence or absence of complement in the second stage of a **complement fixation test** q.v. (2) A mixture containing red blood cells, specific antibody against antigens present on those cells, **complement** components **C1-C9**, Ca^{++}ions and Mg^{++}ions. When such a mixture is incubated at 37°C, **immune haemolysis** occurs.

H antigens. (1) The **flagellar antigens** of motile Gram-negative enterobacteria such as the *Salmonella* group. (2) An antigen of the **ABO blood group system** (*see* **H-substance**).

haplotype. Literally 'half-a-genotype'; refers to the complete set of **MHC** loci, and the closely associated loci, inherited from one parent. Each somatic cell will have two haplotypes, one paternally derived and one maternally derived. Because of the close linkage between MHC region loci, haplotype inheritance can be traced in family pedigrees, and may be a useful marker in studies of MHC and disease associations. Some haplotypes show strong **linkage disequilibrium** (q.v.) between alleles of different loci.

hapten. Substance that can combine with antibody, but cannot initiate an **immune response** unless it is bound to a **carrier** before introduction into the body. Most haptens are small molecules (mol.wt.<1000) and carry only one **antigenic determinant**. Haptenic groups can be **conjugated** to carriers *in vitro* and may then be regarded as isolated determinants capable of reacting with antibody but requiring the carrier molecule in order to become **immunogenic** *in vivo*. *See* **diazotization**.

hapten inhibition test. Any **inhibition test**[2] technique by means of which an **antigenic determinant** is characterized serologically or its molecular configuration elucidated by using **haptens** of known structure to block the combining site of an antibody directed against it, e.g. oligosaccharides may be used in such a test to discover the sugar sequences that determine specificity in polysaccharide antigens.

Harderian gland. One of the tear-secreting glands in the orbit of the mammalian and avian eye. In birds, large, and a major local source of **IgG, IgM** and **secretory IgA**. In these species also, systemic immune responses may be initiated from this organ.

Hashimoto's thyroiditis

Hashimoto's thyroiditis. A disease of the human thyroid characterized by chronic inflammatory change, including infiltration with **lymphocytes, plasma cells** and **macrophages**, and sometimes formation of **germinal centres**. The gland is enlarged and firm. The acinar epithelium may be increased, but is progressively destroyed and thyroid function is commonly depressed. It is considered to be an **autoimmune disease,** and **autoantibodies** against thyroid antigens (thyroglobulin, acinar cell microsomal antigen, thyroid colloid) are present in the serum in most cases. Related to non-progressive focal chronic thyroiditis, and to primary hypothyroidism which is probably an atrophic variant.

Hassall's corpuscles. Epithelial whorls or islands of cells found in the medulla of the **thymus**. They tend to undergo central degeneration and may become cystically dilated. The peripheral cells contain endocrine secretion granules.

hay fever. Acute nasal catarrh and conjunctivitis in **atopic** subjects caused by the inhalation of antigenic substances such as pollens (**allergens** q.v.) that are innocuous in normal persons. Due to **immediate hypersensitivity (type I reaction)** following the reaction of cell-fixed **reagin**[1] (homocytotropic antibody, IgE) with the causative allergen. Often seasonal depending on concentration of the relevant antigen in air. Often associated with **asthma**.

H chain. *See* **heavy chain**.

HD$_{50}$. More usually known as **CH$_{50}$** (q.v.).

Heaf test. A form of **tuberculin test** which employs an automatic multiple puncture instrument to effect intradermal injection. This has 6 needles which penetrate the skin to a depth of 2-3 mm.

heat aggregated protein antigen. Protein antigen whose antigenicity has been modified by mild heating, e.g. to 63°C. This causes some **denaturation,** makes the protein less soluble and reveals new **antigenic determinants. Rheumatoid factor** is an **autoantibody** which reacts *in vitro* with heat-aggregated **gamma globulin** more strongly than with native gamma globulin.

heat inactivation. Destruction of biological activity by heating. Especially, in immunology, the destruction of **complement** activity by heating serum to 56°C for 20 minutes. This inactivates the heat-labile factors **C1, C2** and **factor B**.

heat labile antibody. **Antibody** whose ability to react with antigen is destroyed by heating to 56°C.

heavy chain. A polypeptide chain present in all **immunoglobulin** molecules. Mol. wt. 50 000 in human **IgG**, 65 000 in **IgM**. Each heavy chain is linked, usually by **disulphide bonds,** to a **light chain** and to another identical **heavy chain** (*see* illustration on p108). The heavy chain consists of a **variable region** V_H and a **constant region** composed of three or four **domains** (C_H1–C_H4) depending on class. Heavy chains bear the **antigenic determinants** that differentiate the **immunoglobulin classes** q.v. and also **immunoglobulin subclass** determinants. They are different in each class, see γ **chain**, μ **chain**, etc.

heavy chain class. The group into which a heavy chain is placed by virtue of features of its primary or **antigenic** structure, common to all individuals of the same species, which distinguish it from heavy chains of other classes. These structural differences are found in the **constant region**. The heavy chain classes are μ, γ, α, δ and ε. *See also* **immunoglobulin class.**

heavy chain disease. Rare **paraproteinaemia** in man associated with tumours of lymphoid tissue. Free **immunoglobulin** fragments are present in the plasma and urine. The fragments contain the N-terminal amino acids of the γ-chain linked to the **constant region**, the rest of the **variable region** being deleted. *See also* γ-chain disease.

heavy chain subclass. The subgroup into which a **heavy chain** is placed by virtue of features of its primary or **antigenic** structure, common to all individuals of the same species, which distinguish it from other heavy chains of the same class. These structural differences are found in the **constant region** but the differences between heavy chain subclasses are smaller than the differences between **heavy chain classes.** Examples of heavy chain subclasses are human γ1, γ2, γ3, γ4; α1, α2; etc.

helminth vaccines. *See* **lungworm vaccine, hookworm vaccine**, also **zooprophylaxis**.

helper T lymphocyte. A thymus-derived lymphocyte ($Ly1^+$ in mouse, $T4^+$ in man, *see* **T-antigens**) whose presence (help) is required both *in vitro* and in *in vivo* for the production of normal levels of antibody by **B lymphocytes**. This help requires the presence of **accessory cells** which carry **syngeneic Class II antigens**. *See* **MHC restriction.**

hemagglutination

hemagglutination, etc.   American spelling of **haemagglutination,** etc.

HEP.   High Egg Passage (i.e. passed many times) **rabies vaccine**[c] used in cattle.

hepatitis vaccines (a) **Active immunization**; No vaccine against hepatitis A virus is yet available. The vaccine against hepatitis B consists of purified hepatitis B surface antigen given in three sequential intramuscular doses to persons at risk. (b) **Passive immunization**; Pooled normal human immunoglobulin ('gamma-globulin') gives short term specific protection against hepatitis A. For protection against hepatitis B, it is necessary to prepare the antibody against the hepatitis B surface antigen from human immune sera.

herd immunity.   A concept embracing a variety of factors that make a large natural group of persons or animals (the herd) insusceptible to infection. It may, therefore, have nothing to do with **specific immunity**. Thus, herd immunity may be brought about by providing pure water or good drainage and, e.g. epidemics of plague no longer occur because in modern societies the man-flea-rat contact has been broken. Specific immunity may, however, play a part in herd immunity, e.g. when a sufficiently large percentage of the herd is **immune**[1], epidemics cannot spread.

hereditary angioneurotic oedema.   Disease transmitted as Mendelian dominant. Characterized by recurrent, acute, circumscribed transient oedema of skin and mucosae. May threaten life in its laryngeal form. There may be absence of (or functionally inactive form of) serum **C$\overline{1}$ inhibitor** (which is also an inactivator for the **kinin** system) and low serum levels of **C2** and **C4** especially during attacks.

Herxheimer reaction.   A **hypersensitivity** reaction that follows effective drug treatment of certain chronic diseases. It is possibly of the **serum sickness** type, produced by the liberation of large quantities of antigen from the microorganism into the circulation where antibodies are already present. Classically follows the use of a rapidly acting chemotherapeutic agent as in the treatment of syphilis, where it was ascribed to liberation of toxic products of the organism. Also seen in the treatment of trypanosomiasis and acute brucellosis. The fever seen as each antigenic variant population in a trypanosome infection is destroyed, may have a similar basis.

heteroantibody.   **Autoantibody** capable of cross-reaction with antigen derived from another species. Cf. **isoantibody**.

heteroantigen. **Antigen** derived from one species and capable of stimulating an **immune response** in another species.

heteroclitic antibody. **Antibody** produced in response to immunisation with one **antigen** that has higher **affinity** for another antigen that was not present during the immunisation. The second antigen may have a molecular structure related to that used for immunisation, e.g. immunisation with **DNP**-protein conjugates sometimes results in the production of antibodies with higher affinity for **TNP** than for DNP.

heterocytotropic antibody. **Antibody** with an affinity for cells of heterologous species that is often greater than for those of its own species. Thus human **IgG** fixes to guinea-pig skin cells to give positive **passive cutaneous anaphylaxis** tests, but does not fix to human cells to the same extent. Cf. **homocytotropic antibody**.

heterogeneic. *See* **xenogeneic** *(preferred term)*.

heterogenetic antigen. *See* **heterophil antigen**.

heterograft. *See* **xenograft** *(preferred term)* and **transplantation terminology**.

heterologous. Derived from a different species.

heterologous vaccine. Any **vaccine** which protects against pathogens not present in the vaccine. Contains microorganisms which share **cross-reacting antigens** with the pathogen in question. Examples include the use of **vaccinia** in **smallpox vaccination**; of measles vaccine in canine distemper; and of Shope fibroma virus against myxomatosis in rabbits.

heterophil (heterophile) **antibody**. Antibody against **heterophil antigens** q.v., *see also* **isophil antibody**.

heterophil antigen. **Antigens** occurring on the surface of tissue cells of many different animal species, plants and bacteria and showing extensive interspecies cross relationship. Introduction of heterophil antigen into the tissues of a species which does not carry it stimulates the formation of **heterophil antibody**.

heterophil granulocyte. A general term used to describe the **neutrophil leucocytes** of all species whatever differences there may be in the staining reactions of their granules. Infrequently used except in respect of those of birds which present an appearance markedly different from those of most mammals when stained with the standard blood stains.

heterospecific

heterospecific. Derived from or having specificity for a different species (*syn.* **heterologous**).

heterotopic graft. Organ or tissue grafted or transferred to an anatomical site where that organ or tissue is not normally found. Cf. **orthotopic graft.**

heterotypic vaccine. *See* **heterologous vaccine.**

HEV. *see* **high endothelial venule.**

HGG. Human **gamma globulin.**

hidden determinant. *Syn.* cryptodeterminant. **Antigenic determinant** which is so positioned on a molecule or cell that it is not accessible for recognition by **lymphocytes** or **antibody** and is neither capable of binding specifically to them, nor of stimulating an **immune response,** unless some stereochemical change causes the hidden determinant to be revealed.

high dose tolerance. **Acquired tolerance** following the administration of very large single (polysaccharide) or repeated (protein) doses of antigen to **immunologically competent** animals. Cf. **low dose tolerance.**

high endothelial venule (HEV). Specialized venules found in the **thymus dependent area** of the **lymph node**, characterized by prominent, high endothelial lining cells. Recirculation of **lymphocytes** from blood to **lymph** takes place through the walls of these vessels (see illustration on p.141).

high responder. Term referring to **inbred strains** of mice which give strong immune responses to specified antigens (compared to other strains). Related to presence of **Ir genes** determining the response in question.

hinge region. A flexible, proline-rich region on the **immunoglobulin** molecule which probably acts as a hinge on which the **Fab fragments** can rotate. The angle between the Fab subunits may vary between 0 and 180°. The hinge region is adjacent to the sites of **papain hydrolysis** and **pepsin digestion** (*see* illustration on p.108).

histamine. A **vasoactive amine**, vasodilator and smooth muscle constrictor, widely distributed in biological tissues and found in high concentration in **mast cells.** Histamine and histamine-like substances are released when cell-bound **reagin**[1] (usually **IgE**) reacts with antigen. They cause the classical vascular lesions **(weal and flare** response) of **immediate hypersensitivity. Anaphylatoxin** also mediates release of histamine.

histiocyte. A **macrophage** found within the tissues, in contrast to those found in the blood **(monocytes)** or serous cavities, etc. Some histiocytes appear to remain at the same site for long periods of time, e.g. those that retain dye particles in the skin after tattooing. They have a strong affinity for silver and other heavy metal stains.

histocompatibility antigen. Genetically determined **isoantigen** carried on the surface of nucleated cells of many tissues (and easily detected on blood **leucocytes**). Coded for by **MHC genes** (HLA, H-2) q.v. When tissue is grafted onto another individual of the same species whose tissues do not carry that antigen, may incite an **immune response** which leads to graft rejection. The most closely studied histocompatibility antigens are those of the H-2 system in mice and of the HLA system in man. *See* **H-2,** and **HLA histocompatibility system.**

histocompatibility gene. Gene coding for a **histocompatibility antigen** q.v. *See also* **HLA histocompatibility system, H-2 histocompatibility system.**

histocompatibility locus. Genetic locus on chromosome at which the **histocompatibility genes** which determine formation of **histocompatibility antigens** are situated. *See* **HLA** and **H-2 histocompatibility systems.**

histocompatibility testing. Tests carried out before tissue grafting in man. The donor most closely matched to the recipient is first chosen by **tissue typing. A mixed leucocyte reaction** may then be carried out to detect the presence of other, unidentified, **histocompatibility antigens** or **priming** of the recipient against the donor's antigens.

histoplasmin test. **Skin test** for detection of **delayed hypersensitivity** to *Histoplasma capsulatum,* a fungus and the causative organism of human histoplasmosis. Gives **tuberculin test**-type skin reaction in positive cases indicating past or present infection with *H.capsulatum.*

HLA-DR

HLA-A. Class I human **histocompatibility antigen**, present on nucleated cells, including lymphocytes. There are at least 19 allelic products of the *HLA-A* locus.

HLA-B. Class I human **histocompatibility antigen,** present on nucleated cells, including lymphocytes. There are over 40 allelic products of the *HLA-B* locus. The population frequency of some HLA-B antigens is altered in some diseases e.g. HLA-B8 in juvenile onset insulin dependent diabetes, HLA-B27 in ankylosing spondylitis and reactive arthritis.

HLA-C. Class I human **histocompatibility antigen,** present on nucleated cells, including lymphocytes. The role of the HLA-C products (there are at least 8 allelic forms) in graft rejection is probably small and the function(s) of this group of antigens are poorly understood. *HLA-C* probably arose as a result of reduplication of the *HLA-A* gene.

HLA-D. Class II **histocompatibility antigens** in man: never defined serologically, only by use of **mixed lymphocyte culture**, cellular typing (q.v.). Detected by proliferative response in MLC using mononuclear cell suspension. Responding cells (mainly T lymphocytes) 'recognise' foreign **HLA-D** antigens on stimulating cells (mainly **B lymphocytes**). Macrophages and/or **T helper cells** appear to be necessary for full response. At least twelve allelic products can be detected, most but not all of which, correspond to the serologically determined **HLA-DR** antigens (q.v.). HLA-D molecules have not been biochemically characterized largely because of the apparent lack of specific antisera i.e. HLA-D antigens do not appear to stimulate alloantibody production. The HLA-D locus is very closely linked to that for the **HLA-DR** antigens, and they may both be part of a single complex 'supergene'.

HLA-DR. Class II human **histocompatibility antigens**, expressed on **B lymphocytes.** Detectable also on cells of monocyte/macrophage lineage (e.g. **Langerhans' cells**) and on mitogen-activated **T lymphocytes**, but not on normal circulating cells. These antigens are detectable by microcytotoxicity testing using enriched B lymphocyte preparations from peripheral blood, with **alloantibodies** and murine **monoclonal antibodies**. Twelve or more allelic forms exist for the DR series of antigens. There are probably at least two other loci coding for the Class II products (not including HLA-D). These are recognised using immunochemical procedures, with murine monoclonal antibodies, and by modified **mixed lymphocyte culture** techniques. The two best characterized series are known as DC and SB.

HLA histocompatibility system. The major histocompatibility system of man, containing many genes which control the presence of cell surface **isoantigens,** as well as the capacity to mount immune responses (**Ir genes**). The genes controlling the formation of some **complement** components (**C2** and **factor B**) are also within the HLA locus. The HLA isoantigens on cell surfaces are of primary importance in tissue transplantation inasmuch as HLA **incompatible** grafts are more likely to be rejected than incompatible grafts of other isoantigen groups. *See* diagram below for arrangement of major loci and definitions above for details of major loci.

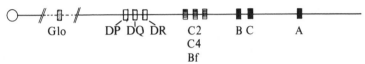

    Glo   DP DQ DR   C2   B C   A
                             C4
                             Bf

■ Class I loci   : 40–45K, associated with β_2 m

☐ Class II loci : 33K and 28K as dimers

? Possible locus for Class II molecules

▤ Class III loci : complement C2, C4, Bf (order not determined)

Human HLA :chromosome 6

Hodgkin's disease. Disease of lymphoreticular tissue. One of a group of diseases known as the **lymphomas**. Characterized by destruction of normal architecture of the **lymph nodes** and replacement with **reticular cells**, Reed-Sternberg giant cells, **neutrophil** and **eosinophil leucocytes** and **lymphocytes**. There is enlargement of the lymph nodes and spleen and infiltration of other tissues frequently occurs. Immunologically, there is a deficiency of **cell-mediated immunity**, so that **skin tests** of the **tuberculin test** type are usually negative and patients are susceptible to severe and sometimes unusual infections.

holoxenic. Conventionally reared animal. Cf. **axenic, gnotobiotic**.

homocytotropic antibody. Strictly *any* antibody molecule that becomes attached to cells of animals of the same species, but not those of other species, cf. **heterocytotropic** antibody. However, the term is commonly used to imply only that type of homocytotropic antibody that, on combination with antigen causes the release of **histamine** and other vasoactive mediators from mast cells, etc. i.e. **reagin**[1] or **IgE**.

homograft. Graft from one individual to another of the same species. Includes **allogeneic** grafts (**allografts**), between genetically dissimilar individuals, and **syngeneic** grafts between genetically identical individuals, e.g. identical twins. The latter terms are more informative and are preferred by transplantation immunologists. *See also* **transplantation terminology**.

homograft reaction. An immunological reaction of the tissues of the recipient of a **homograft** (**allograft**) against the antigens of the graft.

homograft rejection. Rejection of a **homograft** (**allograft**) due to a specific immune response mounted by the recipient's tissues against the graft. Caused by **incompatibility** of **histocompatibility antigens** between donor and recipient. The homograft rejection is essentially due to **cell-mediated immunity** and is characterized by infiltration of the graft by **lymphocytes**. Humoral immunity is usually of less importance.

homologous disease. *See* **allogeneic disease**.

homology region. A sequence of the **immunoglobulin heavy** or **light chain** of approximately 105–115 amino acid residues which shows similarities of primary structure with other sequences of similar size. Each homology region contains an intrachain **disulphide bond** in a similar position and is folded to form a globular **domain** of similar shape. DNA sequencing has shown that the homology regions are encoded by **exons** separated from each other by **introns**. Immunoglobulins probably evolved from a single polypeptide the size of a homology region by gene duplication. The homology regions of the light chains are designated V_L and C_L; those of the heavy chains V_H, C_H1, C_H2, etc.

homotransplantation. The transplantation of **homografts**.

hookworm vaccine. *Vet.* **Vaccine** used for protection against *Ancylostoma caninum,* a parasite of the dog. A live vaccine similar to **lungworm vaccine** q.v., it contains larvae which have been X-irradiated to prevent their development to adults. Similar vaccines have been proposed for the protection of man against the hookworms *Ancylostoma duodenale* and *Necator americanus.*

hormone immunoassays. *In vitro* assay techniques based on competitive binding of known amounts of labelled (often radioactively labelled, *see* **isotope labelling**) hormone and unlabelled hormone in the serum or tissue fluids from the patient to highly avid (*see* **avidity**) anti-hormone antibody molecules. Various techniques are then used to separate free hormone from that bound to the antibody, e.g. by precipitation as in the **Farr test**, or chromatography or electrophoresis, etc., so that measurements can be made. The technique has been applied to the assay of about twenty different hormones, e.g. insulin, human growth hormones, thyroid stimulating hormone, glucagon, etc.

horror autotoxicus. Concept introduced by Paul Ehrlich in 1901 affirming the existence of a mechanism whereby **autoantigens**, tissues and cells, potentially antigenic in other animals, do not cause a response of **autoimmunity** q.v.

horse serum reactions. **Hypersensitivity** reactions to **therapeutic antisera** prepared in the horse.

horse-type antibody. Precipitating antibody, obtained from any species, which resembles that produced by the horse in that it forms **immune complexes** which are extremely soluble both in **antibody excess** and in **antigen excess**. Thus, antibody of this type forms sharply peaked precipitation curves (*see* **optimal proportions**) and thin, well-defined lines in **gel diffusion tests**. Cf. **rabbit type antibody**.

house dust allergy. Respiratory **hypersensitivity** reaction, e.g. **allergic rhinitis**, **asthma**, in **atopic** persons on inhalation of house dust. Chiefly of **immediate hypersensitivity** type (**type I reaction**). Major **allergen** is the house-dust mite *Dermatophagoides pteronyssinus*.

HSA. Human **serum albumin**. Frequently employed as an antigen in investigations with experimental animals.

H substance. Most human red cells bear an antigen, genetically related to the **ABO blood group system**, called H. H substance is present in soluble form in the body fluid of **secretors**. Anti-H occasionally occurs naturally in the serum of non-secretors.

HTLA (human T lymphocyte antigen). A surface marker present on human **T lymphocytes** throughout maturation, i.e. on **pre-T lymphocytes**, cortical **thymocytes**, and on the various **subsets** of **T lymphocytes**, but absent from **B lymphocytes**.

HTLV. *see* **T cell leukaemia viruses**.

humoral antibody. Antibodies present in the 'humours', i.e. **plasma, lymph** and tissue fluids of the body, and responsible for **humoral immunity.** Cf. **cell bound antibody** which is also a mediator of 'humoral immunity'.

humoral immunity. Specific immunity mediated by **antibodies** which are present in the **plasma, lymph,** and tissue fluids of the body, and which may also become attached to cells (**cytophilic antibody**). Cf. **cell-mediated immunity,** and **cellular immunity.**

hybrid antibodies. **Immunoglobulin** molecules in which **antigen-binding sites** are of different specificities. Produced artificially by dissociating two antibodies of different specificities and then recombining them. Mixed immunoglobulin molecules are also produced by **hybridomas** resulting from the fusion of two immunoglobulin-producing cells. Not found naturally.

hybridoma. (1) **B-cell hybridoma.** A cell line obtained by the fusion of a **plasmacytoma** cell with a normal **plasma cell.** The resulting cell line, which has properties of both constituents, continues to secrete the **antibody** produced by the normal plasma cell and, since the cell line is cloned, the antibody produced is monoclonal. The **immunoglobulin** derived from the plasmacytoma cell also continues to be secreted, resulting in mixed molecules, but non-producing cell lines suitable for fusion are available. Mouse, rat and human hybridomas have been successfully produced but hybridomas of mixed species tend to be unstable. (2) **T-cell hybridoma.** A cell line obtained by the fusion of a T lymphoma cell with a normal **T-lymphocyte.** *See* also **monoclonal antibody.**

5-hydroxytryptamine. *See* **serotonin.**

hypergammaglobulinaemia. Raised serum **gammaglobulin** level. Diffuse (i.e. not restricted to a single **immunoglobulin class**) increase in serum gammaglobulin is associated with any condition where continued antigenic stimulation causes production of large amounts of antibody, e.g. chronic infection, **autoimmune diseases** and, irregularly, various chronic diseases of unknown causation. In **paraproteinaemias** a sharp, high electrophoretic spike of **mono-clonal immunoglobulin** is seen.

hyperimmune state. A state, following repeated injections of a single antigen, in which very large quantities of specific **antibody** are present in the serum. Commonly used to describe the immune status of animals employed for the production of **therapeutic antisera** following a **hyperimmunization** procedure.

hyperimmunization. Any method of **immunization** designed to stimulate the production of very large quantities of **antibody**. Especially applied to the immunization of horses, etc. for the production of **therapeutic antisera** by the repeated administration of antigen, in ever increasing quantity, at intervals of a few days.

hypersensitivity. State of the previously immunized (*see* **immunization**[1]) body in which tissue damage results from the immune reaction to a further dose of antigen. Hypersensitivity may be antibody mediated as in **immediate hypersensitivity** or in the **Arthus reaction** (*see also* **type I, II and III reactions**) or it may be a reaction of **cell-mediated immunity** as in **delayed hypersensitivity** (*see also* **type IV reaction**). The term hypersensitivity implies a heightened reactivity to antigen but it is difficult to define all hypersensitivity reactions, particularly cell-mediated reactions, in such terms.

hypervariable region. Within the **variable region** of **immunoglobulins**, residues in certain positions show much higher variability from one molecule to another than do other residues. These hypervariable residues are grouped in regions which, when the protein is folded, are believed to determine the conformation and specificity of the **antigen-binding site** and also the **idiotypic variations** between immunoglobulins secreted by different clones of cells.

hypocomplementaemia. Any condition in which serum **complement** levels are low. Seen in conditions where *in vivo* **complement fixation** by **immune complexes** is sufficient to depress serum levels, e.g. the active phases of proliferative **glomerulonephritis, serum sickness, systemic lupus erythematosus**. Levels may also be low in any protein deficiency state.

hypogammaglobulinaemia. Lowered serum **immunoglobulin (gammaglobulin)** level. May be physiological in neonates or follow increased protein loss or decreased immunoglobulin production. It is also characteristic of **antibody deficiency syndromes** either familial (e.g. **infantile sex linked hypogammaglobulinaemia**) or following replacement of lymphoid tissue by **lymphoma**, leukaemia, etc.

hyposensitization. Administration of a graded series of doses of an **allergen** to subjects suffering from **immediate hypersensitivity** to it, in order to reduce the likelihood of future reactions on casual contact with that antigen. The allergen is given to provoke production of large amounts of **IgG** (or **blocking antibody**[2]). This IgG either has a direct effect by inhibiting further **IgE** synthesis, or combines with the allergen and prevents the latter from combining with IgE (**reagin**) on the surfaces of mast cells. Hyposensitization may also be achieved by giving the allergen in a **water-in-oil emulsion adjuvant**.

Ia antigens. **Class II** histocompatibility antigens (q.v.) found on the surface of mouse **B lymphocytes, macrophages** and **accessory cells**. Also found on **granulocyte** precursors but disappear from these during maturation.

iC3B. The inactivated form of **C3b**. Often also referred to as C3bi.

-id reaction. Spontaneous **hypersensitivity** reaction in the skin to antigens derived from bacteria or fungi at a distant focus of infection. The offending organism cannot be isolated from the -id reaction site. The latter responds to treatment of the primary focus of infection but not to local treatment. Term derived from epidermophytid, trichophytid, etc. reactions named after the infecting organism.

identity, reaction of. *See* **reaction of identity**.

idiopathic thrombocytopenic purpura. Human disease characterized by haemorrhagic tendency and purpura (small haemorrhages into the skin) associated with low blood **platelet** count. Probably associated with the presence of **autoantibodies** against platelets in the serum, but technical difficulties in detecting such antibodies have made it very difficult to assess their importance.

idiotope. (*Syn.* **idiotypic determinant**). Any **antigenic determinant** that is characteristic of the **immunoglobulin** produced by a single clone or a small minority of clones of cells. Idiotopes are believed to be confined to the **variable regions**, and therefore in most cases the **antigen-binding sites** of immunoglobulin, *see also* **idiotype**.

idiotype. Set of one or more **idiotopes** (q.v.) by which a clone of **immunoglobulin**-forming cells can be distinguished from other clones. Some, known as individual idiotypes or IdI's, appear to be unique to individuals. Others, known as inherited idiotypes or cross-reacting idiotypes or IdX's, are found in many members of the same animal species. Examples of inherited idiotypes in mice include A5A, T15, J558, ARS and NP.

idiotypic determinant. *See* **idiotope**.

idiotypic variation. Antigenic variability of individual proteins due to variations in the controlling genes. Idiotypic variation is seen in the variable regions of **immunoglobulins** where individual **antibodies** and **myeloma proteins** each vary from one another in amino acid sequence and in **antigenic determinants** even within the same isotype (*see* **isotypic variation**) and **allotype**. *See also* **idiotypic determinant, idiotype, idiotope, anti-idiotype antibody**.

IE. *See* **immunoelectrophoresis**.

IEF. *See* **isoelectric focusing**.

IEP. *See* **immunoelectrophoresis**.

IFN. *See* **interferon**

Ig. *See* **immunoglobulin**.

IgA. The major **immunoglobulin** of the external secretions (intestinal fluids, saliva, bronchial secretions, etc.) in man where it is found as a dimer linked to **secretory** (or transport) **piece** q.v. Also present in serum (concentration 150-400 mg/100ml) as a monomer and in polymerized forms. Mol. wt. of monomer 170 000, $s_{20,w}$ = 7S (dimer in secretions mol. wt. 400 000, $s_{20,w}$ =11S). Does not cross human placenta, present in human colostrum, but is *not* major colostral immunoglobulin of pig, bovine or sheep. Does not apparently fix **complement** except in presence of **lysozyme** or, in polymerized form, via **alternative pathway**. Many **antibody** activities. Synthesis primarily in lymphoid tissue of gut, respiratory tract and Harderian gland of the bird. Secretory form probably not derived from serum but synthesized locally. At least two subclasses in man (*see* **immunoglobulin subclass**). Forms major specific humoral defence mechanism on mucosal surfaces. See illustration below.

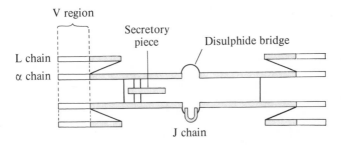

A schematic diagram of human IgA1. In human IgA2m(1) and mouse IgA the L chains are not linked to the α chains by disulpide bridges but to each other. The precise arrangement of disulpide bridges linking J chain and secretory piece to the α chains is not known.

IgD

IgD. **Immunoglobulin** present in low concentration in human serum (0.3-40 mg/100 ml). Mol. wt. 184 000, $s_{20,w}$ =7S. Confined to intravascular space. Low concentration partly attributable to rapid catabolism, i.e. short half-life. Present in large quantities as membrane immunoglobulin on the surface of **B lymphocytes** and may, therefore, have an important role in recognition of antigen and the initiation of antibody synthesis.

IgE. The **immunoglobulin** associated with **reagin**[1] or **homocyto-tropic antibody** activity in man. Present in serum in very low concentration (20-500 ng/ml) but elevated in allergic **asthma, hay fever** and intestinal helminth infections. High affinity for surfaces of mast cells which carry a surface **Fc receptor** specific for IgE. Mol. wt. 188 000, $s_{20,w}$ = 8.2S. High carbohydrate content (11 per cent). Present in external secretions and a major site of synthesis is lymphoid tissue of gut, respiratory tract.

IgG. The major **immunoglobulin** in the serum of man. Homologous immunoglobulins are found in most species from amphibians upwards, but are not present in the serum of fish. Human IgG has been intensively studied and its structure is known in some detail. Mol. wt. of human IgG 150 000, $s_{20,w}$ =7S, fixes **complement**, crosses human placenta. Four subclasses in man IgG1, IgG2, IgG3, IgG4 but number varies in other species (*see* **immunoglobulin subclass**). **Antibody** activity of many types. Normal serum concentration in man 800-1600 mg/100 ml.

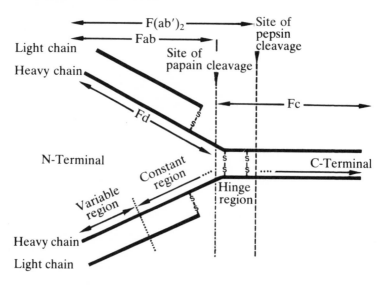

IgG1, IgG2, IgG3, IgG4. The **immunoglobulin subclasses** (q.v. for details of differences) of human **IgG**. A similar nomenclature is used for IgG subclasses in other species, e.g. in the mouse IgG1, IgG2a and IgG2b. *See* **mouse myeloma.**

IgG(t). *See* **T globulin.**

Characteristics of the human immunoglobulins

	IgG	IgA	IgM	IgD	IgE
Old nomenclatures	γG, γ_{ss}, γ_2, 7Sγ	γA, β_2A,γ_1A	γM, γ-macroglobulin, 19Sγ, γ_1M,β_2M	γD	γE
Electrophoretic mobility	γ_2 to γ_1	γ_1 to β	γ_1	γ_1	γ_1
Molecular weight	150 000	170 000 in serum (forms polymers) Dimer in secretions M.W. 398 000	970 000	184 000	188 000
Sedimentation coefficient (approx.)	7S	7S (monomer) 11S (dimer)	19S	7S	8S
Concentration in human serum (mg per 100 ml)	800-1600	150-400	50-200	0.3-40	20-500ng per ml.
Per cent of total present in intra-vascular (serum) pool	48-62	40	65-100	63-86	
Catabolic rate as per cent of intravas-cular pool per day	4-7	14-34	14-25	18-60	
Valency	2	2 (monomer) 4 (dimer)	5-10	2	2
Heavy chain type	γ	α	μ	δ	ϵ
Light chain type	$\varkappa$ and λ	$\varkappa$ and λ	$\varkappa$ and λ	$\varkappa$ and λ	$\varkappa$ and λ
Where found	Plasma, Tissue fluids	External secretions (saliva, milk, etc.) Plasma	Plasma	Plasma	Plasma, Secretions
Complement fixing activity	Yes (subtypes IgG1 and IgG3)	No (in absence of lysozyme)	Yes	?	No
Placental transfer	Yes	No	No	No	No

IgM

IgM. High molecular weight (970 000, $s_{20,w}$ = 19S) **immunoglobulin**. Phylogenetically the most primitive immunoglobulin, present in all vertebrates from lamprey upwards. In mammals it is mainly in the form of a cyclic pentamer of five basic units of heavy and light chains linked by **disulphide bonds.** A monomeric form ($s_{20,w}$ = 7-8S) is found on the surface of B lymphocytes. In other species the predominant form may be a monomer (e.g. dogfish) tetramer (e.g. carp) or hexamer (Xenopus). **Heavy** (μ) **chain** larger than that of other immunoglobulins (mol. wt. 70 000). High carbohydrate content. Fixes **complement**. Does not cross placenta in man but may in certain other species (e.g. rabbit). **Antibody** activity usually destroyed by reduction of inter-subunit disulphide bonds (*see* **mercaptoethanol**). Normal serum concentration in man is 50-200 mg/100 ml. See illustration below.

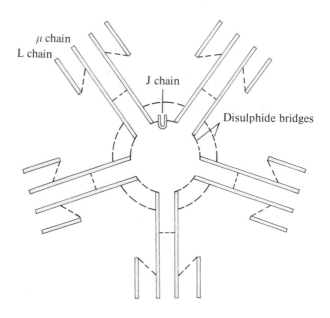

IgT. Name formerly given by some researchers to the **T lymphocyte antigen receptor**, then considered to be a special class of **immunoglobulin,** (do not confuse with IgG(t)). (*See* **T globulin**).

I-K. *See* **immunoconglutinin**.

IL-1. *See* **interleukin-1**.

IL-2. *See* **interleukin-2**.

ImD$_{50}$. The dose of an **antigen**[2] or **vaccine** sufficient to **immunize**[1] 50 per cent of a test group of animals.

immediate hypersensitivity. **Antibody**-mediated **hypersensitivity** characterized by lesions resulting from release of **histamine** and other vasoactive substances (*syn.* **type I reaction**). The ability to react in this way can be transferred to another individual by serum alone (cf. **delayed hypersensitivity**). The antibody is **reagin**[1] or **homocytotropic antibody** usually of **IgE** type which fixes to cells (especially **mast cells**). On contact with antigen, the cell releases vasoactive substances. So named because of rapidity of appearance of lesion after contact with antigen (a few seconds to 30 min). Detected by **skin tests** and **RAST** in man and **passive cutaneous anaphylaxis** in animals. For examples *see* **anaphylactic shock, hay fever, asthma** and **urticaria**.

immobilization test. Technique for the detection and/or titration of antibody against a motile bacterium or protozoon, etc. by observing the effect of antibody in inhibiting movement. This inhibition may be caused by (a) adhesion together (in effect **agglutination**) of the cilia or flagella of organisms, e.g. *Trichomonas fetus, Paramoecium* spp., or motile bacteria, (b) damage to the cell wall in the presence of **complement** as in **Treponema pallidum immobilization test**.

immune. (1) Protected against disease either by (a) specific or (b) non-specific mechanism; e.g. in (a) those who have been vaccinated against or have recovered from smallpox are immune to it, and in (b) all men are immune to canine distemper. (2) A state in which, following contact with **antigen**[1,2] the tissues show a specific alteration in their reactivity to subsequent doses of that antigen, inasmuch as they now exhibit a response of **humoral**, or **cell-mediated immunity** against it.

immune adherence. Adherence of **antigen-antibody complexes** or **antibody** coated bacteria, etc. to primate erythrocytes, rabbit platelets, macrophages and polymorphs. In the case of macrophages and polymorphs immune adherence stimulates phagocytosis. The phenomenon is **complement**-dependent and occurs when **C3** is bound and is a property of **C3b** and C4b (*see* **C4**). May be used as sensitive detector system for complement-fixing antibody. *See* **trypanosome adhesion test, Rieckenberg reaction**.

immune antibody. In blood group **serology,** an **antibody** provoked by antigenic challenge, e.g. by transfusion, as opposed to **natural antibody**; thus immune anti-A, etc.

immune clearance. *See* **immune elimination**.

immune complex. *Syn*. antigen-antibody complex. A macro-molecular complex of **antigen** and **antibody** molecules bound specifically together. May be present in soluble form especially in **antigen excess** or as a precipitate especially at **optimal proportions**. **Complement** components may be bound by immune complexes. Important in pathogenesis of certain **hypersensitivity** reactions, *see* **Arthus reaction (type III reaction)**. *See also* **immune complex disease, serum sickness, glomerulonephritis.**

immune complex disease. Tissue damage mediated by **immune complexes** especially seen in human and experimental **glomerulonephritis.** Essentially **hypersensitivity** of **Arthus reaction** type (**type III reaction**) q.v. *See also* **serum sickness, Masugi nephritis** and **Goodpasture syndrome.**

immune cytolysis. (1). Lysis of cells by **antibody** in the presence of **complement**. Term usually used of cells other than erythrocytes, cf.**immune haemolysis**. (2). Lysis of **target cells** by **cytotoxic T lymphocytes** or **K cells**.

immune deviation. Selective alteration in the immune response to an antigen, caused by prior administration of that antigen. For example, in guinea pigs given antigen in **complete Freund's adjuvant** the **corneal response** and γ_2 **globulin** antibody production are depressed if the same antigen has previously been given without Freund's adjuvant.

immune elimination. (1) Exponential elimination of antigen from the body as a result of removal and destruction by antibodies and/or effector cells. This commences a few days after the first administration of the antigen and radiolabelled antigens can be shown to be eliminated from the circulation much more rapidly in **immune**[2] than in **non immune** hosts. (2) Technique used to measure the antibody response by following the rate of removal of a labelled antigen from the circulation of an **immunized**[2] animal.

immune exclusion. Process by which entry of **antigen** into the body is prevented by a specific immune response directed at the antigen. The term is most frequently applied to the regulation of antigen absorption by mucosal surfaces.

immune haemolysis. **Complement**-dependent mechanism by which fresh serum (i.e. complement containing) lyses erythrocytes coated with anti-erythrocyte antibody (i.e. **sensitized cells**[2] or **haemolytic system**[1]).

immune response. The development of specifically altered reactivity following exposure to an antigen. This may take several forms, e.g. **antibody** production, **cell-mediated immunity**, **immunological tolerance**.

immune serum. **Antiserum** especially in context of **protective immunity**.

immune state. (1) The state of responsiveness of a host to any antigen, e.g. tolerant (*see* **immunological tolerance**), non immune (*see* **non immune animal**), immune[1,2], etc. (2) Used in a more restricted sense in prophylactic **immunization**[2] to describe the degree of **protective immunity** which an individual possesses against a pathogenic organism, e.g. solid immunity, partial immunity, etc.

immune tolerance. *See* **immunological tolerance**.

immunity. (1) *Synonyms:* **protective immunity** and functional immunity. Non-susceptibility to the invasive or pathogenic effects of foreign organisms or to the toxic effects of antigenic substances. *See also* **active immunity, passive immunity** and **non-specific immunity**. (2) State of heightened responsiveness to antigen, such that antigen is bound or eliminated more rapidly than in the **non immune** state; thus inclusive of all types of **humoral** and **cell-mediated immunity** but not of **immunological tolerance**.

immunity deficiency syndrome. *See* **immunodeficiency**.

immunization. (1) Administration of antigen in order to produce an **immune response** to that antigen. (2) Administration either of **antigen**[1,2] to produce **active immunity**, or of **antibody** to produce **passive immunity**, in order to confer protection against the harmful effects of antigenic substances or organisms.

immunize. (1) To produce increased protection against the harmful effects of an **antigen**[2] by procedures designed to produce **passive immunity** or **active immunity**. (2) To alter the reactivity of a host to an antigen by exposing it to that antigen in such a way that it produces an **immune response** q.v.

immunizing dose

immunizing dose. Term used in standardization of vaccines. Thus in biological assay of vaccines, the **ImD$_{50}$** is the dose sufficient to immunize (*see* **immunization**[2]) 50 per cent of the animals tested as judged by any given measure of the **immune response**.

immunoadsorbent. Any insoluble preparation of an **antigen** used to adsorb (*see* **adsorption**) antibodies specific for that antigen from a mixture, so that the antibodies can later be eluted (*see* **eluate**) in a pure form. Also used to remove unwanted antibodies from an **antiserum,** so making it more specific. Soluble antigens can conveniently be linked by **covalent bonding** to insoluble carriers such as diazotized (*see* **diazotization**) polyaminopolystyrene for this purpose.

immunoblast. *Syn.* **Lymphoblast.**

immunoblotting. *See* **western blotting**.

immunochemistry. Chemical techniques and concepts as applied to immunology. Of particular importance in structural studies of **antibody, immunoglobulins, antigens, haptens** but not yet extensively applied to **cell-mediated immunity**.

immunoconglutinin. **Autoantibody** against fixed **complement** components, especially C$\overline{3}$, also C$\overline{4}$ (*see* **C$\overline{n}$**), i.e. **C3b** and C4b (*see* **C4**). Serum immunoconglutinin levels reflect extent of **complement fixation** by *in vivo* immune reactions and are raised in many bacterial, viral and parasitic infections and **autoimmune diseases**. Not to be confused with **conglutinin** q.v.

immunocyte. Any **immunologically competent** cell.

immunocytoadherence. A **rosette** technique by which cells which carry **immunoglobulin** on their surfaces (either because they have formed the immunoglobulin or because it has become bound to the cell) can be detected. Erythrocytes coated with antigen are mixed with the cells and bind to those cells bearing antibody to form a 'rosette'.

immunodeficiency. Any condition in which a deficiency of **humoral** or **cell-mediated immunity** exists. *See* **severe combined immunodeficiency syndrome, cell-mediated immunity deficiency syndromes, infantile sex linked hypogammaglobulinaemia** and **antibody deficiency syndrome**.

immunodiffusion. *See* **gel diffusion.**

immunodominance. An immunodominant portion of an **epitope** is a part that contributes a disproportionately large portion of the binding energy. Many **haptens** are immunodominant.

immunoelectroadsorption. A method for the quantification of antibody. On to a metallized glass slide is adsorbed (*see* **adsorption**), first a layer of the antigen, and then antibody from the serum being examined. Both adsorptions are carried out with the aid of an electric current. The thickness of the layer of antibody can be measured and is a function of its concentration in the serum.

immunoelectroosmophoresis. *See* counter **immuno-electrophoresis.**

immunoelectrophoresis. Technique in which proteins are first separated by **electrophoresis** and then allowed to react with an **antiserum** so that a pattern of **precipitation** arcs is developed. Proteins are thus characterized by (a) electrophoretic mobility and (b) antigenic character. Used for the analysis of complex mixtures such as **serum.** *See also* **counter immunoelectrophoresis.**

immunoferritin technique. The electron microscopic visualization of **antigenic determinant** sites by the attachment to them of antibody molecules labelled with **ferritin.** The labelled antibody may either be applied directly to the specimen, or a ferritin-labelled **antiglobulin** may be used for an indirect technique analogous to those used in the **indirect fluorescent antibody technique.**

immunofluorescence. Technique in which **antigen** or **antibody** is conjugated to a **fluorochrome** and then allowed to react with the corresponding antibody or antigen in a tissue section or smear. The location of tissue antibodies or antigens can thus be determined by microscopic observation of the resulting pattern of fluorescence. For various immunofluorescence methods, *see* **double layer fluorescent antibody technique, sandwich technique, single layer immunofluorescence technique** and illustrations on p.122 and p.202.

immunogen. A substance that when introduced into the body stimulates **humoral** or **cell-mediated immunity** as opposed to **immunological tolerance.**

immunogenic. Capable of inducing **humoral** or **cell-mediated immunity** but not **immunological tolerance.** Cf. **tolerogenic.**

immunogenicity. The potential of an **antigen**[1] (or **immunogen**) to stimulate an **immune response**, in a given species of animal. Immunogenicity probably depends on the size of the antigen and on the extent to which its **antigenic determinants** differ from those of the immunized animal. Distinguish from **adjuvanticity**.

immunoglobulin. Member of a family of proteins each made up of **light chains** q.v. and **heavy chains** q.v. linked together, most commonly by **disulphide bonds**. The members are divided into **immunoglobulin classes** and **subclasses** (q.v.) determined by the amino acid sequence of their heavy chains. Most mammals probably have five immunoglobulin classes (**IgM, IgG, IgA, IgD, IgE**), although lower organisms have less, e.g. the cartilaginous fishes have only one immunoglobulin closely related to IgM. All **antibodies** are immunoglobulins; however, it is not certain that all immunoglobulin molecules function as antibodies. Present in serum, body fluids, etc. of all vertebrate species higher than the hagfish. On electrophoresis show γ or β mobility relative to other serum proteins. *See* illustrations on pp.107, 108 and 110.

immunoglobulin A. *See* **IgA**.

immunoglobulin class. The group into which an **immunoglobulin** is placed by virtue of one or more unique **antigenic determinants** on its **heavy chains** specific for a particular class and which distinguish it immunologically from other classes. The γ chain of **IgG**, for instance, is antigenically and structurally different from the α chain of **IgA**. IgA, IgD, IgE, IgG and IgM are immunoglobulin classes distinguishable respectively by their possession of α, δ, ε, γ and μ chains. *See* table on p.109.

immunoglobulin D. *See* **IgD**.

immunoglobulin domain. The three-dimensional structure formed by a single homology region of an **immunoglobulin heavy** or **light chain**, i.e. V_L, C_L, V_H, C_H1, C_H2, C_H3 or C_H4.

immunoglobulin E. *See* **IgE**.

immunoglobulin G. *See* **IgG**.

immunoglobulin gene.

The structure of light and heavy chain genes from an IgM-producing cell. L = light chain gene, μ = μ chain gene, Lp = leader peptide exon, V = variable region gene, D = D exon (heavy chain only), J = J exon, C_L = light chain constant region gene, $C\mu$1-4 = μ constant region gene exons. T_s = tail sequence, Tm = exons coding for the C-terminal amino acids of the membrane-bound form of μ chain. All coding regions (exons) are shown as blocks. Introns I_1-I_2 are shown as straight lines.

immunoglobulin M. *See* IgM.

immunoglobulin subclass. Subdivision within each **immuno-globulin class**, based on structural and antigenic differences in their **heavy chains.** Thus human **IgG** has four subclasses: IgG1, IgG2, IgG3 and IgG4, each bearing common γ chain antigenic determinants but each also bearing determinants unique to the subclass. The subclasses differ structurally from one another, e.g. IgG1 and IgG4 have two inter-heavy chain **disulphide bonds**, IgG2 has four and IgG3 may have as many as 10-15. They also differ functionally. IgG1, 3 and 4 attach to guinea pig skin cells while IgG2 fails to do so. IgG4 fails to fix **complement**. Human **IgA** has two subclasses. Immuno-globulins of other species also show subclass differences.

immunological (*Amer.* immunologic). Referring to **specific immun-ity**, e.g. as in **immunological tolerance**, or to the study of immunology, e.g. immunological journals.

immunological adjuvant. *See* **antigen adjuvant**.

immunological barrier. Anatomical barrier that prevents or attenuates an immune response against an antigen. Examples are: the placenta (prevents rejection of mammalian fetus) and the aqueous humor of the eye (allows alloantigenic grafts to be made to the anterior chamber).

immunological competence. Capacity to produce an **immune response**; used of cells, tissues, etc.

immunological deficiency state. Preferred term now is **immunodeficiency** q.v.

immunological enhancement

immunological enhancement. An increased rate of tumour growth in animals immunized (*see* **immunization**[1]) with the antigens of the tumour. Seen especially in experimental tumours transplanted to animals which have antibody to the tumour. Attributed to the coating of tumour antigens with antibody which prevents access of **lymphocytes** (agents of **cell-mediated immunity**) to the tumour cells but may also involve suppression of cell-mediated immunity by **suppressor T lymphocytes**.

immunological inertia. A specific depression of **immunity**, other than **immunological tolerance**, towards the **histocompatibility antigens** of a partner in viviparity, i.e. of mother or of fetus.

immunological memory. Concept formulated to explain the capacity of the immunological system of the body to respond much faster and more powerfully to subsequent exposures to an antigen than it did at the first exposure. Postulates that **primed** cells (memory cells) are capable of storing information so that on subsequent **challenge**[1], a more rapid and more efficient **immunological reaction**[1] is triggered off.

immunological paralysis. *See* **acquired tolerance** (*preferred term*) and **immunological tolerance**. Note that this term does not indicate any inability of the animal to move.

immunological reaction. (1) *In vivo*. Any reaction or response stemming from the contact of **primed** or **unprimed** lymphoid cells with, or the combination of **antibody** with, an **antigen**, e.g. cell division, **lymphocyte transformation,** antibody production, induction of **immunological tolerance, graft rejection, hypersensitivity**, etc. (2) *In vitro*. Any measurable change resulting from the combination of antibody with, or response of primed lymphocytes to, an antigen, e.g. **precipitation**, virus neutralization, **macrophage migration inhibition**, etc.

immunological rejection. Destruction of foreign cells or tissues inoculated or grafted into a recipient due to a specific immune reaction (*see* **specific immunity**) against them by the recipient's **lymphoid tissues**.

immunological response. The specific response to **antigen**[1,2]. Thus includes the responses of **cell-mediated immunity, humoral immunity** and **immunological tolerance**.

immunological surveillance. Postulated continuous monitoring of the cells of the body by its immunological system so that aberrant

118

cells arising by somatic mutation and containing new antigens are rapidly destroyed. Suggested by Burnet as control mechanism in prevention of neoplasia.

immunological tolerance. An **immunological response** consisting of the development of specific non-reactivity of the **lymphoid tissues** to a given antigen capable in other circumstances of inducing **cell-mediated** or **humoral immunity**. May follow contact with antigen in fetal or early post-natal life or, in adults, administration of very high or very low doses of certain antigens (*see* **acquired tolerance**). **Immunological reactions**[1] to unrelated antigens are not affected by the induction of tolerance to any given antigen.

immunological unresponsiveness. Failure to respond to contact with antigen. May be specific for a given antigen, as in **immunological tolerance** and **Ir gene** (q.v.) defects, or generalized inasmuch as there is non-specific unresponsiveness to many antigens as, for example in **immunodeficiency states** or following therapy with an **immunosuppressive agent**.

immunologically activated cell. **Immunologically competent cell** that has reacted on contact with antigen, i.e. has been **primed**. The reaction may take several forms, i.e. **lymphocyte transformation, immunological memory**, antibody production, response of **cell-mediated immunity, immunological tolerance**.

immunologically competent cell. Any cell capable of specific recognition of, or specific response to antigen.

immunoosmophoresis. *See* **counter immunoelectrophoresis**.

immunopotentiation. Term used for artificial augmentation of the immune response in a very general sense. Is thus the opposite of **immunosuppression**. Produced by a wide variety of agents, e.g. **adjuvants, Levamisole®** etc.

immunoprophylaxis. The prevention of disease by the use of **vaccines** or **antisera**.

immunoosmoelectrophoresis. *See* **counter immunoelectrophoresis**.

immunosuppression. The artificial suppression of **immune responses** by the use of drugs (**antimetabolites**), irradiation or agents such as **anti-lymphocyte serum**. Used to enhance survival of **allografts**. *See also* **immunosuppressive agent**.

119

immunosuppressive agent

immunosuppressive agent. A physical (e.g. x-irradiation), chemical (e.g. **azathioprine** or **mercaptopurine**), or biological agent (e.g. **anti-lymphocyte serum**), that inhibits the stimulation of an **immune response** by an antigen.

immunotherapy. Treatment of disease by **active** or **passive immunization** or by the use of agents designed to potentiate or suppress the actions of immune cells.

inaccessible antigens. *See* **hidden determinant**.

inactivated vaccine. A **vaccine** containing organisms or viruses that are incapable of replication. In the case of viral vaccines of this type the virus is usually inactivated by an agent such as formaldehyde (e.g. influenza virus), phenol (e.g. Semple rabies vaccine), or β-propiolactone (e.g. duck embryo rabies vaccine, Newcastle disease virus). Formaldehyde, phenol, acetone or heat are employed to inactivate bacterial vaccines. The object, in all cases, is to cause as little damage as possible to the **protective antigens** of the organism concerned.

inactivation. (1) Any procedure used to destroy any biological activity. (2) Destruction of **complement** activity in serum, e.g. by heating at 56°C for 20 min or by treatment with **hydrazine**, etc. *See* **heat inactivation**. (3) The use of heat, formaldehyde, phenol, or β-propiolactone to kill a pathogenic virus, bacterium or other organism before preparing an **inactivated vaccine** from it.

inbred strain. Experimental animals produced by sequential brother–sister matings. In immunology, the term usually refers to animals in the 20th and subsequent generations of such matings. Such animals are so homogeneous at histocompatibility loci (*see* **histocompatibility gene**) that grafts can be freely exchanged between them without provoking **graft rejection**. Note that, due to mutations and evolutionary pressure, sublines of inbred strains kept in different laboratories, may gradually lose syngeneity.

incompatibility. Antigenic non-identity between donor and recipient, e.g. in blood transfusion or tissue transplantation, such that harmful reactions may occur when donor material is introduced into the recipient.

incomplete antibody. (1) In **agglutination** tests, antibodies that coat erythrocytes or bacteria but do not link them together. Such antibodies lack the capacity to bind to multiple receptors on adjacent cells because either their **valency**[a] is too low (**IgG** antibodies are

120

divalent and often incomplete, **IgM** antibodies usually agglutinate), or they are directed against **antigenic determinants** so positioned on the cell surface that agglutination is hindered for steric reasons, or the shape of the antibody molecule is such that it cannot form links between the cells. The presence of non-agglutinating antibodies can often be detected by the **antiglobulin test**. (2) Sometimes used to describe a univalent antibody fragment produced by enzymatic digestion, i.e. **Fab fragment.**

incomplete Freund's adjuvant. A **water-in-oil emulsion adjuvant.** Cf. **complete Freund's adjuvant** and note that the incomplete form does *not* contain mycobacteria.

indirect antiglobulin test. Application of the **antiglobulin test** to the detection of free **incomplete antibody**[1], e.g. in a sample of serum. The test sample is incubated with erythrocytes, bacteria, etc. having the appropriate surface antigen. The cells are then **washed**, and the **antiglobulin** serum is added. If non-agglutinating ('incomplete') antibody has attached to the cells, the subsequent union with antiglobulin antibody results in their agglutination. N.B. The term 'indirect' is applied to the **indirect fluorescent antibody technique,** with a meaning different from that given above, cf. **direct antiglobulin test.**

indirect complement fixation test. Test used to detect antibodies that do not fix guinea pig **complement**, e.g. avian antibodies. Dilutions of serum are allowed to react with the antigen. Complement and rabbit antibody to the antigen are then added to each dilution. Antigen which has not combined with the avian antibody (in the tube where the latter has been diluted out), is available to combine with the rabbit antibody and in so doing fixes the complement. The extent of fixation is detected by adding a **haemolytic system**[1]. Lysis of the cells indicates that avian antibody was initially present in those tubes.

indirect Coombs' test. *See* **indirect antiglobulin test.**

indirect fluorescent antibody technique. A technique for detecting antibody or antigen in which the developing antibody, labelled with a fluorochrome, does not bind directly to the molecule to be detected but to an intermediate antibody or antigen, resulting in increased sensitivity. Examples are the **sandwich technique, double layer fluorescent antibody techniques**, techniques using **fluorochrome**-labelled anti-complement sera, etc.

indirect haemagglutination test

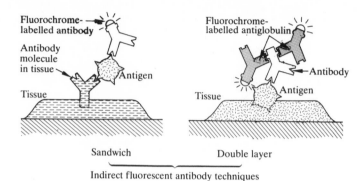

Indirect fluorescent antibody techniques

indirect haemagglutination test. *See* **passive agglutination test.**

indirect template hypothesis. A modification of the **template theory** (q.v.) in which it was proposed that the information required to produce an **antibody** molecule was in some way copied from the **antigen** structure and became encoded in the DNA which was then used to make antibody. Originally postulated by Burnet and Fenner and of historical interest only.

inducer. A substance that induces cell differentiation. *See also* **colony stimulating factors.**

inducer T lymphocyte. A T lymphocyte whose presence is required for induction of immune responses. *See also* **helper T lymphocyte.**

inductive phase. Period of time that elapses between the administration of an antigen and the appearance of a *detectable* **immune response.** The true inductive phase will be much shorter than this.

inert particle agglutination tests. Tests for the presence of antibody which employ small **collodion particles, bentonite** or latex to carry a soluble antigen. The antigen is adsorbed (*see* **adsorption**) to the surface of the particle without the use of a coupling agent, cf. **passive agglutination tests.** The addition of a serum containing antibody to a suspension of particles coated in this way causes agglutination to occur. *See* **latex agglutination test.**

infantile sex-linked hypogammaglobulinaemia. Genetically determined sex-linked **antibody deficiency syndrome** occurring in boys and becoming manifest as soon as maternally derived antibodies (*see* **maternal immunity**) have disappeared from the child's tissues.

Characterized by low serum **immunoglobulin** levels and defective antibody production that leads to repeated bacterial (not viral) infections. **Cell-mediated immunity** is not apparently defective.

infectious bursal agent (IBA). Virus infecting the very young chicken (*Gallus domesticus*) and preferentially multiplying in the cells of the **bursa of Fabricius** which is destroyed (Gumboro disease). Nevertheless, some degree of antibody response to the virus does occur.

infectious mononucleosis (or glandular fever). Disease, chiefly of young persons, characterized by sore throat, lymph node enlargement, the presence of atypical **monocytes** and of large numbers of **large lymphocytes** in the blood. **Heterophil antibodies** are present in serum, which agglutinate the erythrocytes of foreign species, i.e. sheep, horse, ox and which are detected by the **Paul-Bunnell test**. Caused by EB (Epstein-Barr) virus which infects **B lymphocytes**. The blood lymphocytes are **T lymphocytes** reactive against the EB-infected B lymphocytes. *See also* **Burkitt's lymphoma**.

inflammatory cell. Any cell present in an inflammatory lesion as part of the host response, e.g. **neutrophil leucocytes, eosinophil leucocytes, macrophages**, etc.

influenza vaccine. (1) **Inactivated vaccine** containing two or more of the current A and B strains of influenza virus. **Antigenic variation** in the virus makes it essential that the vaccine strains are closely related antigenically to the virus causing outbreaks in the community. Immunity produced is short lived, approximately 6 months. (2) *Vet.* As (1) but containing current strains of the virus that infect horses causing 'stable cough'.

inhibition tests. (1) Tests in which the activity of, e.g. a virus, is inhibited by the addition of dilutions of a serum, containing antibody which is being titrated. *See* **haemagglutination inhibition test**[a], haemadsorption inhibition test. (2) Inhibition of a standard **agglutination**, precipitation, test, etc. by the addition of a purified preparation of the antigen, thus proving the specificity of the reaction. (3) *See* **hapten inhibition test**.

inhibition zone. *See* **prozone** (*preferred term*).

initial serum dilution. Term used in **serology** to indicate that the **end point** of a titration has been quoted as the original dilution that was made of the serum under test, ignoring the further dilution that

innate immunity

has occurred due to reagents added to it. Commonly quoted in, e.g. **agglutination** tests where a single equal volume of a suspension of cells or organisms is added to each tube of the **doubling dilution** of the serum. Cf. **final serum dilution**.

innate immunity. *See* **native immunity**.

inoculation. In immunology refers to introduction of a substance into the body, usually but not exclusively by **parenteral** injection.

instructive hypotheses of antibody production. Early hypotheses suggesting that antibodies have no **specificity** for **antigen**[1] until they or the antibody-producing cells come into contact with it and therefore antigen instructs the cell to synthesize **antibody** specifically reactive against it; e.g. in earlier hypotheses, by acting as a template (*see* **template hypothesis**) on which antibody is formed or, in later versions, by acting as a template for DNA or messenger RNA (*see* **indirect template hypothesis**). Cf. **selective theories of antibody production**.

insulin resistance. A state in which insulin evokes a smaller hypoglycaemic response than would normally be expected. The development of antibodies to injected insulin derived from other species may be one of the causes of this.

Intal®. *See* **disodium cromoglycate**.

interdigitating cell. Cell of dendritic morphology and with **accessory cell** function, found especially in the **thymus dependent areas** of **lymph nodes** and other **peripheral lymphoid organs**.

interfacial test. *See* **ring test**.

interferon. Group of proteins with antiviral activity, originally identified as products released by cells in response to virus infection. When taken up by other cells, the replication of virus within them is inhibited. Activity is species-specific, but non-specific in its spectrum of antiviral activity in that virtually all viruses are susceptible to its action. Interferons appear to act by inducing the production of a second inhibitory protein which blocks translation of viral messenger RNA. Interferons are also released from cells by agents other than viruses, including immunological stimuli. Three types of interferon are now recognized; viz, α-interferon (leucocyte interferon; IFN α), β-interferon (fibroblast interferon; IFN β) and γ-interferon (immune interferon; IFN γ) ; α- and β-interferons (M.Wt. 20 000) are the classical virus-induced forms, but γ-interferon (M.Wt. 45 000) may be released by **T lymphocytes** or activated **macrophages** and is regarded as a **lymphokine** : γ-interferon also differs from α and β-interferons since it is labile at pH 2.0. There are subtypes within these three types. **NK cells** release interferons, and interferons are believed to activate immature NK cells for cytocidal functions. IFN-γ has been shown to possess activity as **macrophage activating factor** and in **B lymphocyte** differentiation.

interleukin-1 (IL-1, lymphocyte activating factor, LAF). A protein secreted by **macrophages** or **accessory cells**, required for the activation (probably indirect through **interleukin 2**) of T and B **lymphocytes** by **antigens** or **mitogens**. Also has direct mitogenic activity for thymocytes. M.Wt. approximately 13 000–16 000.

interleukin-2 (IL-2, T cell growth factor). Soluble product of stimulated **T lymphocytes** which causes activation and differentiation of other T-lymphocytes in an antigen-non-specific manner. Essential factor in maintenance of long-term T lymphocyte cultures in vitro.

interleukin-3. **Lymphokine** identified as a product of mitogen-activated **T lymphocytes**. Is a **colony stimulating factor** for all the bone marrow progenitor cells and a **mast cell** growth factor.

intermediate gel technique. A variant of **crossed immunoelectrophoresis** q.v. in which electrophoresis is carried out in plain gel in one direction and then into two gels in the other direction. The two gels contain antisera to, respectively, one antigen and to all the antigens in the sample. Used to identify specific antigens.

internal image Jerne's **network theory** postulates that, for every **antibody** against an external **antigen**, there is a set of antibodies of unrelated specificities bearing **idiotopes** that fit the **antigen-binding site** of the former antibody. These idiotopes will therefore have structures resembling that of the **antigenic determinant** or **epitope** on the external antigen and for this reason are said to constitute the internal image of the antigen.

International Unit of Immunological Activity. The potency of a given weight of an internationally accepted standard preparation of antiserum or antigen. Applicable as a measure of potency to a number of antitoxins, antibacterial antibodies, immunizing agents such as **pertussis vaccine** and test antigens such as **tuberculin**.

intraepithelial lymphocyte. Any **lymphocyte** found within an epithelium especially the intestinal epithelium.

intron.   A continuous sequence of DNA within a gene that does not code for amino acid sequences in the gene product, c.f. **exon**. Many genes, including those for **immunoglobulin light** and **heavy chains**, contain introns. In immunoglobulin genes, introns separate the **leader sequence** from the **variable region**, the variable region from the **constant region** and the **hinge region** and **homology regions** of the heavy chain gene from each other. *See* fig. on p.117.

Inv allotypes (Inv groups).   Old nomenclature for Km allotypes. **Allotypic** antigenic determinants on the **constant region** of $\varkappa$ **chains** of human **immunoglobulins**. Inv1 (Km1) is formed by a leucine residue at position 191; Inv2 (Km2) is formed by both the leucine at position 191 and an alanine residue at position 153; Inv3 (Km3) is due to the substitution of a valine residue at position 191 and may be independent of residue 153, although this is not certain.

I region.   In the murine **MHC**, the I region appears to include many of the genes coding for Class II histocompatibility products. Six separate genes are recognised (*see* **H-2**), Aα, Aβ, Eα, Eβ, Eβ2 and J. The last (J) is still not well characterized and may not be a separate gene, and the gene for Aα is not precisely characterized. The involvement of the products of this region in many aspects of the immunological response gave it the general name 'I = immune' region. *See* illustration on p.90.

Ir gene.   Immune response gene. Found within the **I region** (q.v.). Determines the capacity of an animal to mount an **immune response** against any defined antigen. *See also* **MHC genes**.

irradiation chimera.   Lethally X-irradiated animal whose **lymphoid tissues** and myeloid tissues have been successfully repopulated by cells transferred from another donor. Adult **bone marrow**, adult **spleen**, infant spleen and fetal liver have been shown to be effective repopulating tissues.

isoagglutinin.   **Isoantibody** which agglutinates cells. *See also* **isohaemagglutinin, isoleucoagglutinin**.

isoantibody.   Antibody against **isoantigen**.

isoantigen.   **Antigen**[1] carried by an individual, which is capable of eliciting an **immune response** in genetically different individuals of the same species but not in the individual bearing it.

isoelectric focusing.   Technique for separating ampholytes (electrolytes, such as proteins and peptides, bearing both acidic and basic groups) according to their **isoelectric point**. A potential difference is applied across a system (liquid column, thin layer gel or cylindrical gel) in which pH increases from anode to cathode. Proteins or peptides present in the system focus into sharp bands in the region of the gradient corresponding to their own isoelectric point.

isoelectric point (pI). The pH at which a given molecule or particle carries no net charge and does not migrate in an electric field. Most substances have a minimum solubility at their isoelectric point.

isogeneic (isogenic). Possessing absolutely identical genotypes, e.g. animals derived from the same egg, identical twins. Often used as a synonym for **syngeneic** as a descriptor of **inbred strains**. However, individuals of the latter are never absolutely identical in the sense inferred by the term isogeneic. *See also* **transplantation terminology**.

isograft. *See* **syngeneic**.

isohaemagglutinin. Antibody capable of reacting with **isoantigens** on the surfaces of erythrocytes and thus of agglutinating the cells. The naturally occurring antibodies against **ABO blood group system** antigens in human serum are examples of isohaemagglutinins.

isoimmunization. **Immunization**[1] with **isoantigen**. Used in blood transfusion serology to refer to immunization of mother by fetal erythrocytes or recipient of a blood transfusion by donor erythrocytes of incompatible **blood groups** (*see* **incompatibility**).

isoleucoagglutinins. Antibody capable of reacting with **isoantigens** on the surface of **leucocytes** and thus of agglutinating the cells. Isoleucoagglutinins are sometimes found in the sera of patients who have had multiple transfusions and in multiparous women. Batteries of these sera are used in **tissue typing** for the identification of **histocompatibility antigens** on leucocytes.

isologous. *Syn.* **isogeneic** or **syngeneic**.

isophil(e) antibody. Antibody against erythrocyte antigens which are unique to the species from which the erythrocytes were derived. Cf. **heterophil(e) antibody**.

isotopic labelling (radionuclide labelling). Introduction into a molecule of a radioactive isotope of any element. This may be

isotype

achieved by internal labelling, e.g. addition of ^{3}H-, ^{14}C- or ^{35}S-labelled amino acids to cultures of tissues which are synthesizing proteins and so allowing the cell itself to incorporate the label during synthesis, or by external labelling in which isotopes (e.g. ^{125}I, ^{131}I) are tagged to molecules which have already been formed. Isotopically-labelled molecules can then be traced by a variety of methods for detecting and measuring radioactivity.

isotype. Classification of a molecule by comparison of its primary or **antigenic** structure with that of closely related molecules found within all members of the same species. Applied to the immunoglobulins, the isotype describes the **immunoglobulin class** and **subclass, light chain type** and **subtype** and can also be applied to the **variable region groups** and **subgroups**. For example a mouse immunoglobulin may have the isotype IgG$_{2a}$ ($\varkappa$) and its light chain may be from the variable region group V$_\varkappa$-10. *Cf*. **allotype, idiotype**.

isotypic variation. Structural variability of antigens common to all members of the same species, e.g. the antigenic differences which distinguish the classes of immunoglobulins and types of immunoglobulin chains. Cf. **allotype, idiotypic variation**.

ITP. *See* **idiopathic thrombocytopenic purpura**.

Jarisch-Herxheimer reaction. *See* **Herxheimer reaction**.

J chain. Polypeptide chain (M.Wt. 15 000) with a high content of cysteine, found in the polymeric forms of IgA and IgM. Has been shown to link together two of the subunits in these immunoglobulins (*see* figs. on pp.107 and 110), thus maintaining the polymeric structure. The J chains from IgA and IgM are identical.

Jennerian vaccination. Jenner in 1798 described the use of infection with **cowpox** to induce **active immunity** in man that protected against smallpox (**variola**). His reputation rests on the fact that he proved the effectiveness of the method by challenging the vaccinated boy James Phipps with virulent smallpox virus. His success was due to the fact that variola virus and cowpox virus share **cross-reacting antigens**[2], yet the latter produces only localized lesions in man. It therefore stimulated protective immunity without causing serious disease. **Smallpox vaccination** as introduced by Jenner is still in use today but the present vaccine virus, **vaccinia**, now differs in some minor respects from the true cowpox virus.

Jerne plaque technique. *See* **haemolytic plaque test**.

128

J exon. J (joining) gene. A short sequence of DNA coding for part of the third **hypervariable region** of the **light chain** or **heavy chain**, found near to the 5′ end of the κ, λ and γ **constant region** genes but separated from them by an **intron**. Not to be confused with **J chain** q.v. Several J exons are associated with each constant region gene. In germ line DNA the variable region gene is separated from the J exon by a large but unknown distance. During the differentiation of a stem cell to a **lymphocyte** a **V-region** gene is translocated to the position immediately 5′ to one of the J exons to which it becomes attached.

Job's syndrome. A syndrome of recurrent, cold staphylococcal abscesses and other infections with persistent eczema, high serum **IgE** levels and a defect of neutrophil leucocyte **chemotaxis**.

Johnin. A substance, similar to tuberculin, used in the **skin test** for the diagnosis of Johne's disease in cattle. Extracted from the medium on which *Mycobacterium johnei* has been growing and prepared in a similar way to purified protein derivative or old tuberculin (*see* **tuberculin**).

Jones-Mote reaction (*see also* **cutaneous basophil hypersensitivity**). Weak **delayed hypersensitivity**-type skin reaction seen on challenge a few days after priming with small amounts of protein antigen in aqueous solution or in **incomplete Freund's adjuvant** (i.e. not in **complete Freund's adjuvant**). A major feature is infiltration with **basophil leucocytes**. Possibly represents **T lymphocyte** mediated hypersensitivity modulated by **B lymphocytes**. Later challenge produces **Arthus reactions** or **weal and flare responses** q.v.

KAF. Obsolete term for **C3b inactivator**.

kallidin. Lysyl-**bradykinin**.

kallikreins (kininogenases). Enzymes with indirect activity in increasing vascular permeability, vasodilatation and smooth muscle contraction. They are esterases which convert kininogens into pharmacologically active **kinins** q.v. Kallikrein activity is inhibited by **CĪ inhibitor** q.v.

Kaminski-Wright technique. A quantitative **gel diffusion test** by which the **optimum proportions** point is determined. Thus, similar to the **Sewell test**.

kappa (κ) chain. One of the two types of **light chain** of immunoglobulins, the other being the **lambda** (λ) chain. An individual immunoglobulin molecule bears either two λ chains or two ϰ chains, never one of each. About 60 per cent of human **IgG** molecules are of the ϰ type, 40 per cent of the λ type. Bears the **Inv (Km) allotype** genetic marker.

Kauffmann-White scheme. A system used for classifying the many serotypes of the bacterial genus *Salmonella*. Based on the characteristics of their **O** (somatic or cellbound) **antigen** q.v. and **H** (flagellar) **antigens**[1] q.v.

Kawasaki's disease (mucocutaneous lymph node syndrome). A self-limiting disease of children who exhibit hypertrophied lymph nodes, maculopapular skin rashes and mucosal inflammation. Commonest in Japan. There is a high proportion of T4-positive lymphocytes in the circulation (*see* **T antigens**) and an imbalance of immune induction. An excess of **helper T lymphocyte** activity has been postulated.

K cell. The effector cell of **antibody-dependent cell-mediated cytotoxicity** , thus an **Fc-receptor** bearing lymphocyte-like cell. cf. **killer cell**, q.v.

Kern. An antigenic marker of human **lambda chains** resulting from the presence of glycine (Kern⁺) or serine (Kern⁻) at position 153. These are not allotypic (*see* **allotype**) markers. In combination with the **Oz** markers they define three **isotypes** of human λ chains.

keyhole limpet haemocyanin. This substance, and haemocyanins obtained from other molluscs are excellent **antigens**[1] in most vertebrates. Often used as **carrier** in experiments designed to investigate the immune response to **haptens**.

killed vaccine. *See* **inactivated vaccine**.

killer cell. Term used for **K** cells, the effector cells in **antibody-dependent cell-mediated cytotoxicity**, but there are a variety of other 'killer' cells, including **natural killer** (NK) cells, **cytotoxic T cells, neutrophil leucocytes** and **macrophages**.

kinetic neutralization test. A type of neutralization test used to measure the effectiveness (k) with which a given serum can neutralize a virus. Virus and serum are mixed, samples are then taken at intervals, diluted with saline to stop the action of the antibody, and the number of surviving virus particles assayed.

kinins. Peptides formed by action of esterases known as **kallikreins**

(kininogenases) and of **PF/dil** on substrate kininogens present in plasma. Kinins have activity as vasodilators, increase vascular permeability and cause contraction of smooth muscle. One of them, **bradykinin** q.v., has been shown to be present in the blood during **anaphylaxis**.

KLH, KLHC. *See* **keyhole limpet haemocyanin.**

Km allotypes *See* **Inv allotypes.** The Km nomenclature has now superseded the Inv nomenclature.

Koch's phenomenon. First observed by Robert Koch in 1891 when he inoculated living or dead *Mycobacterium tuberculosis* into guinea pigs that were already infected with the organism. A marked necrotic reaction occurred at the site, which sometimes became generalized and caused death. The same dead bacilli inoculated into healthy guinea pigs were innocuous. This reaction of **cell-mediated immunity** is the origin of the **tuberculin test.**

Kupffer cell. A non-motile **macrophage** of the **mononuclear phagocyte system** found lining the blood sinuses of the liver. As Kupffer cells are phagocytic and positioned in an area of high blood flow they are highly active in removing foreign particles from the blood. In certain pathological conditions they also remove erythrocytes, and the remains of their haemoglobin form golden-brown haemosiderin particles.

Kurloff cell. Cell found in the peripheral blood, spleen and other organs of pregnant or oestrogen-treated guinea pigs. Contains a large inclusion body composed of mucoprotein and sulphated mucopolysaccharide that can be stained with **PAS**[1] and has been postulated to be a type of modified **lymphocyte** of unknown function.

Kveim test. **Skin test** used in diagnosis of **sarcoidosis** in man. A saline suspension of sarcoid tissue, usually spleen or lymph node is injected intracutaneously. In a positive reaction, a papule develops at the injection site. Histological examination 4–6 weeks after injection, which is an essential part of the test, shows an epithelioid cell **granuloma**[2], resembling a sarcoid lesion.

LAF (lymphocyte activating factor). *See* **interleukin- 1.**

lambda (λ) **chain.** One of the two types of **light chain** of immunoglobulins, the other being the **kappa** (κ) chain. An individual immunoglobulin molecule bears either two κ chains or two λ chains, never one of each. The ratio of κ to λ chains varies with species, e.g.

about 60 per cent of human IgG molecules are of the ϰ type, 40 per cent of the λ type, whereas in the mouse the ratio is 95 per cent ϰ chains to 5 per cent λ chains.

lamina propria. Layer of connective tissue supporting the epithelium of the digestive tract and with it, forming the mucous membrane. Site of accumulation of **lymphocytes, plasma cells**, and of **mast cells** in immunological reactions involving the gut.

Lancefield precipitation test. A **ring test** used for the classification of streptococci. Group specific polysaccharides are extracted from pure cultures of the organisms either by acid (HCl), formamide, or an enzyme from *Streptomyces albus*. The extract is layered onto group- specific antisera in a test tube and **precipitation** is observed at the interface.

Langerhans cell. An **accessory cell** of dendritic appearance found in the epidermis and characterized by the presence of cytoplasmic Birbeck granules (tennis-racket-shaped granules of unknown function). Can be stained with gold chloride or visualized by the ATPase reaction. Bears **C3b receptors** and IgG **Fc receptors** and **Class II antigens** (Ia). Considered by some to be of **mononuclear phagocyte** lineage and originates in the bone marrow.

lapinized vaccine. An **attenuated vaccine** that has been produced by passaging an organism through rabbits until it has lost its virulence for its original host, e.g.**rinderpest vaccine**[b].

large granular lymphocyte. *See* **natural killer cell**.

large lymphocyte. Any **lymphocyte** with a diameter of approximately 12 μm or more.

large pyroninophilic blast cell. **Blast cell** found in preparations of the **thymus dependent areas** of **peripheral lymphoid organs** that have been stained with **methyl green pyronin stain**.

late phase reaction. **Immediate hypersensitivity,** IgE mediated, skin test reaction to antigen that begins about 5 hours after the initial rapidly developed (2–3 minutes) asymptomatic, oedematous, erythematous lesion. The late phase reaction is characterized by inflammation, pruritis and a minimal cellular infiltration.

latent allotype. The phenomenon whereby a third **allotype** at an **antibody** locus can sometimes be detected (usually at low levels) in the serum of animals nominally heterozygous for another two alleles at that locus. Found in the rabbit a locus of the V_H **region**, it indicates that more complex processes than simple Mendelian allotypy underlie allotype expression at that locus.

latex agglutination test.   Test in which polystyrene latex (a suspension of very small spherical particles of the plastic) is used as a carrier to adsorb (*see* **adsorption**) soluble antigens. On addition of specific antibody, **agglutination** of the coated latex particles takes place. Used especially to detect **rheumatoid factor**.

latex fixation test.   *See* **latex agglutination test.**

LATS.   *See* **long acting thyroid stimulator.**

lattice hypothesis.   An hypothesis to explain the phenomenon that maximal **precipitation** is only seen at the point of **optimal proportions** when antibody and dilutions of **soluble antigen** are mixed. Postulates that *divalent* antibody molecules combine with the **antigenic determinants** of *polyvalent* antigen molecules to form an insoluble macromolecular lattice at optimal proportions and soluble complexes in **antibody excess** and **antigen excess** q.v. First suggested by Marrack in 1934 and has received support from immunochemical and electron microscope studies of the antigen-antibody reaction.

Laurell crossed immunoelectrophoresis. *See* **crossed immunoelectrophoresis.**

Laurell rocket test.   Rapid immunoelectrophoretic method for the quantitative estimation of protein antigens. Samples are placed in a row of wells in a sheet of **agarose®** that contains an antiserum to the antigen. Electric current passed in a direction at right angles to the row causes the antigen to move into the agar. Two lines of immune precipitate grow from each well and come together to form a point when the antigen is exhausted. The length of the 'rocket' from the well to point of precipitate is proportional to the quantity of antigen originally present.

lazy leucocyte syndrome.   Generic name for syndromes in children with recurrent infections, characterized by defective neutrophil leucocyte locomotion or **chemotaxis**, but with otherwise normal leucocyte function.

LCA (Leucocyte common antigen). A glycoprotein found on **thymocytes, T lymphocytes** and **B lymphocytes** and on other

L chain

haemopoietic cells. LCA's on the different cell types are all anti-genically similar but have different molecular weights, possibly due to different levels of glycosylation.

L chain. *See* **light chain**.

LCM. *See* **lymphocytic choriomeningitis**.

LD$_{50}$. The dose of toxin, or bacterial suspension, etc. that kills 50 per cent of a test group of animals within a specified time. Used in the estimation of toxicity or virulence and for the measurement of the **challenge**[2] doses of pathogenic organisms that are used in testing **vaccines**.

LDCF (lymphocyte-derived chemotactic factors). **Lymphokine** chemotactic factors. The best characterized has specificity for **mononuclear phagocytes**.

L$_+$ dose of toxin (Limes Tod dose). The smallest amount of **diphtheria toxin** that, when mixed with one unit of **diphtheria antitoxin** and injected subcutaneously just kills a 250g guinea pig on the 4th day. *See also* **L$_0$** *dose of toxin*.

L$_0$ dose of toxin (Limes Nul dose). The largest dose of **diphtheria toxin** that, when mixed with one unit of **diphtheria antitoxin**, and injected subcutaneously into a 250g guinea pig produces, on average, no observable reaction. In practice it is taken as the dose that, in these circumstances causes minimum local oedema when injected intradermally, i.e. the L$_r$ dose of toxin. *See also L$_+$ dose of toxin*.

L$_r$ dose of toxin. The smallest amount of diphtheria toxin that, when mixed with one unit of **diphtheria antitoxin** and inoculated intradermally into a 250g guinea pig, produces a minimal skin reaction. In practice equivalent to an L$_0$ dose of toxin.

leader peptide. A sequence of 20, mainly hydrophobic, amino acids found at the **N-termini** of nascent **light** and **heavy chains** and other secreted proteins, but absent from secreted **immunoglobulin**. The peptide is rapidly cleaved from the light and heavy chains once they are released into the **cisternal space** of the **endoplasmic reticulum** and is believed to be responsible for vectorial release of the polypeptide chains and hence their secretion from the cell: the **signal hypothesis**.

LE cell (lupus erythematosus cell). **Neutrophil leucocyte** with phagocytosed homogeneous nuclear material, from one or more other neutrophils, present in its cytoplasm. Demonstrable especially in patients with **systemic lupus erythematosus** (SLE) after *in vitro* incubation of their blood, and amongst normal white cells which have been suspended in SLE serum containing a **7S antibody** against leucocyte nuclei known as LE factor.

lectin. Protein derived from plants that binds specifically to sugars and oligosaccharides, including the surface glycoproteins of many cells. Thus certain lectins **agglutinate** cells and may show **blood group** specificity in agglutinating erythrocytes. Many lectins act as **mitogens** and are widely used in immunology in studies of **lymphocyte transformation**. Examples of lectins of immunological interest are:-

Lectin	Source	Sugar specificity	Mitogenic activity*	
			T	B
Concanavalin A (Con A)	*Canavalia ensiformis* (Jack bean)	α-D-man>α-D-Glc >α-D-Glc NAc	+	−
Phytohaemagglutinin (PHA):	*Phaseolus vulgaris* (Red kidney bean)			
Leucoagglutinin		?	+	−
Erythroagglutinin		β-D-Gal(1–4)-Glc NAc	−	−
Wheat germ agglutinin (WGA)	*Triticum vulgaris* (Wheat germ)	β-D-Glc NAc(1–4)-β-D-Glc NAc (1–4)-Glc NAc	−	−
Pokeweed mitogen (PWM)	*Phytolacca americana*	?	+	+

*See table of **mitogens**, p.151.   T = **T lymphocytes**   B = **B lymphocytes**

LE factor. *See* **LE cell**.

LEP (Low egg passage). **Rabies vaccine**[c] used for the immunization of dogs and cats.

lepromin test. Skin test of **tuberculin test** type conducted with a suspension of *Mycobacterium leprae* prepared from lepromatous patient's skin lesions. An early reaction (**Fernandez** q.v.) peaks at 24–48 hours, a late reaction (**Mitsuda** q.v.) at about 4 weeks. The reaction is negative in lepromatous leprosy (in which bacilli are numerous) and positive in tuberculoid leprosy patients and in normal adults. In normal persons it is negative in newborns, but gradually gains reactivity in nearly all normal adults. It has no diagnostic value but is an aid in the classification of leprosy and in estimating the prognosis.

LE test. Test in which normal **leucocytes** are incubated with serum from patients with **systemic lupus erythematosus** (the patient's own cells may also be used). During incubation at 37°C, **LE cells** form due to the action of antibody in the patient's serum against cell nuclei.

leucoagglutinin. **Antibody** capable of causing **agglutination** of **leucocytes**. *See also* **isoleucoagglutinin**.

leucocidin. Cytolytic toxin produced by bacteria especially staphylococci. Toxic for **polymorphonuclear leucocytes**, less so for **monocytes**. Non-haemolytic. At subtoxic doses, inhibits polymorph locomotion. Consists of F-component and S-component which together bind to the cell membrane and cause permeability changes.

leucocyte (*Amer*. leukocyte). All the **white cells** of the blood and their precursors (*see* **myeloid cell series, lymphoid cell series**) but sometimes used to indicate **granulocytes** q.v. exclusive of lymphocytes.

leucocyte common antigen. *See* **LCA**.

leucocyte groups. Allelic **isoantigenic** groupings of **histocompatibility antigens** that are detectable on the surface of **leucocytes**. Analogous to the blood groups of red cells. Examples are **HLA histocompatibility antigens, H-2 histocompatibility antigens**.

leucocyte migration inhibitory factor. *See* **LIF**.

leucocyte transfer. *See* **adoptive transfer**.

leucocytosis. Increase above normal of the number of **leucocytes**, especially in blood.

leukocyte. *Syn*. **leucocyte**.

leukotaxis (*Amer*.). **Chemotaxis** of leucocytes.

leukotrienes. Pharmacologically active substances generated from arachidonic acid by the action of lipoxygenases. They form a series of hydroxyeicosatetraenoic acids the most biologically active of which are:-

leukotriene B_4, (5, 12-dihydroxyeicosatetraenoic acid) which is chemotactic (*see* **chemotaxis**) for **neutrophils** and other **leucocytes**.

leukotriene C_4, (5 hydroxy, 6 glutathionyl, eicosatetraenoic acid).

leukotriene D_4, a 6-sulphido-cysteinyl-glycine metabolite of leukotriene C_4.

leukotriene E_4, a 6-sulphido-cysteine metabolite of leukotriene D_4.

leukotrienes C_4, D_4 and E_4 together possess the activity of **slow reacting substance of anaphylaxis** (SRS-A), i.e. they cause contraction of some types of smooth muscle, especially bronchial muscle, and they increase vascular permeability. Leukotrienes may be released from **mast cells, platelets** and various leukocytes, and SRS-A activity can be generated as a result of the combination of **antigen** with **IgE antibody.**

Levamisole®. 2,3,5,6-tetrahydro-6-phenylimidazo[2,1-*b*] thiazole. An immunostimulant drug reported to potentiate or restore the activities of **T lymphocytes** and other **leucocytes.** N.B. Levamisole is also extensively used as a broad spectrum antihelminthic in domestic animals and birds.

Lf unit (limit of flocculation). The amount of **diphtheria toxin** corresponding to one unit of **diphtheria antitoxin** in the mixture that first shows flocculation in a **Ramon titration.** A unit of antitoxin was originally the smallest amount that would neutralize 100 **minimal lethal doses** of toxin in the guinea pig. It is now defined in relation to the international standard antitoxin (*see* **International units of immunological activity**).

Liacopoulos phenomenon. Induction of non-specific **immunosuppression** to a given antigen using large doses of an unrelated antigen. *See also* **antigenic competition.**

LIF (leucocyte-migration inhibitory factor). A **lymphokine** with protease activity that inhibits migration of **neutrophil leucocytes** from capillary tubes or wells in agarose®.

ligand. Something which binds. Term especially used of molecules which bind to cells or to other molecules.

light chain. A polypeptide chain present in all **immunoglobulin** molecules. Mol.wt. 22 000 in man. Most immunoglobulins are made up of two identical light chains linked to two **heavy chains** usually by disulphide bonds (*see* illustration on p.108). Light chains are of two types, kappa and lambda (*see* **kappa** (ϰ) **chain** and **lambda** (λ) **chain**) and a single immunoglobulin molecule always has two (or more) ϰ chains or two (or more) λ chains, never both types. Light chain type is not related to **immunoglobulin class** differences, i.e. all immunoglobulins of whichever class have ϰ or λ chains. Light chains have an **N terminal, variable region** forming part of the antibody combining site and a **C terminal, constant region** which is light chain subtype

invariable with the exception of in man the **Inv** and **Oz allotype** markers.

light chain subtype. The subgroup into which a **light chain** is placed by virtue of features of its primary or **antigenic** structure, common to all individuals of the same species, which distinguish it from other light chains of the same type. These structural features are found in the **constant region** but the differences between light chain subtypes are smaller than the differences between **light chain types**. E.g. human λ chain subtypes are determined by the Oz^+, Oz^-, $Kern^+$ and $Kern^-$ markers. Three subtypes of mouse λ chains are known : λ_1, λ_2 and λ_3.

light chain type. The group into which a **light chain** is placed by virtue of features of its primary or **antigenic** structure, common to all individuals of the same species, which distinguish it from other light chains. Only two light chain types have been found in all species examined to date, designated $\varkappa$ and λ.

limiting dilution. A technique of, supposedly, producing aliquots containing single cells (or micro organisms) by diluting a suspension to the point at which aliquots each contain a single cell. Effectively used to originate clones in e.g. **monoclonal antibody** production. May mislead unless additional tests are employed as, e.g. at the dilution at which, on average, one cell is present per aliquot, the cells will be distributed according to the Poissonian distribution to give 37% of aliquots with no cells and 63% with one or more than one cell each. Authentic clones can only be produced by methods that involve confirmation of the presence of a unique originating cell by visual or electronic means.

limiting dilution assay. Any assay designed to quantify cells or microorganisms by diluting a suspension of them until aliquots on average contain single cells of the type being tested. In e.g. assays for lymphocyte precursors, the original suspension may contain an excess of other cells, the presence of which is required to enable detection of the assayed cell's activity. *See also* **limiting dilution**.

lipopolysaccharide. (1) Any compound in which lipid is linked to polysaccharide. (2) Term frequently used to refer to bacterial lipopolysaccharides, especially components of **O-antigen** (**endotoxin**) complex of Gram negative bacilli especially enterobacteria such as *Escherichia coli*, *Salmonella* and *Shigella* spp. and probably also of *Haemophilus* and *Bordetella pertussis*. These all differ in antigenic structure but not in physiological effect. Bacterial lipopolysaccharides are characterized by their ability to produce shock (fall in blood pressure), an initial leucopenia followed by a **leucocytosis,** pyrexia (hence called pyrogens) and general and local **Shwartzman reactions** q.v. They are also potent **adjuvants** (*see* **triple vaccine**) this activity being associated with lipid A and are mitogenic (*see* **mitogen**) for **B lymphocytes**. Chemically they consist of anti-genically specific polysaccharides linked to the phospholipid, 'lipid A' of the **O antigen** q.v.

liposome. Spherical microstructure formed when mixtures of phos-pholipids with or without sterols are dispersed in aqueous solutions. Liposomes are made up of concentric phospholipid bilayers, and so form simple models of cell membranes which can be used for experimental studies. If antigens are incorporated in them, liposomes have been reported to act as **adjuvants**.

lissamine rhodamine (RB200). A red dye with an orange fluoresc-ence (*see* **fluorochrome**). When treated with phosphorus pentachlor-ide it forms a reactive sulphonyl chloride used for labelling proteins for **immunofluorescence** techniques.

live vaccine. A **vaccine** containing either: (1) An attenuated strain of the pathogen that is entirely non- pathogenic, or causes acceptable reactions, e.g. **anthrax vaccines**[a,b] **BCG, poliomyelitis vaccine**[a], **rinderpest vaccine**[b,c], **measles vaccine**[a], **yellow fever vaccine**. (2) A different pathogen or attenuated strain of it that gives cross protection, e.g. **vaccinia**, *see* **heterologous vaccines**. (3) The actual pathogen against which protection is desired. This is given either by an abnormal route, *see* **contagious bovine pleuropneumonia vaccine**[a], or at the same time as an antiserum, *see* **serum virus vaccination**. (4) *See* **lungworm vaccine**.

local anaphylaxis. An IgE mediated *local* reaction due to release of histamine from mast cells. An example of a **type I reaction** of immediate hypersensitivity and more commonly encountered than acute generalized anaphylaxis (**anaphylactic shock**). Produces **hay fever** and asthma in man and is often observed as cutaneous anaphylaxis in animals.

long acting thyroid stimulator. Serum antibody with thyroid stimulating effect, found in patients with thyrotoxicosis. It is an **autoantibody** of **IgG** class, reactive against thyroid cell receptors for thyroid stimulating hormone. Thus it mimics the biological effects of the latter hormone.

long lived lymphocytes. Small **lymphocytes** which survive without dividing for months or even years, considered by many to be mainly derived from the **thymus,** thus **T lymphocytes.** *See also* **short lived lymphocytes**.

low dose tolerance. Immunological tolerance (**acquired tolerance**) in an immunologically mature animal induced by repeated very small doses of an antigen. Antigens that can be employed to induce tolerance sometimes induce it in both high and low dosage ranges, but stimulate a normal **immunological response** at intermediate dose ranges. Low dose tolerance is due to an effect on **T lymphocytes,** probably inactivation of **helper T lymphocytes,** the **B lymphocytes** being capable of responding if primed helper T lymphocytes are provided. Cf. **high dose tolerance.**

low responder. Term referring to inbred strains of mice which give poor immune responses to specified antigens (compared to other strains). Related to lack of **Ir genes** determining the response in question.

LPR. *See* **late phase reaction.**

LPS. *See* **lipopolysaccharide.** This abbreviation is frequently used for **endotoxin** q.v.

LSGP (leucocyte sialoglycoprotein). A heavily glycosylated protein found on **thymocytes** and **T lymphocytes,** but not on **B lymphocytes**.

lungworm vaccine. *Vet.* X-irradiated second stage larvae (the infective stage) of *Dictyocaulus viviparus,* the nematode worm causing 'husk' or 'hoose' in cattle. These are incapable of development to adults, but when given orally, they enter the tissues and exsheath (moult). An immune response to the exsheathing fluid follows which inhibits the development of virulent larvae picked up from the pasture. It should be noted that although this is a **live vaccine,** the larvae used are attenuated, so that they reach, and make the required antigen, in the right place before dying. *See also* **hookworm vaccine.**

lupus erythematosus (discoid LE, cutaneous LE). Skin disease with red scaly patches in exposed areas especially butterfly area over the nose and cheeks. Not to be confused with lupus vulgaris, which is tuberculosis of the skin, nor with **systemic lupus erythematosus** q.v. of which cutaneous lupus erythematosus is often a sign and to which it is related.

Ly antigen. Alternative abbreviation for **Lyt antigens**.

Lyb.   Nomenclature for **B lymphocyte** surface markers, cf. **Lyt**

lymph.   The fluid found in the lymphatic vessels. Similar in composition to the tissue fluids but that draining the intestine and liver contains more protein. Fat in the form of chylomicrons is copiously present in mesenteric lymph. Most (80–85 per cent) of the cells in lymph are **small lymphocytes**. Medium and **large lymphocytes, monocytes** and **macrophages** are relatively rare. A few erythrocytes and **eosinophil leucocytes** may be present. Lymph contains clotting factors but the clot formed is much looser than that of blood.

lymph gland.   *See* **lymph node** (*preferred term*).

lymph node.   Small organ made up largely of **lymphocytes**, together with **macrophages** and **dendritic cells** held in a loose reticulum. Distributed widely throughout the body, frequently in groups which drain a given area, e.g. inguinal lymph nodes, axillary lymph nodes, etc. This drainage is achieved by lymphatic vessels that pass into the node from the peripheral tissue (afferent vessels) and which pass from the lymph node to more central chains of nodes and, eventually, to the thoracic duct (efferent vessels). The lymph nodes thus act as filters through which foreign materials must pass and come into close contact with macrophages, **accessory cells** and lymphocytes. They are important centres for **phagocytosis** and for the initiation and development of responses of **humoral** and **cell-mediated immunity**. It should be noted that in some mammals, e.g. the pig, the main features of the classically described structure shown in the figure are reversed, the 'cortex' being close to the efferent lymphatic. *See* **germinal centre, thymus dependent area, high endothelial venule.**

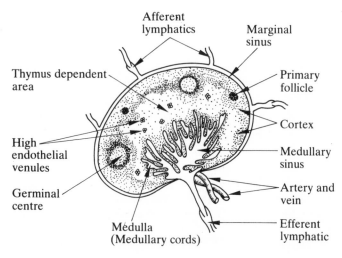

lymphadenoid goitre

lymphadenoid goitre. *See* **Hashimoto's thyroiditis**.

lymphoblast. A **blast cell** (q.v.) of the **lymphoid cell series** with a nuclear pattern characterized by fine chromatin and basophilic nucleoli. Lymphoblasts are formed *in vivo* or *in vitro* following antigenic or mitogenic stimulation (*see* **lymphocyte transformation**), and divide to form populations of **effector** lymphocytes. There are also many established lymphoblast lines (usually B lymphoblasts) in tissue culture, usually transformed by Epstein-Barr virus.

lymphocyte. A spherical cell, from 7–12 μm in diameter (*see* **large** and **small lymphocytes**), with a large, round nucleus (usually indented when observed under the electron microscope) and very scanty cytoplasm. The latter is transparent, does not show basophilic staining, but may contain azurophilic granules. Lymphocytes are actively motile (*see* **uropod**). They do not contain a well-developed **endoplasmic reticulum** (Cf. **plasma cells**). The term lymphocyte is essentially a morphological one that is used to refer to cells associated with all aspects of **specific immunity**, some (**B lymphocytes**) being associated with **humoral immunity** and others (**T lymphocytes**) with **cell-mediated immunity**. Lymphocytes are the chief constituents of the **lymphoid tissues**.

lymphocyte activating factor (LAF). *See* **interleukin-1**.

lymphocyte determinants. **Antigenic determinants** on **target cells**[1] which are recognized by **lymphocytes** from specifically immunized hosts rather than by antibody. Cf. **serological determinants** and **MHC genes**.

lymphocyte transfer reaction. *See* **normal lymphocyte transfer reaction**.

lymphocyte transformation. The name given to the change in morphology seen when **lymphocytes** are cultured in the presence of a **mitogen**, e.g. **phytohaemagglutinin**, or of an antigen to which they are **primed**. They increase in size, the cytoplasm becomes more extensive, and nucleoli are visible in the nucleus, which becomes less densely stained; after about 72 hours these cells resemble **lymphoblasts**.

lymphocytic choriomeningitis. A viral disease of mice in which the lesions appear to result from a **hypersensitivity** reaction to the virus. Lesions are only seen in mice infected as adults; any that become infected *in utero* show no symptoms and are **immunologically tolerant** to the virus.

lymphocytopenic centre. *See* **germinal centre.**

lymphocytosis. Rise above normal of the number of **lymphocytes,** especially in blood.

lymphocytotoxin. *See* **lymphotoxin.**

lymphoid cell. Any cell of the **lymphoid cell series** q.v.

lymphoid cell series. Cell series which includes all cells having the morphology of **small** and **large lymphocytes,** their precursors and cells that may be derived from them, e.g. **plasma cells.** Cf. **myeloid cell series.**

lymphoid follicle. *See* **primary nodule.**

lymphoid tissues. Body tissues in which the predominant cells are **lymphocytes.** They comprise the **lymph, spleen, lymph nodes, thymus, Peyer's patches, pharyngeal tonsils,** adenoids, and in birds the **caecal tonsils** and **bursa of Fabricius.**

lymphokine. Generic name for non-antibody proteins released by **primed lymphocytes,** probably chiefly **T lymphocytes,** on contact with antigen, and which act as intercellular mediators of the immune response. Important in many immunological situations, e.g. **delayed hypersensitivity** and immunoregulation. *See* **macrophage activating factor, migration inhibition factor, LIF, lymphotoxins, interleukins, interferons** *inter alia.*

lymphoma Neoplastic disease of lymphoreticular tissue, i.e. involving cells of **lymphoid cell series** or of **mononuclear phagocyte system.** Includes Hodgkin's disease, lymphosarcoma, reticulosarcoma, giant follicular lymphoma, lymphatic leukaemia, **Burkitt's lymphoma,** etc.

lymphoreticular tissue. Term used to describe tissues composed largely of **lymphocytes** and **macrophages.** Included thymus, spleen, lymph nodes, pharyngeal tonsils, Peyer's patches, bone marrow and, in birds, the bursa of Fabricius and caecal tonsils. *See* **lymphoid tissues.**

lymphotoxin. A **lymphokine** with cytolytic (*see* **lysin**) activity for non-lymphocytic cells.

lysin

lysin. (1) Antibody which causes cell lysis, e.g. **haemolysin**[1], bacteriolysin (*see* **bacteriolysis**). (2) Other substances, especially bacterial toxins, which lyse cells.

lysosome. A cytoplasmic organelle, limited by a membrane and containing hydrolytic enzymes (acid hydrolases). Present in many cells throughout the animal kingdom. Lysosomal enzymes are inert until released from the particle. These enzymes play an important part in intracellular digestion and are involved in many types of cell injury. They may also be released from the cell by exocytosis. For role of lysosomes in **phagocytosis** *see* **phagosome**.

lysozyme. Enzyme, first described by Fleming in 1922, present in tears, nasal secretions, on the skin, and, in lower concentrations, in serum. Lyses certain bacteria, chiefly Gram-positive cocci. *Micrococcus lysodeikticus* is especially sensitive. A saccharolytic enzyme, it splits the muramic acid- β(1-4)-N-acetylglucosamine linkage in the cell walls of Gram positive bacteria. It also potentiates the action of **complement** on Gram negative bacteria (*see also* **IgA**).

Lyt 1,2,3. A group of surface **antigens** defining subpopulations of mouse **T lymphocytes**. *See* **subset** and table of mouse, rat and human T lymphocyte antigens on p.213.

MΦ. Macrophage.

MAC. *See* **membrane attack complex**. (There is also a macrophage-specific monoclonal antibody, named MAC-1.)

macroglobulin. Any **globulin** with a molecular weight above about 400 000. The best-studied serum macroglobulins are **IgM** (mol. wt. 900 000) q.v. and α_2-macroglobulin (mol. wt. 820 000). Many lipoproteins are also macroglobulins.

macroglobulinaemia. Increase in serum **macroglobulin** level. Usually refers to rise in **IgM** level. May follow antigenic challenge, e.g. in trypanosomiasis, or be due to **paraproteinaemia** either primary as in **Waldenström's macroglobulinaemia** or secondary to diseases such as **lymphoma** or carcinoma, especially in alimentary tract.

macrophage. Cell of the **mononuclear phagocyte system** q.v. Most macrophages are believed to be derived from blood **monocytes** which migrate into the tissues and differentiate there. They are strongly phagocytic (*see* **phagocytosis**) of a wide variety of particulate materials, including microorganisms. They contain **lysosomes**, and possess microbicidal capacity. Macrophages are strongly adherent to, and spread on, glass and plastic and show **chemotaxis**. They possess **Fc- and C3b receptors**. Stain positively for **non-specific esterase** and peroxidase. They can be divided into **Ia-negative** and **Ia-positive** populations. The former are classical phagocytes, but the latter also have an important role as **accessory cells** in antigen-presentation to lymphocytes and in induction of immune responses. *See also* **activated macrophage, elicited macrophage, resident macrophage**.

macrophage activating factor. **Lymphokine** that enhances the microbicidal and tumoricidal capacity of **macrophages** (*see* **activated macrophage**). Probably identical to **migration inhibition factor** q.v. **Interferon-γ** has macrophage-activating activity.

macrophage cytophilic antibody. **Cytophilic antibody** with affinity for the cell surface of **macrophages** (e.g. able to bind to **Fc receptors**) and capable of reacting with antigen while on the cell surface. May be detected by the **immunocytoadherence** test (**rosette** technique) q.v.

macrophage disappearance reaction. A reduction in the number of macrophages in the peritoneal fluid of guinea pigs or mice following intraperitoneal injection of an antigen, e.g. PPD or BSA, to which the animal has been primed. The reaction is cell-mediated in nature and is analogous to delayed hypersensitivity as measured *in vitro* by the **macrophage migration inhibition test**. The reaction is mediated by **lymphokine** activation of clotting factors (e.g. fibrinogen) on the macrophage surface causing adherence to the lining of the peritoneal cavity.

macrophage immunity. *See* **cellular immunity[1]**.

macrophage migration inhibition factor. *See* **migration inhibition factor**.

macrophage migration test. An *in vitro* test used to detect and measure **cell-mediated immunity**. **Macrophages** and **lymphocytes** are packed into small pieces of capillary tube and incubated overnight in a tissue culture medium. In normal medium the macrophages migrate out of the tube; if the medium contains an antigen to which the lymphocytes have been **primed**, migration is inhibited due to release of macrophage **migration inhibition factor** by the lymphocytes.

MAF. *See* **macrophage activating factor**.

major histocompatibility complex

major histocompatibility complex (MHC). The collection of genes coding for the major **histocompatibility antigens,** *see* **HLA** and **H-2 histocompatibility systems.**

major histocompatibility complex restriction. *See* **MHC restriction.**

major histocompatibility system (MHS). *Syn.* **major histocompatibility complex.**

Malpighian corpuscle. *See* **spleen.**

Mancini test. *See* **single radial diffusion test.**

Mantoux test. An intradermal **tuberculin test** (q.v.) widely used in man. A positive test indicates **delayed hypersensitivity** to *Mycobacterium tuberculosis* and implies past or present infection with the bacillus. The test is negative during early stages of infection (about 3 weeks) and in rapidly progressing disease. After successful **BCG** vaccination a previously negative Mantoux test becomes positive. Cf. **Heaf test** and *see* **single intradermal tuberculin test** for test used in cattle.

marginal zone. A loosely packed area of **T** and **B lymphocytes** and **macrophages** around the periarterial lymphatic sheath of the mammalian **spleen** q.v., particularly well-defined in rodents. The macrophages in this zone play a major role in the early phase of **phagocytosis** of **antigens** and particulate matter, following intravenous injection. *See* figure on p.206.

margination. Attachment of blood **leucocytes** to vascular endothelium. At any time, half of the **neutrophils** in the blood are normally marginated. Margination also occurs near sites of inflammation and is followed by leucocyte migration out of the vessels.

mast cell. Tissue cell (10–30 μm diameter) bearing strongly basophilic cytoplasmic granules, similar to, but smaller than, those of blood basophil leucocytes. The granules contain **serotonin, histamine,** heparin, *inter alia*, and release of these and other, newly-formed, pharmacological mediators, such as **leukotrienes** (SRS-A), and **platelet activating factor** is mediated by antigen binding to mast-cell bound **IgE** antibody, or by **anaphylatoxins.** There are two populations of mast cells. One, 'mucosal mast cells', has sparse granules, a lymphoid appearance, is dependent on **T lymphocytes** for differentiation and is found in the gut in intestinal nematodal infections. The other population, 'connective tissue mast cells', is richer in granules, T lymphocyte-independent, and present in immediate hypersensitivity lesions.

Masugi nephritis. Experimental **glomerulonephritis** produced in one species (e.g. rat) by injection of antibody obtained from a second species (e.g. rabbit) that has been immunized with rat glomerular capillary basement membrane. If the dose of antibody is large, glomerulonephritis develops within 12 hours due to a reaction of the injected antibody with the (rat's) basement membrane followed by **complement** mediated tissue damage (*see* **immune complex disease**). With smaller doses of antibody, glomerulonephritis takes a few weeks to develop and results from an immune response to the foreign (rabbit) **IgG** which has become fixed to the basement membrane. Progressive chronic disease may follow from suitable dosing with antibody.

maternal immunity (maternally-transferred immunity). **Passive immunity** (of **humoral immunity** type) acquired by the newborn animal from its mother. In man and other primates this is chiefly obtained before birth by the active transport of immunoglobulins across the placenta. The young of ungulates, in whom **antibody** is not transferred across the placenta, acquire it from the **colostrum** (q.v.) their intestines being permeable to immunoglobulins for a few days after birth. The young of birds acquire maternal immunity from antibody in the egg yolk. In all species secretory **IgA** in colostrum provides passive protection of the gut mucosa.

MBSA. Methylated bovine **serum albumin**.

MDP. *See* **muramyl dipeptide**.

measles vaccine. (a) **Attenuated** (virus) **vaccine** used for the **immunization**[2] of children. A single injection is given between the ages of 12 months and 10 years, but preferably in second year of life. It should not be given to children with a history of allergy or convulsions. (b) *Vet*. Attenuated virus employed as a **heterologous vaccine** for the protection of puppies from infection with canine distemper during the first few weeks of life when they possess **maternal immunity** that prevents effective vaccination with live **canine distemper vaccine**[b].

medullary cord. Area of the medulla of a **lymph node** close to the efferent lymphatic, composed largely of **macrophages** and, after antigenic stimulation, containing many **plasma cells**. *See* illustration on p.141.

medullary sinus. Potential spaces in the medulla of a **lymph node** into which **lymph** drains befoe entering the efferent lymphatic. *See* illustration on p.141.

membrane immunofluorescence. An **immunofluorescence** technique using suspensions of *living* cells so that when the fluoro-chrome-labelled reagent is applied it does not enter the cell and is only able to react with structures on the outer surface of the plasma membrane. Widely used to study changes in topography of membrane components, e.g. clustering, **patching, capping**, etc and to identify cell surface markers, e.g. surface **immunoglobulin** on B lymphocytes or **T-antigens** q.v. Also used to identify variant surface antigen of trypanosomes (*see* **antigenic variation**[a]) avoiding complications due to presence of antibodies to internal, common, antigens.

memory cells. T and B **lymphocytes** which mediate **immuno-logical memory**.

mercaptoethanol (2-mercaptoethanol). $HS(CH_2)_2OH$. A reducing agent which breaks **disulphide bonds** in proteins. Used in immuno-chemistry (a) to separate the **heavy** and **light chains** of immuno-globulins, and (b) to test for the presence of **IgM** antibodies, which lose their agglutinating ability when the sensitive inter-subunit disulphide bonds are broken. *See* **mercaptoethanol agglutination test**.

mercaptoethanol agglutination test. Test for agglutinating (*see* **agglutination**) antibody of **IgM** class. If serum containing agglutinating antibody is treated with 2-**mercaptoethanol**, any IgM antibodies present are split by reduction and lose their ability to agglutinate whereas other immunoglobulins are still active. Used in diagnosis of brucellosis.

mercaptopurine (6-mercaptopurine). Chemotherapeutic agent used for the treatment of neoplasia (particularly acute leukaemia in children) and known commercially in Britain as Purinethol®. It is also a potent **immunosuppressive** agent the introduction of which marked a major advance in organ transplantation techniques.

metalophilic cells. Cells which take up metal-containing stains, e.g. silver stains. This is a property of many cells of the **mononuclear phagocyte system** including the fixed **macrophages** of the lym-phoid tissues.

methyl green pyronin stain. A histological stain which colours DNA green and RNA red. It is useful for demonstrating cells whose cytoplasm contains large numbers of RNA-containing ribosomes, e.g. **plasma cells, lymphoblasts**, or actively secreting pancreatic exocrine cells, etc.

MHC. *See* **major histocompatibility complex.**

MHC genes. Major Histocompatibility Complex genes. They code for the cell membrane major **histocompatibility antigens** (H-2 in mouse, HLA in man). *See* **HLA histocompatibility system** and **H2 histocompatibility system** and illustrations on pp 90 and 101.

MHC restriction. The recognition by **T lymphocytes** (**cytotoxic** or **helper cells**) of foreign **antigen** on the surface of a cell, e.g. a virus-infected cell, **macrophage** or **dendritic cell**, only in association with self-antigens of the **major histocompatibility complex**. Cytotoxic T lymphocytes usually respond to foreign antigen in association with **Class I** MHC **antigens**, whereas helper T lymphocytes respond to foreign antigen in association with **Class II** (Ia) **antigens.** *See also* **altered-self** and **dual recognition hypotheses.**

MHD. (1) *See* **minimal haemolytic dose** (of **complement**, in a **complement fixation test**). (2) *See* **minimal haemagglutinating dose** (of virus, in a **haemagglutination inhibition test**[a]).

MHS. Major histocompatibility system, *see* **major histocompatibility complex.**

microfilaments. Long, fine strands about 5–8 nm wide found, often as a network, in the cytoplasm of many eukaryotic cells including all immunological cells. Microfilaments are believed to mediate movement of the whole cell and of organelles within it. Composed chiefly of helically polymerized actin, they form a contractile system which functions by the interaction of actin with myosin. Cytoplasmic actin exists in equilibrium between a soluble and a polymerized form, so that microfilaments may undergo rapid assembly and disassembly as required by the cell. Microfilament function is probably essential in cell locomotion, **phagocytosis**, phagosome-lysosome fusion, exocytosis, cell division, etc.

microglobulin. Any **globulin** or globulin fragment of relatively low molecular weight (40 000 or below). Has been used of low M.Wt. proteins such as **Bence-Jones protein** in urine or similar proteins in serum. *See* β_2 **microglobulin.**

microphage. Metchnikoff's term to describe **polymorphonuclear leucocytes** and other phagocytic cells of the **myeloid cell series** in contrast to **macrophages** q.v.

Microtitre® technique

Microtitre® technique. *See* **Takatsy technique.**

microtubules. Long hollow cylindrical structures (tubular in cross-section) with an outer diameter of about 20–25 nm, found in the cytoplasm of eukaryotic cells including **lymphocytes, phagocytes** and **mast cells.** Composed chiefly of tubulin, a protein which exists in equilibrium between a soluble form and the polymerized tubular form, thus microtubules exist in equilibrium between assembly and disassembly. Form the mitotic spindle, and may form a rigid cytoskeleton essential for coordination and polarization of other motile functions mediated by **microfilaments.** For example, microtubules are not essential for cell locomotion, nor for **chemotaxis,** but are important for the fine coordination of cell movement.

Middlebrook-Dubos test. A **passive agglutination test** in which the patient's serum is incubated with sheep (or human O blood group, *see* **ABO blood group system**) erythrocytes which have been coated with polysaccharide derived from tubercle bacilli. Has been used in the investigation of tuberculosis but is not of much practical use since positive results correlate poorly with the presence of tuberculous disease.

MIF. *See* **migration inhibition factor.**

migration inhibition factor. **Lymphokine** that inhibits migration of macrophages (e.g. out of capillary tubes *in vitro*) possibly by increasing their adhesiveness. There are at least two forms, one a protein with a pI of 3–4 and mol.wt. 65 000, the other with a pI of about 5 and mol.wt. approx. 25 000. Probably biochemically identical to **macrophage activating factor** q.v.

milk ring test. A very sensitive test used to detect infection of cows with *Brucella abortus*. One drop of a suspension of killed *B.abortus* stained with haematoxylin is added to a sample of milk and shaken up. If **antibodies** are present, the bacterial cells are agglutinated (*see* **agglutination**) and rise up with the fat globules of the cream to form a deep blue ring. Otherwise the cream that separates out is white above blue milk. Antibodies in serum e.g. from calves or bulls, can also be detected by the test, by mixing the serum with negatively reacting milk.

minimal haemagglutinating dose (MHD). A term used when standardizing **haemagglutination inhibition tests**[a] for **antibodies**

against viruses such as the influenza virus. It is the smallest quantity of a haemagglutinating virus that will fully agglutinate (*see* **agglutination**) the cells in one volume of a standard suspension of erythrocytes. In the test itself, 4 MHD of virus are added to each tube of a **doubling dilution** of antiserum. Erythrocytes are then added to indicate, by agglutination, in which of the tubes the virus has not been neutralized. *See also* **sedimentation pattern**.

minimal haemolytic dose (MHD).   The lowest dose of **complement** capable of causing complete lysis of a set volume of a standard suspension of **sensitized**[2] erythrocytes.

mitogen.   Any agent which induces mitosis in cells. In immunology often used to refer to substances that are able to induce transformation (*see* **lymphocyte transformation**) in a wide (polyclonal) range of **lymphocytes**.

Action on **T and B lymphocytes**

Mitogen	Mouse		Human	
	T	B	T	B
concanavalin A	+	−	+	−
phytohaemagglutinin	+	−	+	−
pokeweed mitogen	+	+	+	+
lipopolysaccharide	−	+	−	−
PPD (*see* **tuberculin**)	−	+	−	−
dextran	−	+	−	−
dextran sulphate	−	+	−	−

+ = causes **lymphocyte transformation**

mitogenic factor.   In immunology a term frequently used to describe a **lymphokine** with activity as a **mitogen** for lymphocytes.

Mitsuda reaction.   Reaction to intradermal injection of lepromin (*see* **lepromin test**) characterized by slow development of a papule or nodule. Maximal at about 4 weeks, i.e. rather later than the **Fernandez reaction** q.v. Positive in normal adults and in tuberculoid leprosy, negative in lepromatous leprosy; thus of importance in differentiating these two variants of leprosy, but of no diagnostic value.

mixed agglutination reaction.   Formation of mixed aggregates of two different cell types by antibody reacting with similar **antigenic determinants** on the two different cells.

151

mixed antiglobulin reaction. Method for demonstrating antibody adsorbed on to cell surfaces. To the cell suspension under test are added erythrocytes coated with **antiglobulin.** The antiglobulin will bind to **immunoglobulin** on the test cells so that a mixed aggregate of test cells and erythrocytes is formed.

mixed haemadsorption. A term used to describe the **mixed antiglobulin reaction** when used to show the presence of antibody against a virus, the virus in the test being grown in a monolayer of tissue culture cells.

mixed leucocyte reaction. *See* **mixed lymphocyte culture.**

mixed lymphocyte culture. The formation of **lymphoblasts** when equal numbers of lymphocytes from two individuals are cultured together for 3-5 days. The number of lymphoblasts seen appears to be directly related to the degree of **incompatibility** present between the **histocompatibility antigens** of the two donors.

mixed vaccine. A **vaccine** containing **antigens**[2] derived from several different *species* of pathogens, which gives protection against several diseases simultaneously. *Syn.* combined prophylactic. Cf. **polyvalent vaccine.**

MLC. *See* **mixed lymphocyte culture.**

MLD. *See* **minimal lethal dose.**

MLR. mixed leukocyte reaction. *See* **mixed lymphocyte culture.**

M macroglobulin. Paraprotein of **IgM** type, especially in **Waldenström's macroglobulinaemia.**

modulation. *See* **antigenic modulation.**

Moloney test. Test for **hypersensitivity** to diphtheria prophylactics (*see* **diphtheria immunization**) carried out by intradermal injection of **diphtheria toxoid,** and noting the skin reaction. Done in addition to Schick control (*see* **Schick test**).

monoclonal. Pertaining to or derived from a single clone.

monoclonal antibody. Antibody produced by a single clone of cells or a clonally derived cell line, and therefore having a unique amino acid sequence. Commonly used to describe the antibody secreted by a

hybridoma cell line (*q.v.*) although strictly this is only **monoclonal** if one of the fusion partners is a non-producer.

monocyte. A large motile, amoeboid, phagocytic (*see* **phagocytosis**) cell with an indented nucleus. Found in normal blood (200-800 cells per mm^3 or 2-10 per cent of the total white cell count in man). Derived from promonocytes in bone marrow and is the blood representative of the **mononuclear phagocyte system**. Monocytes remain in the blood for a short time (about 24 hours mean half-life) and then migrate into the tissues to become **macrophages.**

monokine. Generic term for secreted products of **mononuclear phagocytes** with regulatory effects on **lymphocyte** function, e.g. **interleukin-1** q.v., or on other immunological events.

mononuclear cell. A vague term often used to refer to cells of the **mononuclear phagocyte system** or to **lymphocytes** as seen in histological sections or fractionated blood leucocyte samples; in contrast to **polymorphonuclear leucocytes**.

mononuclear phagocyte system. The system of phagocytic cells of which the mature functioning form is the **macrophage**. The term mononuclear phagocyte system was introduced to replace the term 'reticulo-endothelial system' which is now considered inaccurate. All mononuclear phagocytes are considered to share a common origin from the **bone marrow** pro-monocytes and to share a common function, i.e. **phagocytosis** and digestion of particulate material. A classification is given below but it is probable that, under certain circumstances, macrophages of one type may take on the properties of another.

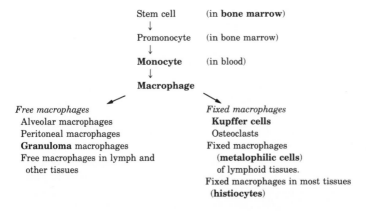

Stem cell	(in **bone marrow**)
↓	
Promonocyte	(in bone marrow)
↓	
Monocyte	(in blood)
↓	
Macrophage	

Free macrophages
 Alveolar macrophages
 Peritoneal macrophages
 Granuloma macrophages
 Free macrophages in lymph and
  other tissues

Fixed macrophages
 Kupffer cells
 Osteoclasts
 Fixed macrophages
  (**metalophilic cells**)
  of lymphoid tissues.
 Fixed macrophages in most tissues
  (**histiocytes**)

monospecific antiserum.   **Antiserum** against a single **antigen**[1] or antigenic determinant. *See also* **monoclonal antibody**.

Montenegro test.   A test used for the diagnosis of South American leishmaniasis caused by *Leishmania brasiliensis*. It is a **skin test** in which either a culture of the organism or a polysaccharide antigen extracted from it is inoculated intradermally and a response of **delayed hypersensitivity**, observed.

Moro test.   A **tuberculin test** carried out by the inunction of an ointment containing **tuberculin**, onto the skin.

Mott cell   Plasma cell containing multiple large, refractile, eosinophilic inclusion bodies, probably **Russell bodies**. Found in the brain in late stage African trypanosomiasis, typically in periarteriolar 'cuffs'. Also called the morula cell of Mott and considered pathognomonic for sleeping sickness.

M protein.   (1) Monoclonal **immunoglobulin** or immunoglobulin fragment, e.g. **myeloma protein**. (2) Type-specific cell surface antigens of Group A β-haemolytic streptococci. *See* **streptococcal M protein**.

MRT.   *See* **milk ring test**.

μ(mu) chain.   The **heavy chain** of **IgM**.

μ_m.   The membrane form of μ **chain**. *See also* **tail peptide**.

μ_s.   The secreted form of μ **chain**, i.e. that found in serum **IgM**, cf. μ_m.

multiple emulsion adjuvant.   *See* **water-in-oil-in-water emulsion adjuvant**.

multiple myeloma.   *See* **myelomatosis**.

multivalent vaccine.   *See* **polyvalent vaccine**.

mumps vaccine.   **Attenuated vaccine** containing virus grown in chick-embryo cell cultures. Not yet officially recommended.

muramyl dipeptide (MDP).   N-acetyl-muramyl-L-alanyl-D-isoglutamine. The simplest structural unit of bacterial peptidoglycans capable of replacing the mycobacteria in **complete Freund's adjuvant** (q.v.) to produce delayed hypersensitivity and an elevated antibody response. Is a pyrogen, and produces platelet lysis and transitory leucopenia. However many chemical derivatives of the molecule have been made that are free from these defects, and may have clinical application as **adjuvants** and immunostimulants.

myasthenia gravis. Disease characterized by progressive muscular weakness on exercise caused by faulty neuromuscular transmission. The patients' sera contain **autoantibodies** including an antibody against the acetylcholine receptor on the postsynaptic membrane of the neuromuscular junction. This antibody is the putative cause of the symptoms. Relieved by rest, anticholinesterase drugs and often treated by thymectomy. Experimental autoimmune myasthenia gravis can be produced in animals by injection of the anti-acetylcholine receptor antibody.

mycobacterial adjuvants. Whole, heat killed, dried, mycobacteria (*M.tuberculosis, M.avium, M.phlei, M.smegmatis*, etc.) that, when suspended in mineral oil and emulsifier as in **complete Freund's adjuvant** have **adjuvant** activity in respect of any antigen given with them. The **immunological responses** to the antigen are greatly enhanced, especially that of **cell-mediated immunity**. They are commonly used to induce experimental **autoimmune diseases**, e.g. **experimental allergic encephalomyelitis** and, also, in the absence of added antigens, **adjuvant arthritis** q.v. Extracts of some mycobacteria, e.g. mycobacterial **wax D** and **mycobacterial peptidoglycolipids** have similar adjuvant activities. *See also* **muramyl dipeptide.**

mycobacterial peptidoglycolipid. A component of mycobacterial **wax D**; the type obtained from the human strain of *M.tuberculosis* having the adjuvant properties of the **mycobacterial adjuvants**. Electron microscopic visualization of **peptidoglycolipids** can be obtained by negative staining. Those showing adjuvant activity appear as homogeneous filaments intertwined like spaghetti.

mycobacterial wax D. *See* **wax D.**

myeloid cell series. A series of **bone-marrow** derived cell lineages which includes as mature forms the granular leucocytes (**granulocytes**) of blood. Derived from a single line of stem cells which form different lines of progenitor cells (*see* **colony stimulating factors**) which mature into myeloblasts then to myelocytes which, in turn, mature into granulocytes. The **neutrophil leucocyte, eosinophil leucocyte** and **basophil leucocyte** types are usually termed myeloid cells, though their development is separate. These latter are all released into the circulation and are present in normal blood. This maturation process is known as myelopoiesis. Neutrophils and

myeloma

mononuclear phagocytes develop from the same precursors (GM-CFC). *see also* lymphoid cell series.

myeloma. A tumour of plasma cells, *see* plasmacytoma, myelomatosis.

myeloma protein. Protein produced by neoplastic plasma cells in myelomatosis in man, in plasmacytomas in mice, and similar conditions in other species. Structurally and electrophoretically homogeneous (monoclonal) paraprotein.

myelomatosis. Disease characterized, in man, by neoplastic proliferation of plasma cells throughout the bone marrow. The neoplastic cells are monoclonal and produce large amounts of structurally identical immunoglobulin (paraprotein) usually of IgG or of IgA type though IgD and IgE types have also been reported, forming a sharply localized band on serum electrophoresis and characteristic monoclonal banding pattern on isoelectric focusing. Bence-Jones protein appears in the urine in a proportion of cases. Myelomatosis may present with anaemia due to bone marrow replacement or with spontaneous fractures of bone. Commonest in men over 50 and usually fatal. *See also* plasmacytoma; paraproteinaemia.

myeloperoxidase. Peroxidase found in the azurophil granules of the neutrophil leucocyte, which, together with hydrogen peroxide and halide, forms a bactericidal system. Families with myeloperoxidase deficiency have been reported.

myoid cell. A cell containing skeletal myofibrils. Found in the thymus of man and many other species including reptiles such as the turtle. In man, most easily found in neonatal glands but identification in adults has been claimed.

native immunity. Non-specific immunity resulting from the genetic constitution of the host, e.g. immunity of man to canine distemper.

natural antibody. Antibody present in serum of normal individuals not known to have been immunized (*see* immunization[1]) against the relevant antigen. Examples in man include the isohaemagglutinins of the ABO blood group system and Forssman antibodies. They possibly result from an immune reaction against some closely related antigen, e.g. blood group antibodies may be directed against closely related antigens of bacteria or food in the intestine of the infant.

natural fluorescence. *See* **autofluorescence.**

natural immunity. *See* **native immunity.**

natural killer cell (NK cell). **Lymphoid cell** which kills a range of sensitive tumour cell targets in the absence of prior **immunization** and without **antigen specificity**. In man, morphologically distinguishable by presence of large granules visible under the light microscope (large granular lymphocytes).

naturally acquired immunity. Immunity[1,2] acquired by random exposure to antigen as opposed to immunity acquired as a result of deliberate **immunization**[1,2].

NBT. *See* **nitroblue tetrazolium test.**

necrotaxis. **Chemotaxis** of leucocytes towards dead and damaged cells and tissues.

negative phase. A drop in antibody **titre** seen immediately after the administration of a second or later dose of antigen to a **primed** animal. Due to combination of the antigen with pre-existing antibody in the circulation.

neoantigen. An **antigen** detected in the body during a disease state which is not found in health. Does not apply to the commonly recognised antigens of pathogenic organisms. Term used particularly in tumour studies, when a tumour antigen is found which is not detected in normal fetal or adult tissues.

neonatal thymectomy syndrome. *See* **wasting disease.**

network theory. A theory postulated by N.K. Jerne in 1974 that the immune system is controlled by a network of interacting **antigen-binding sites (paratopes)**, which may be on **immunoglobulin** molecules or **lymphocyte receptors**. Each paratope is capable of recognizing an **epitope** on an external **antigen** and also an **idiotope** on another immunoglobulin molecule (the '**internal image**'). Since each immunoglobulin molecule bears an idiotope, for which there is a corresponding paratope, this results in a network of interactions. It is postulated that interaction between two components of the system can result in stimulation or suppression, depending upon the nature of the interaction, the end result being a balanced system. This system is disturbed by the introduction of an external epitope, resulting in an immune response.

neuraminidase

neuraminidase. Enzyme, produced by viruses of the myxovirus and paramyxovirus group and by bacteria, including *Vibrio cholerae* and *Clostridium perfringens*, which splits the glycosidic link between neuraminic acid or sialic acid and other sugars. Neuraminic acid is an important structural component of the surface glycoproteins of many cells and contributes largely to the net negative charge of cells. Thus neuraminidase-treated cells may show less coulombic repulsion from one another than normal cells, and show an increased tendency to agglutinate (*see* **agglutination** and **agglutinin**[2]). Neuraminidase-treated cells (e.g. sheep red cells) may activate the **alternative pathway** of complement, whereas the same, untreated, cells do not.

neutralization test. Any test in which antibody is measured by its capacity to neutralize the biological effects produced by an antigen or by an organism bearing it, e.g. neutralization of the infectivity of a virus or the biological effects of a bacterial toxin. *See* **phage neutralization test, toxin neutralization test, virus neutralization tests**.

neutrophil leucocyte. Cell of **myeloid cell series**, the most numerous in normal peripheral blood (normal count in human blood 2500 to 7500 per mm[3] or 40-75 per cent of the total white cell count). A motile, short-lived cell with multilobed nucleus and a cytoplasm filled with **azurophil granules** q.v. and **specific granules** q.v. which do not take up acidic or basic dyes strongly (hence name). Actively phagocytic (*see* **phagocytosis**) and responds to chemotactic stimuli (*see* **chemotaxis**). The major cell in acute inflammatory lesions, e.g. acute bacterial infections, also **Arthus reactions**. Name usually abbreviated to neutrophil. Also known as polymorph or **polymorphonuclear leucocyte** or **granulocyte** (eosinophils and basophils also have multilobed nuclei and cytoplasmic granules), or, inaccurately, as 'pus cell'. It should be noted that in species other than man, the blood cells acting functionally as neutrophils may have granules whose staining properties are not 'neutrophil'. These are sometimes known as **heterophil granulocytes.**

New Zealand black mice. *See* **NZB mice.**

Newcastle disease vaccines. (a) *Vet.* Inactivated virus (*see* **inactivation**[3]), grown in the chick embryo, combined with **aluminium hydroxide gel** as adjuvant. (b) *Vet.* Live virus grown in the chick embryo and attenuated to different degrees. Medium virulent (mesogenic) strains (Komarov, Mukteswar) are given **parenterally**, but the less virulent (lentogenic) strains may safely be given to birds *en masse* as an aerosol or in their drinking water.

Nezelof syndrome. Immunodeficiency syndrome characterized by thymic hypoplasia, absence of **T lymphocytes** and T lymphocyte function, but with normal **B lymphocyte** function. Cf. **thymic hypoplasia.**

nitroblue tetrazolium test. Test of **neutrophil leucocyte** function. Nitroblue tetrazolium is a soluble yellow dye which is taken up into neutrophils only when they are exposed to a phagocytic (*see* **phagocytosis**) stimulus. Normal neutrophils contain enzymes which reduce the dye which is then deposited as insoluble deep-blue formazan crystals within the cell. Neutrophils from patients with **chronic granulomatous disease** lack the capacity to reduce nitroblue tetrazolium.

NK cell. *See* **natural killer cell.**

non identity, reaction of. *See* **reaction of non identity.**

non-immune animal. Animal which has not been **primed** with a given antigen.

non-secretor. Person whose secretions (gastric juice, saliva, etc.) do not contain **ABO blood group substances.**

non-specific esterase (also known as α-naphthyl acetate esterase). Enzyme identifiable within **mononuclear phagocytes** and some **lymphocytes** by cytochemical staining. **Mononuclear phagocytes** show characteristic diffuse, granular cytoplasmic staining and this is commonly used as a criterion for identifying these cells. A proportion of human **T lymphocytes** also stain for non-specific esterase, but with quite a different appearance of a single, or a small number of localized, discrete dots.

non-specific fluorescence. In **immunofluorescence** tests, fluorescence emitted for reasons other than specific combination between antibody and antigen. May be due to the presence of free **fluorochrome** or to fluorochrome labelling of proteins other than the antibody under test (especially albumin, α, β globulins in serum or unwanted antibodies). Often referred to as 'non specific staining'. *See also* **autofluorescence** and **tissue powder.**

non-specific immunity. Mechanisms for the disposal of foreign and potentially harmful macromolecules, microorganisms or metazoa which do not involve the recognition of **antigen**[1] and the mounting of a specific **immune response.** Such mechanisms include the action of **lysozyme** or **interferon, phagocytosis** and chemical and physical

non-specific T-cell helper factor

barriers to infection. **Protective immunity** in invertebrates is of the non-specific type. Specific and non-specific immunity are so closely linked in vertebrates that it is often impossible to dissociate their actions, cf. **specific immunity**.

non-specific T-cell helper factor. Soluble product of a **helper T-cell lymphocyte** which activates other lymphocytes in a non-antigen-specific manner.

non-specific T-cell suppressor factor. Soluble product of a **suppressor T lymphocyte** which suppresses the immune response in a non-specific manner.

non-sterile immunity. *See* **premunition**.

non-tissue specific antigen. Antigen present in more than one normal tissue or organ, e.g. nucleoprotein. Cf. **tissue specific antigen**.

normal lymphocyte transfer reaction. A reaction seen following the intradermal inoculation of peripheral blood **lymphocytes** into a genetically non-identical (**allogeneic**) animal of the same species. An erythematous lesion appears at the site of injection. This is maximal at 48 hours, and its size is believed to be inversely related to the degree of histocompatibility between the donor and recipient of the cells (*see* **histocompatibility antigens**).

N terminal. Adjective describing the end of a polypeptide chain with a free -NH_2 group. Cf. **C terminal**.

nu nu mice. Mice with congenital absence of the **thymus**, and whose blood and **thymus dependent areas** of the **lymph nodes** and **spleen** are depleted of **T lymphocytes**. These mice are homozygous for the gene 'nude', abbreviation *nu*, hence *nu nu*, and have no hair. They should be distinguished from mice carrying other genes that cause a lack of hair, e.g. shaven *Sha*; hairless, *hr*; bare, *ba*; hair loss, *hl*; etc. All these latter strains have normal thymuses. *See also* **thymic hypoplasia**.

nude mice. *See* **nu nu mice**.

NUL lymphocyte. A **lymphocyte** that has no detectable immuno-globulin or T lymphocyte antigens on its surface, cf. **T** and **B lymphocyte**.

nurse cell *See* **thymic nurse cell**.

NZB (New Zealand black) **mice.** **Inbred strain** of black mice which develop spontaneous autoimmune **haemolytic anaemia**. They show a positive **direct antiglobulin test** between 4 and 10 months of age, at which time glomerular and tubular renal lesions (and extramedullary haemopoiesis) are also seen. There is some evidence that this **autoimmune disease** may be of viral aetiology.

NZW (New Zealand white) **mice.** An **inbred strain** of white mice. The F_1 **hybrid** between these and **NZB mice** develop even more severe **autoimmune disease** than do the latter mice.

OA. *See* ovalbumin.

Oakley-Fulthorpe test. A **double diffusion test**, carried out in a narrow test-tube in which the antigen in solution and the antibody in agar are separated by a layer of plain agar in which the precipitate appears.

O antigen. The somatic antigen or **endotoxin** of Gram-negative bacteria, e.g. genera *Escherichia, Salmonella, Shigella,* etc. Species–specific cell wall antigen with outer oligosaccharide repeating unit side chain which confers specificity and is linked interiorly to 'lipid A' (forming **lipopolysaccharide**) and 'lipid B' thus:

antigenically specific polysaccharide–lipid A–protein–lipid B

'lipopolysaccharide'

O blood group. *See* **ABO blood group system**.

oil emulsion adjuvants. Water-in-oil emulsions that have been prepared with mineral oil and a stabilizer, e.g. **Arlacel**® to form a **depot forming adjuvant**. Oil-in-water emulsions and emulsions prepared with vegetable oils are relatively ineffective as adjuvants (*but see* **Adjuvant 65**®). For examples *see* **complete Freund's adjuvant, water-in-oil emulsion adjuvant, water-in-oil-in-water emulsion adjuvant, solubilized water-in-oil adjuvant, mycobacterial adjuvants**.

oil-in-water emulsion. A fine dispersion of vegetable or mineral oil droplets in an aqueous phase, stabilized with an emulsifier such as **Tween 80**® Such emulsions are relatively ineffective as **adjuvants** for antigens contained in the aqueous phase, cf. **water-in-oil emulsion adjuvants**.

OKT antibodies®. Commercial monoclonal antibodies against human **T-antigens**.

old tuberculin. *See* **tuberculin**.

oligosaccharide determinant. A small number (2-7) of 5, 6 or 7 carbon sugars (pentoses, hexoses or heptoses) joined by glycoside linkages, that form the **antigenic determinant** site or **epitope** on a polysaccharide **hapten.**

opsonin. Factor present in plasma and other body fluids which binds to particles, *esp.* cells and microorganisms, and increases their susceptibility to **phagocytosis.** Opsonins may be (1) **antibodies** which bind to **antigenic determinants** on the particle. Particle–bound antibody can then attach by its **Fc fragment** to the Fc receptors of phagocytes thus initiating phagocytosis of the particle. (2) Products of **complement** activation *esp.* **C3b**. These are known as heat-labile opsonins.
(3) Other non-antibody, non-complement opsonins (e.g. fibronectin) have also been found in biological fluids.

opsonization. Coating of microorganisms and other antigenic particles with **opsonins** thus facilitating their **phagocytosis.**

optimal proportions. In **precipitin tests,** if antibody and antigen are present in such a ratio that the maximum combination between **antigen binding sites** and **antigenic determinants** can occur, they are said to be present in optimal proportions or 'at equivalence'. At this ratio, maximum precipitation occurs. Cf. **antibody excess, antigen excess,** *and see* **lattice hypothesis.**

organ specific antigen. *See* **tissue specific antigen.**

original antigenic sin. Term used to describe a phenomenon in which, after **vaccination** or infection with influenza virus, followed by re-infection or vaccination with a related but not identical virus, the antibody produced in response to the second virus is still directed against the first virus.

orthotopic graft. Tissue or organ grafted to a site normally occupied by that tissue or organ. Cf. **heterotopic graft.**

OT. Old tuberculin (*see* **tuberculin**).

Ouchterlony test. **Precipitin test** of **double diffusion test** type. Wells are cut in an agar plate and filled with appropriate solutions of antigen and antibody which then diffuse through the agar gel and meet to form lines of precipitate. *See* **reaction of identity, reaction of partial identity, reaction of non identity, spur.**

Oudin test. **Precipitin test** of the **single diffusion test** type. A narrow test tube is partly filled with a layer of agar mixed with antiserum. A solution of antigen is poured onto this and diffuses into the agar to form rings of precipitate. *See also* **single radial diffusion test**.

ovalbumin (OA). A negatively charged protein related to the albumin of fowl serum and obtained from the white (albumen) of the avian egg. Frequently used as an experimental antigen.

oxazolone. (4−ethoxymethylene−2−phenyloxazol−5−one). A chemical employed to produce experimental **contact hypersensitivity**.

Oz. Oz^+ and Oz^- are antigenic markers on human λ **chains** defining λ subtypes. Oz^+ λ chains have lysine at position 191 whereas Oz^- chains have arginine at the same position. In combination with the **Kern** markers (q.v.) they define three human λ chain subtypes. The positions of these markers are similar to those of the Km allotypes (*See* **Inv allotypes**) of ϰ chains.

P. Symbol for **properdin**. *See* **Factor P**.

P–80 test. A measure of the antigen precipitating capacity of an antiserum, which yields information similar to that given by a **quantitative precipitation test**. A radioactively labelled antigen is used and tubes are set up each containing the same amount of antigen, but doubling dilutions of antiserum. The end point is that tube in the region of **antigen excess** in which 80 per cent of the antigen added is precipitated. *See also* **Farr test**.

panagglutination. **Agglutination** of all normal erythrocytes by certain sera, or of certain erythrocytes by normal sera (this latter is termed **polyagglutination** q.v.). A laboratory artefact resulting from bacterial contamination of sera or cells. May lead to false positive results in blood-grouping, cross-matching tests, etc.

PAP technique. *See* **peroxidase–anti-peroxidase technique**.

papain. Proteolytic enzyme obtained from the papaw plant (*Carica papaya*). Used in **papain hydrolysis** of **immunoglobulins** and also to treat the surfaces of erythrocytes so as to render them agglutinable by **incomplete antibody**[1].

papain hydrolysis. The reaction by means of which **IgG** molecules are split into three fragments (2 **Fab fragments,** 1 **Fc fragment**) by

163

treatment with **papain** in the presence of cysteine. The papain attacks a histidyl-threonine peptide bond on the **heavy chain** at the site indicated in the illustration on p.108.

paracortical area. *See* **thymus dependent area.**

paradoxical reaction. Obsolete. Von Behring's term for **anaphylaxis.** In his case, the death of animals which had been immunized with **tetanus toxoid,** on subsequent challenge with the same antigen.

paralysis. *See* **acquired tolerance.**

paralytogenic. Capable of inducing **immunological tolerance.**

paraprotein. **Immunoglobulin** derived from an abnormally proliferating clone of neoplastic plasma cells. Paraproteins are structurally homogeneous, an example from a single patient being of a single **immunoglobulin class,–subclass** and **light chain** (ϰ or λ) type. They are usually demonstrable as a sharply localized band on serum electrophoresis. **Myeloma proteins** and the abnormal **IgM** of **Waldenström's macroglobulinaemia** are examples of paraproteins.

paraproteinaemia. Presence in serum of **paraprotein.** A diagnostic feature of **myelomatosis** and **Waldenström's macroglobulinaemia.** (*See also* **benign monoclonal gammopathy, heavy chain disease** and α–**chain disease**). Paraproteinaemias involving all five **immunoglobulin classes** have been reported in man, the frequency in any given class being proportional to the normal serum concentration of that class. Also occurs in mice, *see* **mouse myeloma.**

paraspecific anti-venom. Anti-venom that, though produced against the venom of one species also protects against that of other species, i.e. anti-venom against poison of *Latrodectus mactans* also protects against that of other species of black widow spider. In contrast, anti-venoms against scorpions and many snakes are species specific.

paratope. *Syn.* for **antigen binding site.**

parenteral. Introduced or injected into the body by any route other than through the alimentary canal.

paroxysmal cold haemoglobinuria. Disease in which haemoglobin appears in urine following exposure to cold. Due to presence

in serum of **Donath-Landsteiner antibody** which binds to erythrocytes in the cold and lyses them on warming in the presence of
complement. Many but not all cases are associated with
congenital syphilis.

partial identity, reaction of. *See* **reaction of partial identity.**

particulate antigen. An **antigen**[1] present on a particle such as a
tissue cell, bacterium (or fragments thereof), virus, or inert particle,
either as part of its structure or adsorbed (*see* **adsorption**) on to
it. Such antigens are usually either surface antigens or are recognized following cellular breakdown. Antibodies against particulate
antigens can be demonstrated by **agglutination** tests and are often
of the **IgM** class.

PAS. (1) Periodic acid Schiff. Two reagents used in sequence for
staining polysaccharides. Detects substances containing 1,2-diol
groups including glycogen, sialic acid and mucopolysaccharide.
(2) Para-aminosalicylic acid, an antituberculous drug.

passive agglutination test. A test used to detect antibodies to
soluble antigens. Molecules of the latter are firmly attached to
small particles of uniform size such as polystyrene latex, or erythrocytes. Agglutination of these passive supports occurs when antibody to the antigen is present. *See* **tanned red cell test, latex
agglutination test, bentonite flocculation test, bisdiazotized
benzidine.**

passive Arthus reaction. Artificially induced skin reaction of
Arthus reaction type produced by passively administering large
quantities of precipitating antibody by the intravenous route, and
then inoculating antigen subcutaneously or intradermally. The
antibody need not have been produced in the same species of animal
as that in which the test is carried out, cf. **passive cutaneous
anaphylaxis.**

passive cutaneous anaphylaxis. *In vivo* **passive transfer** technique for recognizing **homocytotropic antibody** responsible for
immediate hypersensitivity reactions. Antibody is injected
intradermally into a homologous animal and a sufficient interval is
allowed for fixation of homocytotropic antibody to cells and diffusion
away of non cell-fixed antibody. Antigen is then injected intravenously mixed with the dye Evans blue. Where the antigen reacts
with cell-fixed antibody, histamine and other **vascular permeability factors** are released, the permeability of the vessel walls
increases and plasma and the dye leak out giving a blue spot on the
skin the size of which can be measured.

passive haemolysis. Erythrocyte destruction brought about by the combination, in the presence of **complement,** of antibody with an antigen attached to the surface of that cell. The antigen is not an integral part of the cell surface, e.g. it may have been deliberately attached as in the **passive agglutination test,** or be a bacterial antigen that has become adsorbed (*see* **adsorption**) to the cell during a disease process.

passive immunity. Immunity [1,2] due, not to the production of a specific **immune response** by the individual himself, but to the presence in his tissues of **antibody** or **primed** lymphocytes derived from another, **immune**[1,2], individual. Examples are the immunity of the neonate against many infectious agents due to placentally–or colostrally–transferred maternal antibody (*see* **maternal immunity,** transfer of) and the use of **antitoxins** to give protection against diphtheria or tetanus. In the case where lymphocytes are transferred, the term **adoptive immunity** is often used.

passive immunization. The use of **antibody** or **primed** lymphocytes from an **immune** individual to produce **passive immunity** against an antigenic substance (e.g. toxin) or organism in a **non immune** individual. Gives short-lived immunity so its use is restricted to therapy or short-term prophylaxis and it is not suitable for long-term prophylaxis, cf. **active immunization.** Examples in man: use of **diphtheria antitoxin, tetanus antitoxin,** and of **gammaglobulin** in **antibody deficiency syndrome.** Amongst numerous applications in animals the passive immunization of newborn lambs against clostridial diseases may be noted. This is accomplished by strategic **vaccination** of the ewes before lambing so that their **colostrum** contains large amounts of antibody at that time. *See* **maternal immunity.**

passive sensitization. Passive transfer of hypersensitivity from a **primed** donor to a normal host by administration of **antibody** or **primed lymphocytes.** *See also* **passive cutaneous anaphylaxis, Prausnitz-Küstner reaction, passive systemic anaphylaxis, adoptive transfer.**

passive systemic anaphylaxis. Passive transfer of anaphylaxis from **primed** to normal animal by injection of **homocytotropic antibody,** especially intravenously, followed by a dose of antigen which, on combination with the antibody, produces **anaphylactic shock.** *See also* **passive cutaneous anaphylaxis.**

passive transfer. Transfer of **immunity**[1,2] or **hypersensitivity** from an **immune**[1,2] or **primed** donor to a previously **non-immune** host either by injection of serum **antibody** (as in **Prausnitz-Küstner reaction**) or by injection of **lymphocytes** (as in experimental transfer of **delayed hypersensitivity**).

patch tests. Tests used in the diagnosis of skin allergies (*see* **allergy**[1]) particularly those of the **contact hypersensitivity** type. The suspected substance is applied to the skin for a short period under an impervious dressing. A positive result is one that reproduces the original allergic condition. A patch test, the **Vollmer test,** has also been used as a **tuberculin test**.

patching. Appearance of cell surface observed using e.g. **membrane immunofluorescence** or other labelling techniques after polyvalent **ligands**, e.g. antibody, have been allowed to react with surface structures on cell membranes, e.g. antigens, this causing clustering of these structures. Depends on the ability of membrane components to diffuse laterally in the plane of the membrane (*see* **fluid mosaic model**). This causes a patchy surface fluorescence which resembles a two-dimensional **agglutination** reaction, one of the reactants being a membrane component. Does not require metabolic energy on the part of the cell and can be demonstrated at 4°C, cf. **capping**.

pattern method. *See* **sedimentation pattern**.

Paul-Bunnell test. Haemagglutination test[1] used in diagnosis of **infectious mononucleosis**. Sera from patients with infectious mononucleosis agglutinate erythrocytes of sheep or horse. In the Paul-Bunnell test, the sheep cell agglutination titre is determined. This **agglutinin**[1] can be absorbed from serum with boiled ox cells but not with guinea pig tissue, a pattern of **absorption** which distinguishes it from other **heterophil antibodies** found in human serum. The agglutinin is different and distinct from the antibodies formed to Epstein-Barr virus (the cause of the disease).

PCA. *See* **passive cutaneous anaphylaxis**. *Also* perchloric acid.

pemphigoid. A fairly rare, blistering skin disease found mainly in elderly persons. Blisters develop at the dermoepidermal junction and the **single layer immunofluorescence technique** shows **IgG** deposition in this region. IgG directed against the same site is also present in the circulation.

pemphigus vulgaris. A rare blistering skin disorder most frequently found in patients of Jewish origin. The histological appearance is of a blister situated within the epidermis and the single layer immunofluorescence technique demonstrates the presence of **IgG** in the intercellular spaces. Circulating IgG directed against an antigen in the same site is also present.

penicillin hypersensitivity. Immediate hypersensitivity to breakdown products of penicillin such as penicilloic or penicillenic acid acting as **haptens** and binding to the patient's own proteins. Often manifested as **serum-sickness** with fever, joint-pains and urticaria following the inoculation of penicillin, but **anaphylactic shock** may also be seen. Cf. **ampicillin hypersensitivity.**

pepsin digestion. Use of the gastric enzyme pepsin to split the polypeptide chains of proteins. It attacks certain peptide links between L-dicarboxylic and L-aromatic amino acids. In immunology, its chief use has been to split the **immunoglobulin** molecule giving a **F(ab')$_2$ fragment** q.v. plus small peptide fragments derived from the remainder of the **Fc fragment**. This has a practical use inasmuch as the **IgG** molecules of **antitoxins** used in **passive immunization** can be treated with pepsin and the F(ab')$_2$ fragments separated. These fragments retain their activity as divalent antibody but, on injection, are less likely to give rise to **hypersensitivity** reactions than the whole molecule.

peptidoglycolipid. A fat or wax whose molecules contain sugar and peptide. *See* **wax D.**

Percoll®. A colloidal suspension of silica used in **density gradient centrifugation** (q.v.)

periarterial lymphatic sheath. The **thymus dependent area** of the white pulp of the **spleen** q.v.

perifollicular zone. Zone surrounding the Malpighian body, in the mammalian **spleen** q.v., particularly well-defined in rodents. It has been shown that **macrophages** in this zone play a major role in the early phase of **phagocytosis** of antigens and particulate matter, following intravenous injection.

peripheral lymphoid organs. Those lymphoid organs that are not essential to the ontogeny of the **immune response**, i.e. **spleen, lymph nodes, pharyngeal tonsils, Peyer's patches.** Cf. **central lymphoid organs.**

peripheral sensitization. In transplantation immunology, the postulated priming (*see* **primed**) of **lymphocytes** at the actual site of the graft, as opposed to central sensitization in which antigens from the graft travel from it to the organs of immunity.

peripolesis. The clustering of **lymphocytes** around **macrophages,** especially seen in tissue culture preparations made from stimulated **lymphoid tissue.** May be of importance for induction of immune responses.

peritoneal exudate cells. Any cells present in a peritoneal exudate. After injection into the peritoneum of guinea pigs, rabbits, etc. of substances such as glycogen, paraffin oil or peptone, an exudate composed mainly of **neutrophil leucocytes** forms within a few hours and this is replaced a few days later by an exudate composed mainly of **macrophages** and **lymphocytes.** However, the yield of the various cell types varies greatly between species and it may be noted that the cells obtained by lavage of the peritoneal cavity of mice, into which no irritant materials have been inoculated, are mainly macrophages.

permeability factors. *See* **vascular permeability factors.**

permeability increasing factor. A **lymphokine** believed to increase vascular permeability.

pernicious anaemia. Disease of man characterized by atrophic gastritis with achlorhydria and lack of gastric intrinsic factor which leads to failure of absorption of dietary vitamin B_{12} and consequent megaloblastic anaemia. Sometimes associated with autoimmune **thyroiditis.** Gastric secretions and also serum of patients contain **autoantibodies** against intrinsic factor (50 per cent of cases) and against a microsomal antigen present in gastric parietal cells.

peroxidase-anti-peroxidase (PAP) technique. A variant of **enzyme labelling** techniques for detecting **antigen** or **antibody** in tissue sections by binding **immune complexes** containing horseradish peroxidase and (normally) rabbit anti-peroxidase. The tissue section is incubated with rabbit antibody specific for the antigen to be detected. This is followed by an excess of anti-rabbit IgG followed by the PAP complexes. The anti-rabbit IgG links the antigen-bound antibody to the PAP complexes which are then stained by incubation with a substrate, producing a coloured product. This method gives greater sensitivity than the simpler enzyme staining methods due to the multiplication effect of the PAP complex. (Diagram overleaf).

pertussis adjuvant

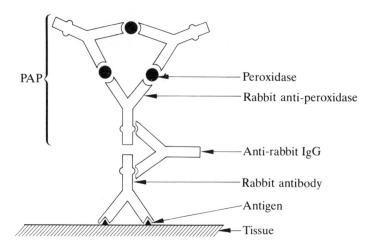

PAP

Peroxidase

Rabbit anti-peroxidase

Anti-rabbit IgG

Rabbit antibody

Antigen

Tissue

pertussis adjuvant. **Adjuvant** mixture in which antigen is injected mixed with a saline suspension of killed *Bordetella pertussis* q.v. Has especially marked activity in eliciting production of IgE in experimental animals, e.g. rats. In **triple vaccine** used for **immunization**[2] of children, pertussis is used as a protective **vaccine** in its own right (against whooping cough) as well as for its adjuvant activity in enhancing antibody production to **diphtheria toxoid** and **tetanus toxoid**.

pertussis vaccine. **Vaccine** against whooping cough prepared from formalin– or merthiolate– killed virulent stains of *Bordetella pertussis* q.v. Usually given as one component of **triple vaccine** in combination with **diphtheria toxoid** and **tetanus toxoid**. *B. pertussis* itself is active as an **adjuvant** and may enhance antibody levels against the latter vaccine. Vaccination carries a slight risk of **hypersensitivity** reactions including encephalitis.

Peyer's patches. Nodules of **lymphoid tissue** in the submucosa of the small intestine, more prominent in the ileum (lower part) than in the jejunum. Contain **lymphocytes,** including **B lymphocyte** precursors of **IgA** producing cells, **germinal centres** and **thymus dependent areas**.

PF/dil. A β **globulin** with an action in increasing vascular permeability. Not found in normal **plasma** but generated on exposure to foreign surfaces, e.g. glass, therefore probably activated by Hageman factor (a proenzyme which is activated by contact with foreign surfaces). Has activity as an esterase and is inactivated by $C\overline{1}$

inactivator. It is not identical to **kallikrein** although it may have a similar activity in **kinin** production.

PFC. *See* **plaque forming cells.**

pFc′. A fragment produced after **pepsin digestion** of **IgG.** It is a non-covalently bonded dimer of the C-terminal **immunoglobulin domains** (i.e. C_H3) of the **Fc fragment.** Differs from the **Fc′ fragment** by retaining the basic **N–terminal** and **C–terminal** peptides of this domain (*see* **immunoglobulin domain**). Cathodic electrophoretic mobility, mol. wt. 27 000.

Pfeiffer phenomenon. Rapid lysis of *Vibrio cholerae* by antibody in the presence of **complement.** (Historical).

PFU. Plaque-forming units: a measure of plaque formation in, e.g. the **haemolytic plaque test, phage neutralization test,** etc.

PHA. *See* **phytohaemagglutinin.**

phacoanaphylaxis. **Hypersensitivity** to proteins of the lens of the eye.

phage neutralization test. An assay of antibody against bacteriophage. Incubation with antibody inhibits the capacity of bacteriophages to infect their host bacterium. This effect of antibody can be measured quantitatively by observing the reduction in the numbers of plaques produced by the mixture after various periods of incubation when subsequently added to a 'lawn' of bacteria. Very low levels of antibody can be detected by this technique.

phagocyte. A cell that is able to ingest, and often to digest, large particles such as effete blood cells, bacteria, protozoa and dead tissue cells. They are also active in ingesting foreign colloidal materials such as finely divided carbon. Examples of phagocytes are **macrophages, Kupffer cells,** and **neutrophil leucocytes.** *See also* **mononuculear phagocyte system.**

phagocytic index. (1) A measure of the *in vivo* activity of the **mononuclear phagocyte system** of the body. It is usually represented by a constant K that characterizes the rate of carbon clearance (*see* **carbon clearance test**) from the blood and is inversely proportional to the dose of carbon injected. (2) Term also used for various measures of phagocytic activity *in vitro*.

phagocytosis. 'Cell eating'. The ingestion of cells or particles by inclusion in a cytoplasmic **phagosome.** In mammals, only cells of the **mononuclear phagocyte system** and **polymorphonuclear leucocytes** are 'professional' phagocytes although other cells may, on occasion, show facultative phagocytosis. The mechanism of phagocytosis is similar to that of macropinocytosis (*see* **pinocytosis**).

phagolysosome. The product of the fusion of **lysosomes** with a **phagosome.** Materials included within it may be digested by hydrolysis. Following such digestion the vesicle may continue to function as a **secondary lysosome.**

phagosome. An intracellular vesicle in a **phagocyte** q.v. formed by invagination of the cell membrane and containing phagocytosed (*see* **phagocytosis**) material. This latter is digested by lysosomal (*see* **lysosome**) enzymes liberated into the vesicle following fusion of the phagosome with cytoplasmic lysosomes. The structure which results from this fusion is known in macrophages as a **phagolysosome** or **secondary lysosome.**

pharyngeal pouch syndrome. *Syn*. for **thymic hypoplasia.**

pharyngeal tonsils. Accumulations of **lymphoid tissue** found in invaginations of the mucous membrane in the area between the mouth and the pharynx. They vary in extent in different species being extensive in man and the horse, and small in cattle. In man they form distinct organs. The most prominent of these are the two palatine tonsils; tubal, lingual and a single nasopharyngeal tonsil complete a ring round the area. *See also* **caecal tonsils.**

(Phe,G)AL. A synthetic **antigen** composed of short polymers of phenylalanine and glutamic acid attached as side chains to a backbone of poly-L-lysine by alanine residues.

phytohaemagglutinins (PHA). **Lectins** extracted from the seeds (beans) of *Phaseolus vulgaris* or *P. communis*. They may be partially purified to yield a protein-rich form PHA-P or a mucoprotein-rich extract PHA-M. Phytohaemagglutinin causes agglutination of certain erythrocytes due to its binding affinity for N-acetyl-β-D-galactosamine residues. In soluble form it is a strong **mitogen** of the **T lymphocytes** of man and mouse. It will also act as a mitogen for **B lymphocytes** if presented to them on an insoluble matrix.

picryl chloride. (1-chloro-2,4,6-trinitrobenzene). A reagent which introduces the picryl group into proteins. Used experimentally as a **hapten** and as an agent for inducing **contact hypersensitivity.**

pigeon fancier's lung. *See* **bird fancier's lung**.

pinocytosis. 'Cell-drinking'. Ingestion of fluid-containing vesicles by cells. There are two forms. (a) *Macropinocytosis:* the ingestion of large fluid-containing vesicles or 'vacuoles' visible in the light-microscope, by an energy-requiring mechanism similar to phagocytosis. This is frequently seen in **monocytes**, macrophages and other cells of the **mononuclear phagocyte system. (b)** *Micropinocytosis:* the ingestion of small droplets as microvesicles about 70 nm in diameter. Micropinocytosis is a property of many cells, not only phagocytic ones, and does not require metabolic energy. It is a selective process, only certain molecules adsorbed (*see* **adsorption**) to the cell surface being taken into the cell. Pinocytosis of ligand-receptor complexes into clathrin-coated vesicles is an important mechanism which many cells use to internalize ligands.

PK test. *See* **Prausnitz-Küstner reaction**.

plague vaccine. Heat or formalin-killed *Pasteurella pestis*. Has been used to produce **immunity**[1] against plague in man in India and probably confers a degree of protection for some months. More recently an attenuated **live vaccine**[1] has been used in Java. This also gave protection but no comparative trial of the two vaccines has been carried out.

plaque forming cells. Cells producing antibody against erythrocytes, or against an antigen coating the erythrocytes, that are seen to be surrounded by plaques of **haemolysis** in the **haemolytic plaque test**.

plaque technique. *See* **haemolytic plaque test, Cunningham plaque technique, phage neutralization test**.

plasma. Fluid obtained from uncoagulated blood after removing the cells. To prevent clotting, an anticoagulant, e.g. heparin, oxalate, or EDTA, is first added to the blood. For most immunological procedures, **serum** q.v. is usually used.

plasma cell. Cell of **lymphoid cell series** with basophilic cytoplasm containing rough-surfaced **endoplasmic reticulum** and a nucleus which is often round and eccentrically placed; **Russell bodies** may also be present. The nucleus has a 'clock face' appearance when stained with haematoxylin. The cytoplasm is pyroninophilic when treated with **methyl green pyronin stain** due to its high content of RNA. The end cell of the **B lymphocyte** line, it is the major **immunoglobulin**-producing cell type and therefore the classical cell of **humoral immunity**. Present in **lymphoid tissue** and increased in numbers in the draining **lymph node** and at the site of entry of antigen following antigenic stimulation. Plasma cell tumours may occur, *see* **myelomatosis.**

plasma half-life ($T^{1/2}$).   Measure of rate of catabolism of any plasma constituent. In immunology commonly used of the time taken for half of the immunoglobulin in the plasma to be catabolised. Measured from the linear part of the plasma immunoglobulin decay curve using a semi-logarithmic plot.

plasma pool.   The quantity of immunoglobulin in the plasma per unit body weight, normally expressed as mg of immunoglobulin per Kg body weight.

plasmablast.   Blast cell characterized by its prominent, clumped nuclear chromatin, and some differentiation of the **endoplasmic reticulum,** and Golgi apparatus. Precursor of the **plasma cell.**

plasmacyte.   *See* **plasma cell**.

plasmacytoma (*syn.* **myeloma**).   A tumour of **plasma cells,** *see also* **myeloniatosis.** Plasmacytomas occur spontaneously and can be induced in rats and mice (especially the **BALB/c mouse** strain) by intraperitoneal injection of paraffin oil, **complete Freund's adjuvant** and other substances. Tumours producing **monoclonal immunoglobulin** of each class and subclass have been obtained in this way and may be maintained by serial transplantation or adaptation to tissue culture. Widely used for studies on immuno-globulin biosynthesis and gene structure, as a source of **monoclonal immunoglobulin** and for fusion with **primed lymphocytes** to produce **monoclonal antibody**.

plasmapheresis.   The technique of obtaining large volumes of **plasma** and thus **antibody** from an animal (or man) without causing anaemia; this involves withdrawal of blood and the return of the erythrocytes to the animal after they have been separated from the blood which has been withdrawn. Used therapeutically to remove harmful substances from the circulation. Machines are available for these purposes which automatically remove the patients plasma and return the erythrocytes with fresh normal plasma. Can also be used to isolate large quantities of antibody.

plasminogen activator.   Enzyme which converts plasminogen to plasmin which degrades fibrin. Secreted by various cells including vascular endothelial cells and certain neoplastic cells.

Immunological interest is that **activated macrophages** secrete much larger amounts than inactivated macrophages, thus plasminogen activator secretion is used as a marker for macrophage activation.

platelet (*syn.* thrombocyte). A small non-nucleated 'cell' (3μm diam.) found in mammalian blood, and derived from the megakaryocytes of **bone marrow.** It is important in blood coagulation as generator of thromboplastin on contact with foreign surfaces and is essential for haemostasis and thrombosis. Also contains **histamine** and may play some part in **hypersensitivity** especially **type I (anaphylaxis)** and **type III reactions** (immune complex).

platelet activating factor *syns* (PAF) (PAF acether). 1-0-hexadecyl-2-acetyl-sn-glycero-3- phosphorylcholine, a lipid released by various cells, including possibly **basophil leucocytes** and **mononuclear phagocytes,** in the presence of antigen. Release may be **IgE**-mediated. Induces **platelet** aggregation and degranulation. Inactivated by phospholipase A.

PMN. *See* **polymorphonuclear leucocyte.**

pneumococcal polysaccharide. Type specific antigenic polysaccharide present in the capsule of *Streptococcus pneumoniae,* its presence being related to the virulence of the organism. Many **serotypes** of this organism exist, each of which has a structurally different polysaccharide in its capsule. These are made up of oligosaccharide repeating units, e.g. type III is composed of repeating units of glucose and glucuronic acid. Type XIV polysaccharide is antigenically related to A blood group substance (*see* **ABO blood group substances**) and is a **thymus independent antigen** q.v. *See also* **pneumococcus capsule swelling reaction** and **C reactive protein.**

pneumococcus capsule swelling reaction. (Neufeld Quellung reaction). Phenomenon first observed by Neufeld in 1902 in which, on additon of type-specific antibody to capsulated pneumococci (*Streptococcus pneumoniae*), the capsule developed a swollen appearance due to combination of antibody molecules with the **capsular polysaccharide.** *See also* **pneumococcal polysaccharide.**

PNH cells. Erythrocytes from patients with paroxysmal nocturnal haemoglobinuria. These cells lyse spontaneously at slightly acid pH. The lytic activity of **complement** for PNH cells is abnormally high, possibly because of a cell membrane defect.

poison ivy hypersensitivity. **Hypersensitivity** (especially **contact hypersensitivity**) to the poison ivy plant (*Rhus toxicodendron*) which grows in North America but not in Europe. The **allergens** of poison ivy have been isolated and are catechols. Lesions are of **delayed hypersensitivity** type (**type IV reaction**).

pokeweed mitogen. This term covers five (Pa 1–5) **mitogens** q.v. obtained from *Phytolacca americana*. Pa 1 is active for both **T** and **B lymphocytes**, but Pa 2,3 and 4 only activate T lymphocytes.

poliomyelitis vaccines. (a) Sabin vaccine, the oral poliomyelitis vaccine now in general use, contains live attenuated strains of the three types of poliomyelitis virus. These multiply in the gastrointestinal tract and stimulate good blood antibody production and local gut **immunity**[1] due to production of **IgA** antibody. Given in three oral doses. It has largely superseded (b) Salk vaccine, prepared from formalin-killed poliovirus and given by three subcutaneous injections.

pollen hypersensitivity. **Immediate hypersensitivity (type I reaction)** occuring in **atopic** subjects, usually on inhalation of pollens. Characterized by respiratory symptoms, **hay fever** or **asthma** (or by **urticaria** if pollen settles on skin abrasions). Many pollens may cause symptoms, especially Timothy grass pollen in Britain and ragweed in U.S.A. Diagnosed by **skin tests** using pollen extracts.

polyacrylamide gel electrophoresis. A high resolution electrophoresis technique carried out in a transparent synthetic polymer gel. The gel acts as a molecular sieve and, in the presence of sodium dodecyl sulphate, the mobility of a protein molecule is inversely proportional to its Mol. Wt.

polyagglutination. Agglutination of normal erythrocytes, which have been acted on by **neuraminidase,** by normal sera which contain antibody against the **T antigen**. Result of bacterial infection *in vivo* (rare) or of bacterial contamination of serum samples. Cf. **panagglutination**.

polyarteritis nodosa. Systemic **collagen disease** in man characterized by nodular lesions in medium-sized arteries in which there is necrosis, fibrinoid degeneration and hyalinization of the intermediate coat with infiltration of **inflammatory cells**. The lesions are widespread and the clinical presentation is that of a disease of many tissues; symptoms and signs referable to the intestinal tract, kidneys, neuromuscular system or lungs are especially common. The lesions resemble those of experimental **serum sickness** in rabbits and polyarteritis nodosa in man may follow administration of potentially **haptenic** drugs, e.g. sulphonamides, but direct evidence of **hypersensitivity** or **autoimmunity** as aetiological factors is lacking.

polyclonal activators.   General term for substances that activate many clones of **lymphocytes,** in contrast to antigen which activates only a restricted number of clones. Certain of these substances activate **T lymphocytes,** others **B lymphocytes** (*see* **mitogen** and **lectin**). B lymphocyte polyclonal activators usually have a high molecular weight and repeated **antigenic determinants.** Many are **thymus independent antigens** such as lipopolysaccharide, polymerized flagellin, **dextrans,** levan, polyvinyl pyrrollidone, type III **pneumococcal polysaccharide.** However, some low molecular weight derivatives with a strong net charge, e.g. dextran sulphate or pentosan sulphate have identical properties.

polygenic inheritance.   Inheritance of a phenotype due to genetic variation at many loci. The observed character results from the effects of many loci, each of which contributes a small part of the total. Polygenic inheritance is responsible for many physiological properties e.g.: susceptibility to specific diseases, various types of immune response, spleen size, life-span, height and weight.

polymorphonuclear leucocyte.   Cell of **myeloid cell series** which in its mature form has a multilobed nucleus and granular cytoplasm. Present in blood and in acute inflammatory exudates. Includes **neutrophil leucocytes** (the commonest type, the term is often used for this type alone), **eosinophil leucocytes** and **basophil leucocytes**. *See also* **granulocyte**.

polystyrene latex test.   *See* **latex agglutination test**.

polyvalent antiserum.   **Antiserum** containing **antibodies** against many **antigens**[1,2], e.g. rabbit anti-human globulin may contain antibodies against 20 to 30 serum globulins.

polyvalent vaccine.   A **vaccine** containing **protective antigens** derived from several strains of a single species of pathogenic organism. Cf. **mixed vaccines**.

post-capillary venules.   Small vessels through which blood flows after leaving the capillaries and before reaching the veins. It is between the endothelial cells of post capillary venules (rather than capillaries) that most **leucocytes** migrate into inflammatory sites. The **high endothelial venules** (q.v.) of lymph nodes are specialized post-capillary venules through which the **recirculating pool** of lymphocytes pass from blood to lymph.

post-rabies vaccination encephalomyelitis. Demyelinating encephalomyelitis in man following **active immunization** for the prophylaxis of rabies (*see* **rabies vaccines**). Closely analogous to the **autoimmune disease,** called **experimental allergic encephalomyelitis** q.v. in animals produced by **immunization**[1] with nervous tissue. In rabies vaccination, repeated doses of rabbit brain containing phenol-killed rabies virus were injected. There was therefore some risk of encephalomyelitis and only the certainly fatal outcome of rabies justified the use of this vaccine. A tissue culture vaccine that does not contain nervous tissue is now used.

post-vaccinal encephalomyelitis. Demyelinating encephalomyelitis, often fatal, occuring rarely as a complication of **smallpox vaccination**. Usually appears about 14 days after primary vaccination especially in infants under one year old and in adults. Similar encephalomyelitis may rarely follow **active immunization** with other organisms.

PPD. Purified protein derivative. *See* **tuberculin**.

Prausnitz-Küstner reaction. (*Historical*) Skin reaction for detection and measurement of human **reagin**[1] (**IgE**). Human serum containing reaginic antibody is inoculated intradermally into a volunteer. Reaginic antibody fixes to the skin cells whereas other immunoglobulins diffuse away. Antigen is injected into the site of attachment of reagin 48 hours later. A **weal and flare response** appears immediately and its intensity can be graded. Not used clinically because of danger of transferring **serum hepatitis**. A similar test, the **passive cutaneous anaphylaxis** test is used in laboratory animals.

pre-B lymphocyte. **Lymphocyte** committed to the **B lymphocyte** lineage which has not yet acquired the characteristics of a mature B lymphocyte.

pre-T lymphocyte. **Lymphocyte** committed to the **T lymphocyte** lineage which has not been processed by the **thymus** and which does not have the characteristics of a mature T lymphocyte.

precipitating antibody. *See* **precipitin**.

precipitation. In immunology, the formation of a visible complex on the addition of soluble antibody to **soluble antigen**. Such complexes are detected in the test tube as a sediment and in agar gels (*see* **gel diffusion**) as a white line appearing where the antigen and antibody interact. Precipitation does not take place with all **immunoglobulin classes**, nor in all proportions of antibody-antigen mixtures even though combination *has* taken place. Also, special conditions may be necessary to effect precipitation with immunoglobulins of the various classes of vertebrates, e.g. a high salt concentration is required for avian sera. *See* **antigen excess, antibody excess, optimal proportions**.

precipitin. Antibody which reacts with antigen to form a precipitate. *See* **precipitation**.

precipitin test. A test in which the reaction of antibody with a **soluble antigen** is detected by the formation of a visible precipitate. *See* **quantitative precipitation test, gel diffusion, precipitation**.

pre-emptive immunity. Insusceptibility of a cell to superinfection with a second virus following infection with a first virus. *See also* **interferon**.

pregnancy tests. Immunological tests used for the diagnosis of pregnancy are **inhibition tests** [2] that detect the presence of chorionic gonadotrophin in the urine of pregnant women (or in the serum of pregnant mares). Tanned erythrocytes (*see* **tanned red cell test**) or latex particles (*see* **latex agglutination test**) coated with chorionic gonadotrophin and already agglutinated with a specific antiserum are used as the reagent. The addition of any urine (or serum) containing chorionic gonadotrophin reverses this **agglutination** due to a redistribution of the antibody molecules between antigen on the particles and that in the supernate (as in **antigen excess**). Non-agglutination therefore indicates pregnancy.

premunition. *Syn*. premunity or non-sterile immunity. A state of **protective immunity** maintained by the persistence of small numbers of the pathogenic organism within the body. Loss of these organisms, e.g. due to drug treatment, may result in a return to susceptibility and acute re-infection. Recrudescence of the premunizing infection in virulent form may also follow debility or splenectomy. Premunity is especially seen in diseases caused by blood-borne protozoa, e.g. babesiosis of cattle and dogs, but may also be the basis of the **tuberculin test** response in man.

primary allergen. In cases of **cross sensitivity** q.v., describes the substance which **primed** the patient.

primary follicle. A tightly packed group of **lymphocytes** in the cortex of a **lymph node,** in the white pulp of the **spleen** or in other **lymphoid tissues,** within which a **germinal centre** develops following antigenic stimulation. *See* illustration on p.141.

primary granule. *See* **azurophil granule.**

primary immune response. The response of the animal body to an antigen on the first occasion that it encounters it. Characteristically, low levels of **antibody** are produced slowly but the **lymphoid tissues** have been **primed** so that a secondary response can be evoked on subsequent challenge. Responses of **cell-mediated immunity** follow a similar pattern. *See* **first set rejection.** Cf. **secondary response.**

primary interaction. A term used to describe the actual binding of an antibody to an antigen whether or not this gives rise to a secondary effect such as **precipitation** or **complement fixation.** Tests that measure primary antigen-antibody interactions are the **Farr test, equilibrium dialysis**, fluorescence **quenching**, fluorescence polarization and tests employing other techniques such as differential centrifugation or electrophoresis to separate bound from unbound antibody molecules. Qualitative demonstrations of primary interactions are given by **radioimmunoelectrophoresis** and the **single layer immunofluorescence technique.**

primary lysosome. A **lysosome** prior to fusion with a **phagosome.**

primary nodule. *See* **primary follicle.**

primed. (a) Of a whole animal: exposed to antigen in such a way that the antigen makes contact with the **lymphoid tissue,** so that the appropriate responsive cells are activated. Further contact of a primed host with antigen usually results in a vigorous, rapid **secondary immune response** q.v. *See* **primary immune response.** (b) Of cells: A primed cell is one that has been specifically activated in respect of a given antigen and can either produce more cells that have been so activated, or synthesize **immunoglobulin,** or mediate the reactions of **cell-mediated immunity**.

primed lymphocyte. Lymphocyte **primed** specifically to an antigen.

priming dose. The first dose of any antigen given to an animal in order to stimulate an **immune response.**

PRIST (paper **radioimmunosorbent test**). Method for measuring **IgE** levels in serum. Similar in principle to the **radioimmunosorbent test**, q.v. except that the anti-human IgE is coated onto filter paper discs instead of Sephadex® beads.

private specificity. Specificity defined by an **antigenic determinant** which is believed to be found only on the product of a single allele, and hence defines that allele. A term commonly applied to **alloantigens** of the **major histocompatibility complex,** though may be used to describe other alloantigenic systems. The term is essentially an operational one. As more antibodies are found (especially **monoclonal antibodies**) against more determinants, alloantigens sharing the same private specificity can sometimes be found to be heterogeneous for other determinants. If this occurs the new antibodies will define new private specificities. *See also* **public specificity**.

privileged sites. Sites in the body lacking normal lymphatic drainage and into which antigens, or tissue grafts, can be placed without stimulating an **immune response**, e.g. the central nervous system, the anterior chamber of the eye, and the cheek-pouch of the hamster.

pro-complementary factors. Substances present in some animal sera (especially pig) that mimic the action of **complement** and complicate the interpretation of **complement fixation tests**. Such substances may activate the **alternative pathway** q.v.

properdin. *See* **factor P**.

prophylactic immunization. The use of **immunization**[2] to prevent disease. Usually, but not always, **active immunization** which has a longer lasting effect than **passive immunization**.

prostaglandins. Biologically active lipids generated by the action of cycloxygenases on arachidonic acid (cf. **leukotrienes**, which are generated by lipoxygenase action). There is a large number of prostaglandins, which have a variety of activities as inflammatory mediators. The actions of different prostaglandins may be mutually antagonistic. **Mast cells** release PGI_2 (prostacyclin), a potent inhibitor of platelet aggregation, a vasodilator, and inhibitor of release of **SRS-A**. They also release PGD_2, a smooth muscle constrictor. Other cyclooxygenase products released during anaphylactic reactions (*see* anaphylaxis) include thromboxane A_2, which causes platelet aggregation, PGF_2 a smooth muscle constrictor, and PGE_2, a smooth muscle relaxant and vasodilator.

protective antigens. Those **antigens**[1] of a pathogenic microorganism that, if given alone, will stimulate an **immune response** capable of providing protection against infection by that organism.

protective immunity. **Non-specific immunity** and/or **specific immunity** that is protective, e.g. against a pathogenic microorganism, in contrast to **immunity**[2] stimulated by an experimental antigen such as ovalbumin, or by an internal antigen of the pathogen. *See* **protective antigen**.

protein A (staphylococcal protein A). Protein found in the cell wall or extracts of *Staphylococcus aureus*. It binds to the **Fc fragment** of **IgG** from a variety of species including human IgG1, 2 and 4, guinea pig IgG1 and 2, mouse IgG2a and 2b and rabbit IgG. Binding may result in **complement fixation**. Has an anti-phagocytic (*see* **phagocytosis**) effect, possibly resulting from its ability to bind to the Fc fragment of opsonizing (*see* **opsonin**[1]) antibody. The ability of protein A to bind IgG makes it a valuable reagent for removing IgG during protein purification and for the detection of IgG antibody-antigen complexes in a variety of techniques, e.g. **reverse plaque assay, radioimmunoassay, western blotting**.

provocation poliomyelitis (provocation paralysis). Rare complication of **immunization**[2]. Poliomyelitis has been observed to be more severe and more often paralytic shortly after vaccination especially with **vaccines** containing alum or *Bordetella pertussis*. The paralysis is especially liable to involve the muscles of the injected limb.

prozone. In **agglutination** and precipitation tests, agglutination/ precipitation may not occur in the tubes containing the highest concentration of antibody but becomes obvious when the antibody is diluted. This absence or weakness of agglutination/precipitation in the presence of the high levels of antibody is known as a prozone. It may be due (a) to **blocking antibody**[1] (**incomplete antibody**[1]) q.v.; (b) to binding of antibody only to single cells or molecules, e.g. an **antibody excess** situation; or (c) to non-specific inhibition by other serum proteins or lipids. In precipitating systems, soluble **immune complexes** formed in antibody excess are present in the prozone, ie. (b).

pseudoallergic reaction. Clinical state that mimics the symptoms and signs of **immediate hypersensitivity** but without evidence for an immunological mechanism.

pseudoglobulin. **Globulin** fraction of serum, more soluble in salts such as ammonium or sodium sulphate than **euglobulin** but less so than albumin. In Howe sodium sulphate precipitation method (*see* **salt precipitation**) refers to protein precipitated between 14.2 per cent and 17.7 per cent sodium sulphate. Term now largely obsolete.

PTAP. Purified diphtheria toxoid adsorbed (*see* **adsorption**) onto hydrated aluminium phosphate. Used prophylactically to produce **active immunity** against diphtheria.

public specificity. Specificity defined by an **antigenic determinant** which is found on the products of more than one allele of an alloantigenic system (*see* **alloantigens**). A term commonly applied to alleles of the **major histocompatibility system** (MHC). In the MHC, public specificities may be found on the antigenic products of several alleles at the same locus; public specificities may also be found on alleles at distinct but related loci (e.g. HLA-A and HLA-B ; H-2K & H-2D).

purified protein derivative (PPD). *See* **tuberculin**.

pyroninophilic blast cells. *See* **large pyroninophilic blast cells**.

pyroninophilic cells. Cells showing red cytoplasm when stained with **methyl green pyronin stain** (Unna–Pappenheim). The reaction indicates the presence of large amounts of cytoplasmic RNA and therefore of very active protein synthesis. It is characteristic of protein-secreting cells such as **plasma cells**.

Qa antigens. Class I murine **histocompatibility antigens,** coded for by genes distal to *H-2 D/L,* and closely linked to *Tla* (see **H-2.**). Identified using alloantisera and monoclonal antibodies, this region has at least 5 loci (Qa1–5) each of which appears to have two alleles, one a null allele.

quantitative corneal test. *See* **corneal response**.

quantitative gel diffusion tests. **Gel diffusion** techniques that enable an estimate of the quantity of an antibody, or more usually, an antigen to be made. *See* **single radial diffusion test, Sewell immunodiffusion technique, Laurell rocket test**.

quantitative precipitation test. **Precipitin test** in which a row of tubes is set up so that the ratio of antibody to antigen is varied (sequentially) from tube to tube. Antigen and antibody are present at **optimal proportions** in that tube in which **flocculation** occurs

Quellung phenomenon

most rapidly and in which the precipitate is most abundant. As all of the antibody capable of forming a precipitate is precipitated in that tube, quantitative estimations of antibody in terms of protein or protein nitrogen can be achieved by Kjeldahl estimations, spectrophotometric measurement, etc. *See also* **Ramon titration, Dean and Webb titration.**

Quellung phenomenon. *See* **pneumococcus capsule swelling reaction.**

quenching. (1) In **immunofluorescence,** reduction of emission of fluorescent radiation from **fluorochromes** or fluorochrome-conjugated protein or from sections labelled with them, as a result of exposure to various agents. May follow from exposure to ultraviolet light under the microscope when the same field of a section is studied for any length of time. May be done deliberately so that a field or cell can be restained with a different fluorochrome-labelled agent, or repeatedly with the same agent in order to measure **primary interaction** of antigen and antibody. (2) Reduction in efficiency of measuring radioactivity in a scintillation counter by a variety of substances, e.g. H_2O_2, ethanol, coloured (especially yellow) substances.

rabbit type antibody. Precipitating antibody, obtained from any species, which resembles that produced by the rabbit. In **precipitin tests** carried out with this type of antibody, precipitation extends well into the zone of **antibody excess** thus giving a broader curve than that seen when **horse type antibody** is used. Rabbit type antibodies do not, therefore, give such clear lines in **gel diffusion tests** as do sera containing the horse type of antibody.

rabies vaccination encephalomyelitis. *See* **post rabies vaccination encephalomyelitis.**

rabies vaccines. (a) A tissue culture vaccine prepared from virus grown in diploid human embryo lung cells (WI38) is now used routinely in man. Produces a high level of neutralizing antibody. (b)*Vet.* Chick embryo adapted vaccine. Used for pre-exposure prophylaxis in animals. Low egg passage material (LEP) was used in the dog but clinical rabies occasionally developed. High egg passage material (HEP) is safe and used for cattle. (c) *Hist.* Pasteur's vaccine was prepared from the spinal cords of rabbits to which the virus had been adapted. Brain-and spinal-cord-derived vaccines were used for many years, but are no longer used because of the danger of **post rabies vaccination encephalomyelitis.**

radial immunodiffusion test. *See* **single radial immunodiffusion test**.

radiation chimera. *See* **irradiation chimera**.

radioallergosorbent test (RAST). Method for measuring extremely small amounts of **IgE** antibody specific for various **allergens**. In clinical work, serum IgE antibody is usually measured. The **serum** is reacted with allergen-coated dextran particles (Sepharose®) and then washed to remove non-reacting proteins. Radiolabelled anti-human IgE **antiserum** is then added and this binds to the IgE antibody, bound to the particle via the allergen. Provided that the amount of allergen supplied and the amount of anti-IgE are in excess, the radioactivity of the Sepharose pellet after **washing** is proportional to the amount of allergen-specific antibody in the serum sample. Cf. **radioimmunosorbent test** which is used to measure total IgE in the serum.

radioimmunoassay. Method of measuring antibody or antigen concentration by employing radioactively labelled reactants. *See* **hormone radioimmunoassay, Farr test, radioimmunoelectrophoresis, radioallergosorbent test.**

radioimmunoelectrophoresis. Refinement of **immunoelectrophoresis** in which any given precipitin arc (*see* **precipitation**) can be identified by addition of the appropriate radioactively labelled antibody or antigen followed by **autoradiography** of the arcs.

radioimmunosorbent test (RIST). Method for measuring **IgE immunoglobulin** in samples of serum. In clinical work the serum is mixed with a standard amount of purified radiolabelled IgE, and the mixture is then exposed to **Sephadex®** particles coated with anti-human IgE (specific for **heavy chain**). After appropriate incubation and washing, the amount of radioactivity bound to the Sephadex is determined. Since IgE in the serum will *compete* with the radiolabelled IgE for the anti-IgE the quantity of the former can be calculated by establishing the reduction of binding of radioactivity in comparison to that of a control (i.e. non-competed) sample which binds 100 per cent of the standard amount of radiolabelled IgE. Cf. **radioallergosorbent test** which is used to measure IgE *specific* to an **allergen.**

Raji cell assay. *In vitro* assay to identify **immune complexes** using the Raji lymphoblastoid B lymphocyte tumour line. These cells have receptors for C3 and for the Fc portion of IgG but no surface immunoglobulins. Complexes bound to their surfaces can therefore be detected using labelled anti-globulin reagents, if the Fc receptors are blocked off.

Ramon titration

Ramon titration. A **quantitative precipitation test** in which the dilution of antibody is varied and the dilution of antigen kept constant (cf. **Dean and Webb titration**), the **end point** being taken as the first tube in which **precipitation** is seen.

RAST. *See* **radioallergosorbent test.**

RB200. *See* **lissamine rhodamine.**

reaction of identity. Reaction on **gel diffusion test** plate (especially **Ouchterlony test**) which demonstrates the antigenic identity of two test solutions. The two solutions of antigen are placed in separate wells and allowed to diffuse towards antibody in a third well. If the resultant line of **precipitation** is continuous, this is known as a reaction of identity.

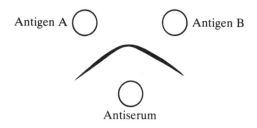

reaction of non-identity. Reaction on **gel diffusion test** plate (especially **Ouchterlony test**) which demonstrates the antigenic non-identity of two test materials. Solutions of these are each placed in a well and allowed to diffuse towards antibody in a third well. If two lines of **precipitation** are seen, each corresponding to one of the antigen solutions, and these lines cross, this is a reaction of non-identity.

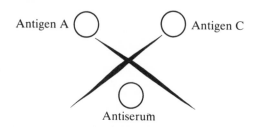

reaction of partial identity. Reaction on **gel diffusion test** plate (especially **Ouchterlony test**) which demonstrates that a given test substance shares **antigenic determinants** with a second substance but has other determinants which are not shared. The antigens are each placed in wells and allowed to diffuse towards antibody in a third well. The resultant line of **precipitation** is continuous, because of the shared determinant, but has a **spur** formed by the unshared determinant.

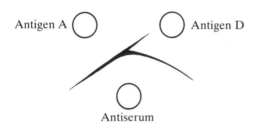

Antigen A   Antigen D

Antiserum

reactive haemolysis. Lysis of unsensitized (*see* **sensitization**[2]) erythrocytes initiated by a stable complex of the activated **C5** and **C6** components (i.e. C$\overline{5}$ and C$\overline{6}$) of **complement.** Phenomenon shown especially by **acute phase sera**.

reagin (reaginic antibody). (1) Antibody which fixes to tissue cells of the same species so that, on reaction with antigen, **histamine** and other vasoactive agents are released. Of specialized **immunoglobulin** type (especially **IgE**). *Syn.* **homocytotropic antibody**. (2) Obsolete term for complement fixing antibody reacting in **Wassermann reaction** with **cardiolipin**.

Rebuck skin window. *See* **skin window**.

receptor. Chemical grouping on a macromolecule or cell which is capable of selectively combining, with a varying degree of **specificity,** with complementary molecules or cells, e.g. enzyme receptors for substrate, cell surface receptors for hormone. In immunology, frequently refers to cell surface sites, e.g. membrane-bound **immunoglobulin** receptors for antigen on **B lymphocytes**. In reference to cell membranes, the term 'receptor' is perhaps best reserved for specific binding sites at which binding is followed by transduction of a signal across the membrane and a response on the part of the cell.

recirculating pool. All the **T** and **B lymphocytes** that continuously recirculate between blood and **lymph**.

recognition. Term used for the interactions by which cells (or molecules such as antibody) discriminate between materials in their environment. Recognition may be a property of specific **receptors** by which molecules are selectively bound (e.g. antigen by antibody), or may be relatively non-specific. Recognition at cell surface receptors is usually followed by activation of cellular function, for example the activation of antibody synthesis in **B lymphocytes** following cell surface binding of antigens.

recombinant inbred strains (RI strains). **Inbred strains** of animals (e.g. mice) which have been made by crossing two different inbred parental strains to yield an F_1 and thence an F_2 generation. Pairs of F_2 mice are then crossed and their progeny inbred until homozygosity is reached at most loci. RI strains are inbred so that all members of the RI strain tend to complete genetic identity and homozygosity. RI strains are recombinant because the combinations of genes in the parental strains are re-assorted (i.e. recombined) in the RI strains. RI strains provide large numbers of virtually genetically uniform and homozygous mice in which the effects of reassorting various parental genes (e.g. **heavy chain** genes) can be studied.

red cell adhesion test (*obs.*) An **immune adherence test** formerly employed to detect antibody in experimental trypanosomiasis. *See* **Rieckenberg reaction**.

red cell-linked antigen antiglobulin test. A **passive agglutination test** used to detect and measure agglutinating antibodies and especially non-agglutinating, **incomplete antibodies**[1]. Antigen-coated erythrocytes are incubated with the test serum, washed and the anti-Ig is added. This results in agglutination of erythrocytes that have bound antibody. *See also* **antiglobulin test**.

red pulp of spleen. *See* **spleen**.

Reiter complement fixation test. *Hist.* Diagnostic **complement fixation test** for syphilis employing as antigen a protein extract of the Reiter strain of *Treponema pallidum*. Detects antibodies to group antigens of *Treponema* species rather than the antibody detected by the **Wassermann reaction** which may be an **autoantibody**.

rejection. *See* **immunological rejection**.

released antigen. An antigen found in **serum** obtained from animals infected with trypanosomes. It is specific to the antigenic type of the organism infecting the host at that time (*see* **antigenic variation**[a]), is identical to antigen forming a coat on the cell surface, and can be used for **immunization** [2] against that antigenic type.

repeating units. Term used of macromolecular structures, especially **antigens**[1], in which an identical configuration occurs repeatedly, e.g. the polysaccharide cell wall antigens of Gram negative bacteria are repeated along the length of the organism. **Pneumococcus polysaccharide** type III consists of a repeating structure of -β-1,4-glucose-β-1,3-glucuronic acid. Antigens with a repeating unit structure are frequently **thymus-independent antigens**.

resident macrophage. **Macrophage** present at a site in the absence of a known eliciting stimulus.

reticular cells. Cells that, together with reticular fibres, make up the framework or stroma of **lymphoid tissues** such as the **spleen** and **lymph nodes** and of the **bone marrow**.

reticular dysgenesis The most complete form of **severe combined immunodeficiency syndrome** in which there is a defect of maturation of all leucocytes, i.e. **lymphocytes, granulocytes** and **monocytes**.

reticuloendothelial blockade. Administration of large quantities of inert particles, e.g. colloidal carbon or iron, by the intravenous or peritoneal routes with the aim of saturating most of the actively phagocytosing cells of the **mononuclear phagocyte system** so that they are temporarily incapable of further **phagocytosis**.

reticuloendothelial system. A term, coined by Aschoff (1913) to describe a system of cells that had the ability to take up and retain certain dyes and particles when these were injected into the living animal. It has been replaced by the term **mononuclear phagocyte system** q.v.

reticulosis. *See* **lymphoma**

reticulum cell. *See* **reticular cells**.

reverse Mancini technique. *See* **reverse radial immunodiffusion**.

reverse passive Arthus reaction. Reaction produced by injecting precipitating (*see* **precipitation**) **antibody** into the skin of an animal followed by intravenous injection of **antigen** after a delay (usually of 30 minutes–2 hours). Thus the normal situation of antibody diffusing from the blood to the tissues and antigen from the tissues to the blood has been *reversed*. Often used in the study of the effect of **Arthus reactions** on joints (i.e. antibody injected into the joints). *See also* **passive Arthus reaction**.

reverse plaque assay. A **haemolytic plaque assay** (q.v.) which detects Ig-secreting cells irrespective of their **antibody specificity.** A suspension of cells in agarose is incubated in a Petri dish at 37°C with **protein-A** coated sheep erythrocytes and anti-Ig plus **complement.** Ig-anti-Ig complexes form around any cell that is secreting immunoglobulin and the complexes bind to the protein A on the sheep erythrocytes resulting in a zone of lysis (plaque). The technique can be made specific for any Ig class by using the appropriate antiserum.

reverse radial immunodiffusion (RRID). A quantitative technique for the estimation of antibody levels. Similar to **single radial diffusion test** except that samples of **antibody** solutions are allowed to diffuse into an antigen-containing gel. The area of the rings of **precipitation** obtained is directly proportional to the concentration of the antibody present in the solution. Sometimes called the reverse Mancini technique.

reversed anaphylaxis. **Passive transfer** of **anaphylaxis** from **primed** to normal animal by giving antigen first, followed by antibody. *See* **reversed passive cutaneous anaphylaxis.**

reversed passive cutaneous anaphylaxis. **Passive cutaneous anaphylaxis** test in which the antigen is injected first and the antibody afterwards. To be effective, the antigen must itself be an **immunoglobulin** capable of fixation to cells (*see* **cytophilic antibody**).

RFc α, ϵ, γ, μ. Nomenclature for the **Fc receptors** for **IgA, IgE, IgG** and **IgM** respectively.

Rhesus antibody. Antibody against **Rhesus antigen** q.v. Most commonly **anti-D.**

Rhesus antigen. Red cell antigen of **Rhesus blood group system.** A number of allelic genes govern the appearance of the Rhesus antigens. Clinically the most important is the D-antigen as antibody against this one occurs most frequently. *See* **Rhesus incompatiblity.**

Rhesus blood group system. Human **blood group** system so named because **antibody** produced in rabbits injected with Rhesus monkey erythrocytes reacted with human Rhesus group **antigens.** The Rhesus blood group system is genetically complex. The most important erythrocyte antigen is that known as the D-antigen. Antibodies against Rhesus antigens do not occur naturally in serum, but **anti-D** antibodies may be produced after transfusion of a Rhesus (D)-negative person with Rhesus (D)-positive blood, and in a Rhesus (D)-negative mother who bears a Rhesus (D)-positive child. This may give rise to **transfusion reactions** in the former, or to **erythroblastosis fetalis** in the mother.

Rhesus incompatibility. Incompatibility of **Rhesus (blood group) antigens** between a mother and her baby or between donor and recipient in blood transfusion. In the former case, the mother forms **antibodies** against the baby's erythrocytes and, in the latter case, the recipient forms antibodies against the donor erythrocytes. Most commonly due to an **immune response** against the D-antigen of erythrocytes. *See* **erythroblastosis fetalis**.

rheumatic fever. Inflammatory disease of fibrous tissue involving chiefly the heart (pancarditis which may lead to scarring of valves) and the joints. Often follows a few weeks after infection with *Streptococcus pyogenes* of Lancefield Group A (*see* **Lancefield precipitation test**). May be recurrent. Characteristic lesions are fibrinoid degeneration and necrosis of fibrous tissue and formation of Aschoff bodies, nodules made up of necrotic fibrous tissue surrounded by **macrophages** (including large multinucleate Aschoff cells), **lymphocytes** and **plasma cells.** Probably a **hypersensitivity** reaction to Group A streptococci, either directly due to presence of antigens derived from streptococci or due to sharing of **cross reacting antigens** between streptococci and the heart muscle. Serum levels of anti-streptolysin O (*see* **anti-streptolysin O test**) and **C reactive protein** are high.

rheumatoid arthritis. Chronic inflammatory polyarthritis with systemic disturbances; toxic febrile illness, anaemia, enlargement of lymph nodes. More common in women. Synovia of joints are swollen and infiltrated with **granulomata** containing **plasma cells, lymphocytes, macrophages** and **germinal centres.** Lesions in other connective tissues throughout the body are also seen. A putative **autoimmune disease** although evidence for autoimmune pathogenesis is not good. Serum contains **rheumatoid factor** q.v. and, in a minority of cases, **anti-nuclear factor** q.v.

rheumatoid factor. Antibody against slightly denatured (*see* **denaturation**) IgG. Present frequently in serum of patients with **rheumatoid arthritis** in whom it can sometimes be shown to be an **autoantibody.** Reacts with human or animal IgG that has been heat aggregated (*see* **heat aggregated protein antigen**) or combined

Rh group

with antigen, but not with normal IgG. Detected by **Rose–Waaler test** or **latex agglutination test**. The factor is thus diagnostically useful, but of doubtful aetiological importance.

Rh group. Rhesus group. *See* **Rhesus blood group system**.

rhodamines. A group of red fluorescent dyes, some of which are used for labelling proteins for use in **immunofluorescence** techniques, e.g. **lissamine rhodamine, tetramethyl rhodamine isothiocyanate**, rhodamine B isothiocyanate.

Rieckenberg reaction. An **immune adherence** test for trypanosomiasis. Citrated blood from animals cured of an infection is mixed with a suspension of live trypanosomes. If these are of the same variable antigen type (*see* **antigenic variation**[a]) as those that caused the infection, they become coated with blood **platelets**. *See also* **trypanosome adhesion test**.

rinderpest vaccines. (a) *Hist.* Hyperimmune serum and virulent virus. (b) Living virus attenuated (*see* **attenuated vaccine**) by passage in goats. This gives good life-long immunity but produces a febrile response and slight mortality. The virus can be attenuated further by passage in rabbits or eggs. (c) Virus adapted to tissue culture (best modern vaccine). (d) Killed virus with an **adjuvant**. This gives relatively poor, short-lived protection.

ring test. **Precipitin test** in which a solution of antigen is carefully layered on to a solution of antibody in a test tube so that an antigen-antibody precipitate is formed at the interface. Used in **Lancefield precipitation test** and **Ascoli's test** and in the identification of blood meals from haematophagous insects.

RIST. *See* **radioimmunosorbent test**.

Rivanol®. 2-Ethoxy-6,9-diaminoacridine lactate; employed to separate **IgG** from serum. Forms insoluble cation complexes with most serum proteins except IgG. IgG, having a high **isoelectric point** does not form a precipitate with Rivanol® at neutral pH. The IgG obtained by this method is not so pure as that obtained by DEAE-cellulose chromatography.

rocket immunoelectrophoresis. *See* **Laurell rocket test**.

Rose–Waaler test. **Passive agglutination test** in which sera are titrated against sheep erythrocytes coated with **gamma globulin**. The sera of a high proportion of cases of **rheumatoid arthritis**

192

contain antibodies against **IgG** whose conformation has been altered, e.g. by heating or by combination with antigen, so that **hidden determinants** are exposed. This antibody, known as **rheumatoid factor**, agglutinates the gamma globulin-coated sheep erythrocytes.

rosette.   Cluster of erythrocytes round a leucocyte or other cell. Rosette assays are often used to classify leucocytes. *See* **EAC rosette forming cell, E-rosette forming cell**.

rubella vaccine.   An **attenuated vaccine** containing virus grown in human embryo or rabbit kidney cells. Used especially for immunization of girls aged 10–13 years; *contraindicated in pregnancy*.

runt disease.   Disease which develops after injection of **allogeneic lymphocytes** into immunologically immature experimental animals. Characterized by loss of weight, failure to thrive, diarrhoea, splenomegaly and often death. An example of a **graft-versus-host reaction**.

Russell body.   An eosinophilic, brightly refractile sphere (**PAS** positive) which develops within the **endoplasmic reticulum** of some (possibly aged) **plasma cells.** They have been demonstrated to consist of **immunoglobulin** of defined specificity.

S.   Abbreviation for **sedimentation coefficient**.

S.   (1) Abbreviation for **Svedberg unit,** e.g. 7S antibody.
(2) Symbol for the site of **complement** activation (usually on a cell surface).

S*.   Symbol for the target site on the surface of a cell for **complement**-induced   **immune cytolysis**. *See also* **E***.

$s_{20,w}$.   Standard sedimentation coefficient. The **sedimentation coefficient** of a particle or molecule at infinite dilution in water at 20°C.

S19 vaccine.   *Vet. See* **brucella vaccines**.

7S antibody.   Immunoglobulin molecules with a **sedimentation coefficient** of about 7S. Term often used as a synonym for **IgG** (*preferred term*).

19S antibody.   Immunoglobulin molecules with a **sedimentation coefficient** of about 19S. Often used as a synonym for **IgM** (*preferred term*).

Sabin vaccine.   *See* **poliomyelitis vaccines**.

SAC 1-*n*. Symbols for action of **complement.** S=antigenic site of complement activation, A=antibody, C=complement, 1–*n* = the first *n* complement components.

saccharated iron oxide. Colloidal preparation of iron oxide used for studying **phagocytosis** of particles by **macrophages** and other cells of the **mononuclear phagocyte system.**

sacculus rotundus. The expanded, thick-walled, terminal portion of the ileum of the rabbit, from which springs the caecum and colon. It is rich in **lymphoid tissue.**

saline agglutinin. Antibody which produces **agglutination** of cells in physiological salt solutions without addition of proteins, enzymes or other substances. Cf. **albumin agglutinating antibody.**

Salk vaccine. *See* **poliomyelitis vaccines.**

salt precipitation. Precipitation of serum proteins in solutions of salts such as sodium sulphate or ammonium sulphate. **Globulins** are precipitated at lower concentrations of such salts than is albumin. **Euglobulins** are precipitated at lower concentrations than **pseudo-globulins**. Used as a crude method for separation of serum proteins.

salting out. *See* **salt precipitation.**

Sanarelli-Shwartzman reaction. *See* **Shwartzman reaction.**

sandwich technique. A **fluorescent antibody technique** for the detection of antibody or antibody-producing cells in tissue sections or smears. A first layer of **antigen** is applied and allowed to react with the antibody in the section. This is followed by a second layer of **fluorochrome**-labelled antibody specific for the antigen. Thus the antigen is 'sandwiched' between two layers of antibody. *See* illustration on p.122.

s antigens. 'Soluble' antigens; an incomplete non-infectious internal component of virus appearing early in a virus infection.

saponin. A surface- and membrane-active glucoside that has **adjuvant** properties. It is often added to **anthrax vaccines** for veterinary use. Saponin is believed to act by causing a local reaction that retards loss of antigen from the inoculation site and attracts antibody-forming cells.

sarcoidosis. Human disease of unknown aetiology characterized by presence of scattered, small **epithelioid cell** granulomata similar to those seen in tuberculosis but with little or no necrosis. Commonest type involves pulmonary hilar lymph nodes; more severe cases are seen with lesions in lungs, liver, skin, eye or other tissues. The lesions may resolve or progress to fibrosis. Patients frequently fail to show **delayed hypersensitivity** as evidenced by positive **tuberculin tests** or **chlorodinitrobenzene** sensitivity tests. The **Kveim test** q.v. is used in diagnosis of sarcoidosis.

Schick test. A test used to gauge the degree of susceptibility or **immunity**[1] of man to diphtheria. A standard quantity of **diphtheria toxin** is injected intradermally into one forearm. In **non immune** persons an area of redness and swelling appears in 1-2 days with a maximum reaction at 4-7 days and subsequent pigmentation and scaling. This is a positive Schick reaction and indicates that **diphtheria immunization** is required. As a control for the test a similar quantity of purified toxoid or of toxin that has been heated to destroy its toxicity is inoculated into the other forearm. A reaction at *both* sites may result from either a pseudo reaction or a combined reaction. *See also* **Moloney test**.

Schultz-Dale test. Biological test for **immediate hypersensitivity**. On addition of antigen to a bath containing uterus or ileum from a guinea pig previously **primed** with that antigen, contraction of the organ is observed. This is due to the action of **histamine** and similar substances which are released when antigen combines with antibody (*see* **homocytotropic antibody**) that is fixed to the tissue cells. The test can also be carried out using ileum, from an **unprimed** guinea pig, that is **passively sensitized** by the *in vitro* application of the appropriate **antiserum**.

Schweiger-Seidel sheath. *See* **ellipsoid**. The ellipsoid structures in the spleen were first described by Schweiger-Seidel.

SCID. *See* **severe combined immunodeficiency syndrome**.

second set rejection. The **immunological rejection** of a graft by a host that has already rejected (*see* **first set rejection**), either tissue from the same donor, or tissue carrying similar **histocompatibility antigens**. Second set rejection is much more rapid than is first set rejection and in this resembles a **secondary immune response**. *See also* **white graft reaction**.

secondary allergen. The substance that produces the symptoms in cases of **cross sensitivity** and which may, superficially, appear to be unrelated to the **primary allergen** q.v.

secondary disease. This term is usually applied to **allogeneic disease** as it occurs in **irradiation chimeras**.

secondary follicle. Follicle in a **peripheral lymphoid organ,** that contains a **germinal centre**. More frequently observed in **secondary immune response,** than in **primary immune response,** hence name.

secondary granule. *See* **specific granule**.

secondary immune response. Secondary response of the body to an antigen with which it has already been **primed** (*see* **primary immune response**). There is very rapid production of large amounts of antibody over a few days followed by a slow exponential fall. The response of **cell-mediated immunity** follows a similar pattern. *See also* **second set rejection** and **negative phase**.

secondary lysosome. A **lysosome** which has fused with a **phagosome.** Following digestion of the contents of the phagosome, secondary lysosomes may remain functional.

secondary nodule. *See* **secondary follicle**.

secretor. Person who secretes **ABO blood group substances** into mucous fluids such as gastric juice, saliva, ovarian cyst fluid. Over 80 per cent of humans are secretors, this status being genetically determined.

secretory IgA. IgA in secretions; mainly in the form of a dimer with **secretory piece** bound to it. Thus distinct from that found in the serum.

secretory piece. Polypeptide of mol. wt. 60 000 found attached to dimers of the secretory form of **IgA**. Structurally unrelated to **immunoglobulins** and synthesised by epithelial cells in the secretory gland, not the plasma cells that synthesise the immunoglobulin. Has strong affinity for mucus thus prolonging retention of IgA on mucous surfaces. May also inhibit the destruction of IgA by enzymes in the digestive tract. Facilitates transport of IgA across epithelium.

sedimentation coefficient (sedimentation constant) s. Defined by the equation

$$s = \frac{dx}{dt}/w^2 x \quad \text{where} \quad \frac{dx}{dt}$$

is the rate of sedimentation of a particle or molecule at distance x from the axis of a centrifuge rotor which has angular velocity w

radians per second. s depends mainly on the weight, size and shape of the particle, also on the temperature and concentration of the solutions, but not on the speed of the centrifuge. Measured in seconds or in **Svedberg units.** Related to the molecular weight (M) by

$$M = \frac{RTs}{D(1-Vp)}$$

where R is the gas constant (8.314JK^{-1}mol^{-1}); T the absolute temperature; D the **diffusion coefficient;** V the volume occupied by unit mass of the substance in solution and p is the density of the solution. *See also* $s_{20,w}$.

sedimentation pattern. Pattern formed by erythrocytes on the bottoms of test tubes, or wells in a plastic plate, after the cells in a **haemagglutination test**[1,2] have been allowed to sediment fully. Where **agglutination** has occurred the cells form an even carpet or mat; where there is no agglutination they slide down to form a round button.

Sedormid® purpura (*historical*). Thrombocytopenic purpura due to hypersensitivity to the drug Sedormid® (allyl-isopropyl-acetyl carbamide). Sedormid® acts as a **hapten** and combines with **platelets**. Antibody formed against the platelet-Sedormid complex causes platelet lysis in the presence of **complement**. This is therefore an example of a cytotoxic or **type II reaction**.

selective theories of antibody production. Theories which suggest that, before exposure to antigen, cells already carry the information necessary to react immunologically. Administration of antigen then stimulates the appropriate predetermined cells to divide and produce antibody or cell-mediated immunity. The best-known examples are **Ehrlich's side chain theory**, Jerne's theory and Burnet's **clonal selection theory**. Cf. **instructive theories of antibody production**.

self antigen. *See* **autoantigen**.

self-cure. In animals infested with intestinal nematodes the suddenly initiated, and thereafter exponential, expulsion from the intestine of the majority of the population of worms. It starts some 10 days after initial establishment of the infestation and is believed to result from an **immune response** by the host. This is probably of the **immediate hypersensitivity** type following release of vasoactive substances (*see* **vasoactive amines**) from **mast cells** in the gut wall. *See also* **globule leucocyte**.

self marker hypothesis. Hypothesis put forward in 1949 by Burnet and Fenner suggesting that the body's own cells carried a marker which allowed recognition of their self character by **immunologically competent cells** which were then inhibited from responding to them. *See also* **clonal selection theory**.

self recognition. Recognition of **autoantigens** by the **immunologically competent cells** such that, in fetal life, **immunological tolerance** of such antigens is developed (*see* **clonal selection theory**).

self tolerance. **Immunological tolerance** to **autoantigens**. Such tolerance to all self antigens, which are accessible to the lymphoid tissues, is thought to be acquired normally during fetal life.

sensitization. (1) Administration of antigen to provoke an immune response, so that, on later **challenge**[1], a more vigorous **secondary response** will ensue. Used especially in context of an initial dose of antigen given in order to provoke a **hypersensitivity** reaction on subsequent challenge. (2) Coating of cells with antibody, e.g. in **complement fixation tests**, and **Schultz-Dale tests** as a preliminary step in the elicitation of an **immunological reaction**[2].

sensitized cells. This term is used with two entirely distinct meanings (1) Any cells which have become immunologically activated (**primed**) by administration of antigen, e.g. **primed lymphocyte.** (2) Cells coated with antibody, e.g. sheep erythrocytes used in **complement fixation tests**.

sensitized lymphocyte. Lymphocyte **primed** specifically to an antigen. *Syn.* for **primed lymphocyte,** a term that seems preferable as less confusing.

sequestered antigen. Any **antigen**[1] or **antigenic determinant** which is hidden from contact with **immunologically competent cells** and thus cannot stimulate an **immune response.** May thus be intracellular antigens or **hidden determinants** on cell surfaces or on soluble molecules, or antigens in **privileged sites**.

serial dilutions. In serological quantification of antigen-antibody reactions, the progressive dilution of serum or antibody in a row of tubes so that the first tube contains the largest amount of antibody and the last tube the smallest. *See also* **doubling dilution**.

serological determinants. **Antigenic determinants** on cells that are accessible to antibodies able to cause destruction of those cells. A

primed animal may simultaneously produce **lymphocytes** capable of killing the same cells (*see* **killer cell**) but these lymphocytes may be directed against different antigenic determinants, i.e. **lymphocyte determinants,** on the cell surface, from those affected by the antibody. *See also* **MHC genes**.

serology. The study of antigen-antibody reactions *in vitro*.

serotherapy. Injection of **antisera** or antibodies (e.g. gamma globulin) derived from them to produce **passive immunity** for the prophylaxis or treatment of infectious diseases. *See* **passive immunization**.

serotonin. 5-hydroxytryptamine (5HT). Causes smooth muscle contraction, increased vascular permeability and vasoconstriction of larger vessels. Found in **platelets** and **mast cells**. Released in anaphylactic reactions in rabbit but there is no direct evidence that it has a role in human **anaphylaxis**.

serotype. Subtype within a bacterial species identified by serological methods, i.e. by detecting differences in the surface antigens of bacteria on addition of specific antibody. Used to classify *Salmonella, Shigella,* streptococci, *Leptospira,* etc.

serum. Fluid expressed from a blood clot as it contracts after coagulation of the blood. The essential difference between **plasma** and serum is that the latter does not contain fibrinogen. Serum is more commonly used than is plasma in immunological procedures because there is no danger of a clot forming when other materials are added to it.

serum albumin. The major protein component of serum in higher species. Soluble in distilled water and in salt solutions such as 50 per cent saturated ammonium sulphate (cf. **globulin**). Overall negative charge at neutral pH, therefore migrates rapidly to anode on electrophoresis relative to globulins. Serum concentration in man 3-5 g/100ml. Mol. wt. 66 000, $s_{20,w}$ =4.6S. Major role in maintaining osmotic balance. Binds anions strongly, especially hydrophobic anions such as fatty acids. Frequently used as experimental antigen.

serum hepatitis (hepatitis B). Serum hepatitis, which often has a long incubation period of 2-5 months, occasionally follows transfer of **serum** or other biological fluids from one human being to another. Hazard of blood transfusion and of **passive transfer** tests, e.g. **Prausnitz-Küstner reaction**.

serum sickness. A **hypersensitivity** reaction to the injection of foreign antigens in large quantity especially those contained in **antisera** used for **passive immunization.** Symptoms appear some days after a single dose of the antigen (cf.**anaphylactic shock**) and consist of local swelling at the injection site, enlarged lymph nodes, fever, urticaria, joint swellings and, more rarely, renal lesions. The symptoms are due to the localization in the tissues of soluble **immune complexes** (*see also* **soluble complex**) formed between antibody produced during the developing **immune response,** and the large quantities of antigen still present. They take the form, therefore, of a generalized **Arthus reaction (type III reaction).** *See also* **immune complex disease.**

serum thymic factor (FTS). A nonapeptide secreted by **thymus** epithelial cells and found in the peripheral circulation, that partially restores T lymphocyte function in thymectomized animals. Induces the differentiation and maturation of immature T lymphocytes. *See also* **thymin, thymosins** and **thymopoietin.**

serum virus vaccination. Obsolete technique for the production of **active immunity** by inoculating live virulent virus at the same time as an **antiserum** against the virus. In man, was recommended for the **vaccination** of **immunodeficient** subjects during a smallpox outbreak. Also, used to control reactions of normal persons to insufficiently attenuated virus vaccine, e.g. early **measles vaccines.** *Vet.* At one time used for the vaccination of dogs against distemper, however, dangerous as may cause spread of disease and no longer in use.

severe combined immunodeficiency syndrome (SCID). The most severe form of congenital **immunological deficiency state** in which thymic agenesis with **lymphocyte** depletion coexists with deficiency of **plasma cells** and **antibody deficiency syndrome**. Also known as Swiss-type hypogammaglobulinaemia. Such infants usually die from infection in early life, although prognosis may be improved by bone marrow transplantation.

Sewell immunodiffusion technique. A **quantitative gel diffusion test** in which the **optimum proportions** point of a set of **antigen-antibody** mixtures similar to those used in the **quantitative precipitation test** is determined.

Sezary syndrome. A disease syndrome characterized by total body erythroderma, thickening of facial skin resulting in a leonine facies, and dystrophic nail changes. Associated with these cutaneous changes is a very high proportion of abnormal lymphoid cells in the peripheral circulation. These are called Sezary cells and have been shown to be **T lymphocytes**. Similar cells are seen in the cutaneous infiltrate.

sheep cell agglutination test. (1) Any test in which sheep erythrocyes are agglutinated by antibody to them, e.g. **Paul-Bunnell test.** (2) In rheumatology, the term is often used as a synonym for the **Rose-Waaler test** q.v. which is a **passive agglutination test.**

short lived lymphocytes. **Lymphocytes** which appear to have a life of 4-5 days only. Their fate and function is unknown. Cf. **long lived lymphocyte.** N.B. The definition of lymphocytes according to their life-span is now little used.

Shwartzman reaction (Shwartzman-Sanarelli phenomenon). Local skin necrosis or generalized disease of kidneys, lungs, liver and heart following the second of two doses of **endotoxin.** Immunological basis is doubtful.

Sia test. (*Obs.*) A rapid, crude test for **macroglobulinaemia.** Based on the poor solubility of **IgM** in water. Serum is dropped into two tubes, one containing water, the other saline. The test is positive when a precipitate appears immediately in water but not in saline.

sIgA. *See* **secretory IgA.**

signal hypothesis. An hypothesis proposing that the **leader peptide** of nascent **heavy** and **light chains** is responsible for attachment of polyribosomes synthesizing these polypeptides to the **endoplasmic reticulum** Also for vectorial release of the chains through the membrane of the endoplasmic reticulum into the **cisternal space,** resulting in secretion of the **immunoglobulin** after assembly of the chains.

silica adjuvants. Crystalline silica (tridymite) and **bentonite** (hydrated aluminium silicate) have both been observed to have activity as **adjuvants.** These are **centrally acting adjuvants** although bentonite, by adsorbing protein antigens, also has a depot action in preventing the rapid diffusion of antigen away from the injection site.

silicosis. Chronic pulmonary disease, due to inhalation of silica dust. Characterized by nodular pulmonary macrophage **granulomata** progressing to fibrosis. It has been suggested that these might represent a **delayed hypersensitivity** reaction to proteins adsorbed onto silica particles. *See* **silica adjuvants.**

Simonsen phenomenon

Simonsen phenomenon. A **graft-versus-host** reaction. Simonsen in 1957 observed splenomegaly in embryo chicks injected with **immunologically competent cells** derived from adult chickens. The embryo **spleens** contained increased numbers of **lymphocytes** partly derived from the donor, partly from the host.

single diffusion test. Gel diffusion test of the **single radial diffusion test** or **Oudin test** type, where one of the reactants is allowed to diffuse into the other. Cf. **double diffusion test**.

single hit theory. Theory that **immune haemolysis** results from a single **complement**-induced lesion of the erythrocyte surface, rather than that lesions at many sites are necessary. Supported by electron microscope studies of lesions induced by **IgM** complement-fixing antibody.

single intradermal tuberculin test. *Vet.* A **tuberculin test** of the **Mantoux test** type used in cattle and other animals. A positive reaction is diagnosed by the degree of increase in skinfold thickness as measured 48 hours after the intradermal inoculation of **tuberculin**. *See also* **comparative single intradermal tuberculin test**.

single layer immunofluorescence technique. *Syn.* direct immunofluorescence. **Immunofluorescence** technique in which antigen in tissue sections is located with a single layer of **fluorochrome**-conjugated antibody or, less commonly, where antibody is located with a single layer of fluorochrome-conjugated antigen.

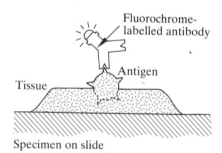

single radial diffusion test. A **quantitative gel diffusion test** in which one of the reactants (usually antibody) is incorporated into a layer of agar into which a well is then cut. The other reactant (usually antigen) is placed in the well and allowed to diffuse into the agar. A ring of precipitate is formed, the area of which is proportional to the concentration of the material in the well. Usually used in the quantitative assay of antigens, especially **immunoglobulins**, incorporating a monospecific anti-immunoglobulin serum in the agar. Frequently referred to as a Mancini test.

Sjögren's disease. Chronic inflammatory disease of salivary and lacrimal glands in man often accompanied by secondary inflammation of the conjunctiva. In many cases, associated with **rheumatoid arthritis**. Sera of patients often contain **anti-nuclear factor** and **rheumatoid factor** as well as antibody against the duct epithelium of the salivary and lacrimal glands. Probably the same as Mikulicz's disease, which causes enlargement mainly of the salivary but also of the lacrimal glands.

skin sensitizing antibody. Antibody capable of attachment to skin cells so that, on subsequent combination with antigen, an **immediate hypersensitivity** reaction (**type I reaction**) occurs. Mainly IgE but also includes antibodies such as human IgG1 (*see* **immunoglobulin subclass**) which give positive **passive cutaneous anaphylaxis** in guinea pig (but not human) skin.

skin test. Any test in which substances are injected into or applied to the skin in order to observe the host's response to them. Used extensively in the study of hypersensitivity and immunity, *see* e.g. **tuberculin test, Schick test**, etc.

skin window. A technique employed to study the sequence of changes that occur in inflammation. The skin is scraped until capillary bleeding occurs. A small coverslip, or, better, a small chamber containing balanced salt solution is then applied and secured firmly in place. At intervals thereafter the cells which have migrated into the chamber are removed, stained, and identified.

SLE. *See* **systemic lupus erythematosus**.

slide agglutination test. Rapid **agglutination** test carried out by mixing drops of a suspension of a particulate antigen (bacteria, erythrocytes, etc.) and of antibody on a microscopic slide. Agglutination, which usually occurs within 30 seconds, is observed by visual or microscopic examination. A good screening test but less accurate than the **tube agglutination test** as the agglutination observed may in fact be due to **cross reacting antibodies** which cannot be distinguished unless the **antiserum** can be diluted.

slide flocculation test. *See* **slide agglutination test**.

S-locus. Murine 'serum-substance' locus (*Ss*), so-called because it

slow reacting substance A

controls quantitative variations in a serum protein (Mol. wt. 200 000) which is the murine equivalent of human **C4.** An allotypic determinant on one sub-class of S-protein is expressed in some strains of mice and in males only (sex-limited). This Ss allotype is controlled by the *Slp* locus, which is postulated to occur in close juxtaposition to the S-locus. *Ss* and *Slp* may code for a single polypeptide precursor for both Slp-positive and Slp-negative Ss molecules.

slow reacting substance A. A pharmacologically active material comprising **leukotrienes** C, D, and E, released by **mast cells** and other cells, causing contraction of smooth muscle, especially bronchial muscle, and increased vascular permeability. Found in lesions of **immediate hypersensitivity** (*see* **leukotriene**).

small lymphocyte. Cell 6-8 μm in diameter with a deeply stained nucleus and narrow rim of cytoplasm. Despite the apparent identity of morphology, such cells may differ in origin, age, motility and function. *See* **lymphocyte** and **T lymphocyte, B lymphocyte, immunologically competent cell, antigen reactive cell, plaque forming cell, long lived lymphocyte, short lived lymphocyte.**

smallpox. *See* **variola.**

smallpox handler's lung. (*Obs.*)   A **farmer's lung** type of disease resulting from the inhalation of dust from smallpox scabs.

smallpox vaccination. Method of producing **active immunity** against smallpox (**variola**). Smallpox is now believed to have been eliminated worldwide, the virus existing only in certain laboratories. **Vaccinia** virus is prepared from the vesicular eruptions of vaccinia on the skin of a calf or sheep. This virus shares **cross reacting antigens**[2] with the variola virus and therefore induces **protective immunity** against smallpox. Vaccination is achieved by the **multiple pressure** technique. Successful primary vaccination is characterized by development of a vesicular lesion at the vaccination site after 6-9 days, the reaction reaching its maximum at the 12th day. In secondary and later vaccination, reactions may be accelerated so that a small vesicle develops at the 4th-5th day and the reaction reaches its height at the 7th day. Primary vaccination is safest given to infants between one and two years old. Revaccinations are required at intervals of three years. Rare complications are generalized vaccinia including **eczema vaccinatum** and **chronic progressive vaccinia** (which may occur particularly in cases of **cell-mediated immunity deficiency syndromes**), and **post vaccinial encephalomyelitis** which is more common after primary vaccination in infants under one year old and in adults. Contra-indicated in **immunological deficiency states, atopic** diseases including **eczema,** in pregnancy, and in patients on corticosteroids or **anti-metabolites.**

Snell-Bagg mice. Inbred strain of pituitary dwarf mice with deficiences of thymic and **lymphoid tissue** and depressed responses of **cell-mediated immunity.**

solubilized water-in-oil adjuvant. A low viscosity **water-in-oil emulsion adjuvant** in which the antigen is contained in a water phase of very small volume, compared to that of the oil, and is dissolved in a mixture of emulsifiers.

soluble antigen. Any **antigen**[1] in aqueous solution or capable of such solution. Cf. **particulate antigen.**

soluble complex. Immune complex in soluble form. Occurs *in vivo* or *in vitro* usually where there is an **antigen excess** over antibody so that a lattice (*see* **lattice hypothesis**) is not formed. Causes tissue damage *in vivo* (especially if **complement** is also bound); e.g. local aggregation of neutrophils by **chemotaxis,** increase in vascular permeability, lodgement of neutrophils, fibrin, platelets on vascular endothelium with oedema or thrombosis and necrosis. *See* **type III reaction, Arthus reaction, serum sickness, glomerulonephritis, immune complex disease.**

somatic antigen. *See* **endotoxin** and **O antigen**[1].

species specificity. Term used of tissue antigens, cell wall antigens, etc. to denote their presence in a single species alone and not in others. Other antigens, e.g. **heterophil antigens** are found in many species.

specific granule. Cytoplasmic granule of the **neutrophil leucocyte** containing lysozyme, lactoferrin, vitamin-B_{12}-binding protein and neutral proteases. Smaller than the **azurophil granule** and probably appears later in development. Fuses more rapidly with phagosomes than the azurophil granule, and its contents are also readily secreted to the exterior.

specific immunity. Immunity resulting from specific recognition of antigen[1] such that antibody (**humoral immunity**) or **primed lymphocytes** (**cell-mediated immunity**) can react specifically with that antigen *or* in which specific **immunological tolerance** to that antigen is produced.

specificity. A term defining selective reactivity between substances, e.g. of an **antigen**[1] with its corresponding **antibody** or **primed lymphocyte**.

spleen. A solid, encapsulated organ, deep red in colour, found in the abdominal cavity. In some animals it is contractile and forms an important circulatory reserve (not man). It is a site of **antibody** production especially against **particulate antigens** administered intravenously. Histologically, two parts can be distinguished. The red pulp consists of large numbers of blood-filled sinusoids in which phagocytosis of effete erythrocytes takes place. Many **phagocytes** and **plasma cells** are found in the cords of Billroth, which correspond to the medulla of a **lymph node**. The white pulp consists of large aggregates of **lymphoid cells** distributed round the arterioles. The macroscopic arrangement of the white pulp was first described by Malpighi, hence the term Malpighian body or follicle, used to define these aggregates. The Malpighian body can be further subdivided into a central zone, immediately round the central arteriole, which is thymus dependent (*see* **thymus-dependent area**), and a peripheral zone where **germinal centre** development usually takes place. *See also* **ellipsoid**.

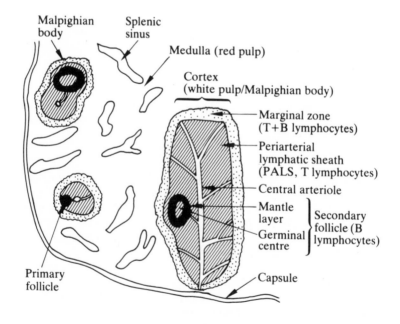

Section of part of the spleen.

splenectomy. Surgical removal of the complete **spleen**. After splenectomy, the **immune response** to intravenously inoculated antigens is greatly reduced. Splenectomized subjects also show an increased susceptibility to septicaemia and blood-borne protozoal infections.

splenic red pulp. *See* **spleen**.

split tolerance. (1) A result sometimes obtained following the experimental induction of **immunological tolerance** to **allogeneic** cells. Tolerance to one antigen, or to a group of antigens on the surfaces of those cells is produced, whilst simultaneously there is an **immune response** to other antigens on the cells.
(2) The term has also been used to refer to immunological tolerance affecting *either* **humoral immunity** or **cell-mediated immunity** but not both at the same time.

S-protein. *See* **S-locus**.

spur. In **double diffusion tests** (especially **Ouchterlony tests**), a spur of precipitate is indicative of a **reaction of partial identity** q.v.

SRBC. Sheep erythrocytes [red blood cell(s)].

SRSA. (slow reacting substance A). *See* **leukotrienes**.

SSPE. *see* **subacute sclerosing panencephalitis**.

SSS III. Example of specific soluble substance (capsular polysaccharide) of *Streptococcus pneumoniae* (pneumococcus). The Roman numeral signifies the type of specific capsular polysaccharide, of which over seventy have been identified. *See also* **pneumococcal polysaccharide**.

stem cell. A large cell with a rim of intensely pyroninophilic cytoplasm (*see* **methyl green pyronin stain**) and pyroninophilic nucleoli within a leptochromatic nucleus (i.e. having narrow strands of chromatin) found in **bone marrow** and other haemopoietic tissues. Capable of both self-replication and generation of a series of progenitor cells by proliferation and differentiation under the influence of **colony stimulating factors**. Known also as CFU-S (colony forming unit - spleen, referring to the tissue in which it was first studied). Its progeny, granulocyte-macrophage lines, lymphocyte lines, etc., are detailed under colony stimulating factors.

steric hindrance. Prevention of interaction between one molecule and another because their shapes prevent proper apposition of the reaction sites, e.g. the **valency** of **IgM antibody** can vary between two and ten depending upon the size of the **antigen.** The larger the antigen the lower the valency.

stimulated macrophage. A vague term, no longer recommended, to refer to macrophages in which one or many functions have been stimulated *in vitro* or *in vivo*. *See* **elicited macrophage, activated macrophage.**

Stormont test. *See* **double intradermal tuberculin test.**

streptococcal M protein. An antigenic protein found in the cell wall of *Streptococcus pyogenes*. Present only in virulent organisms in which it acts by inhibiting **phagocytosis.** Antibody to M protein has, therefore, a protective effect due to **opsonization.**

streptococcal nephritis. **Glomerulonephritis** following infection with *Streptococcus pyogenes* of Lancefield group A and, most commonly, of Griffith type 12. Associated with deposits containing **immunoglobulin** and **complement** in the glomeruli and probably reflects a **hypersensitivity** reaction (chiefly a **type III reaction** due to toxic complexes) either against streptoccocal antigens deposited in the glomerulus itself, or against a glomerular basement membrane antigen sharing antigenic determinants with the streptococcus (in this case a response of **autoimmunity**). Nephritis has been produced after injection of animals with streptococcal antigens but it differs from the human disease in many respects.

streptolysin O test. *See* **anti-streptolysin O test.**

subacute sclerosing panencephalitis. Rare, late neurological complication of measles. A slow virus infection. Despite the presence of high blood and cerebrospinal fluid levels of antibody against measles virus, the viruses escape **immune elimination**[1], possibly due to factors (virus-antibody complexes) which block the function of the antiviral **T lymphocytes.**

subcutaneous tuberculin test. *Hist.* The original test employed by Robert Koch for the diagnosis of tuberculosis in man, it has also been extensively used in cattle. It is not now used in man because of the serious general and focal reactions caused. In cattle, the interpretation of the test depends on the production of a characteristic febrile response following the subcutaneous administration of **tuberculin.**

subset. Term used to classify functionally or structurally different populations of cells within a single cell type. Used especially of **T**

lymphocytes, e.g. **helper T lymphocytes, suppressor T lymphocytes,** immature T lymphocytes, etc. *See also* **Lyt 1,2,3** (mouse), **T antigens** (T4,5,8) (human), and Table on p.213.

suicide (immunological). Technique for eliminating a population of **lymphocytes** with **receptors** for a given **antigen**[1] by allowing them to take up a preparation of that antigen labelled with a high dose of radioisotope sufficient to kill the cells. Alternatively, cells dividing in response to stimulation by antigen may be killed by feeding with high specific activity [^{3}H] thymidine, or bromodeoxyuridine followed by U.V. irradiation.

Sulzberger-Chase phenomenon. A form of **immunological unresponsiveness** to chemical sensitizing agents capable of inducing **delayed hypersensitivity** reactions. Guinea pigs **primed** by the cutaneous route normally show **contact hypersensitivity** to picryl chloride-protein conjugates. If they are first fed with picryl chloride by mouth or given picryl chloride intravenously, they later fail to show skin reactivity to picryl chloride. This unresponsiveness can be abolished by **adoptive transfer** of lymphocytes from guinea pigs primed in the normal way to picryl chloride.

superantigen. (*Hist.*) Hypothetical **antigen** that, after processing by **macrophages,** was postulated to be particularly potent at initiating antibody production, possibly because of complexing with RNA. Relevance to antigen presentation by macrophages is unclear.

superoxide anion (O$'_2$). Oxygen molecule that carries an extra unpaired electron, and is therefore a free radical. Generated in **neutrophil leucocytes** and **mononuclear phagocytes** by one-electron-step reduction of molecular oxygen, by an unidentified oxidase, driven by hexose monophosphate shunt pathway activation. Highly reactive and toxic. O$'_2$ may be further reduced to H_2O_2, or, when two O$'_2$ radicals interact, one is oxidised and the other reduced in a dismutation reaction to form O_2 and H_2O_2. This reaction is catalysed by superoxide dismutase, an enzyme present in phagocytic cells. O$'_2$, H_2O_2 and the hydroxyl radical OH· play a major part in the oxidative microbicidal activity of neutrophils and mononuclear phagocytes (*see also* **myeloperoxidase, peroxidase**).

suppressor cell. A lymphoid cell capable of suppressing antibody production by other cells. Best exemplified by **suppressor T lymphocytes,** a lymphocyte **subset** population.

suppressor T lymphocyte. Subpopulation of **T lymphocytes** which directly suppresses the immune response.

suppressor inducer T lymphocyte

suppressor inducer T lymphocyte. T Lymphocyte which activates **suppressor T lymphocytes** but does not suppress the immune response directly.

suppressor T-cell factor. Soluble product of a **suppressor T lymphocyte**, responsible for suppressing other lymphocyte functions. *See* also **antigen-specific T-cell suppressor factor.**

surface active agent adjuvants. Some substances, e.g. **aluminium hydroxide gel,** alginates, lanoline, phospholipids, that act as **adjuvants** are also emulsifying agents in that they can stabilise oil-water interfaces. Surface active agents are able to do this because their molecules have one end non-polar, and the other polar. Thus they have an affinity for interfaces between water and oil. However, not all surface active agents also act as adjuvants. The cationic quaternary ammonium compounds are adjuvant active but neither the non-ionic agents (e.g. **Arlacel A®** and **Tween 80®**) nor the anionic agents, e.g. aluminium stearate etc., have adjuvant activity.

surface immunoglobulin. *See* **B lymphocyte receptor**

Svedberg unit. A unit in which **sedimentation coefficients** are measured. Symbol S. One Svedberg unit equals 10^{-13} seconds.

Swiss type hypogammaglobulinaemia. *See* **combined immunodeficiency syndrome** (*preferred term*).

switch region. (1) The sequence of amino acids at the junction of the **variable** and **constant regions** of a **light** or **heavy chain.** The functional significance of this region in linking the **V-** and **C-regions** is determined by the **D** and **J exons** that code for this region. (2) The region of DNA 5′ to each **heavy chain C-region** gene containing the **switch sites** q.v.

switch site. A short sequence of DNA 5′ to each **heavy chain C-region** gene which acts as a recognition site for translocation of the **V-region** gene during switching of gene expression from one class of heavy chain to another. Each C-region gene has multiple switch sites contained within the **switch region**[2] q.v.

sympathetic ophthalmia. Inflammatory disease of a sound eye following perforating injury of the other eye. Characterized by **lymphocyte** and **epithelioid cell** infiltration and **granuloma**[2] formation, especially in the uveal tract. Postulated reaction of **cell-mediated immunity** against antigens, normally sequestered, liberated by injury to the opposite eye, thus an **autoimmune disease**.

syngeneic (syngenic).   Genetically identical, usually applied to grafts made within an **inbred strain**. *See also* **transplantation terminology**.

synthetic antigen. **Antigen** synthesized in the laboratory as opposed to antigens derived from living tissues, e.g. **(T,G)AL, (Phe,G)AL**.

systemic anaphylaxis. **Anaphylaxis** or **immediate hypersensitivity** in which many tissues show lesions, as contrasted with **local anaphylaxis** which occurs at one single site. Seen especialy after systemic (e.g. intravenous) administration of antigen. May lead to death from **anaphylactic shock**.

systemic lupus erythematosus.   Disease of man, characterized by widespread focal degeneration, 'fibrinoid necrosis' of connective tissue and disseminated lesions in many tissues including skin, joints, kidneys, pleura, peripheral vessels, peripheral nervous system, blood, etc. May follow administration of drugs or other antigenic substances. Numerous immunological abnormalities include presence in serum of **antinuclear factor,** LE factor (*see* **LE cell**), complement fixing antibodies (*see* **autoimmune complement fixation reaction**), and high serum **immunoglobulin** levels. Putative **autoimmune disease** possibly associated with breakdown of **immunological tolerance** to **autoantigens** followed by a complex **hypersensitivity** reaction against these antigens involving **type II, III** and **IV reactions** to varying degrees. The glomerular lesions are particularly serious and have been shown to result from deposition of **immune complexes** in the glomerular capillaries. Cf. **lupus erythematosus**.

T_m.   **C-terminal** polypeptide (**tail peptide,** q.v.) of the heavy chain of membrane **immunoglobulin**.

T_s.   (1) Suppressor T lymphocyte, see **suppressor cell**. (2) **C-terminal** polypeptide (**tail peptide,** q.v.) of the heavy chain of secreted **immunoglobulin**.

T_sF.   *See* **suppressor T-cell factor**.

T6 marker.   Mouse chromosome originally derived from an irradiated male. It is about half the length of the shortest pair of autosomes, and has a marked secondary constriction near the centromere. It is a useful cell marker, easily identifiable in squash preparation of somatic tissues and can therefore be used for tracing the fate of cells transferred to another mouse. Present in the **inbred strain** CBA/H-T6.

TAB vaccine. **Vaccine** used in prophylaxis of enteric fevers. Contains heat-killed, phenol-preserved *Salmonella typhi* and *Salmonella paratyphi A* and *B*. The organisms are in the smooth specific phase and possess their normal complement of **O antigens**[1] and **Vi antigens.** Given in repeated subcutaneous doses. Contains **lipopolysaccharide**[2]. Therefore some pyrexia and local inflammation usually follows injection. TABC also contains *Salmonella paratyphi C.* TABT also contains **tetanus toxoid** (used in servicemen).

TAF. *See* **toxoid antitoxin floccules**.

T agglutinin. **Natural antibody** present in normal human sera which agglutinates erythrocytes that have been in contact with bacteria or that have been incubated with **neuraminidase** (receptor-destroying enzyme) which reveals the **T antigen** present on normal erythrocytes. May give false-positive results in blood grouping or cross-matching tests using a suspension contaminated with bacteria.

tail peptide. A polypeptide at the C-terminus of a **heavy chain** which is not a part of the **C-terminal domain.** The secreted forms of **IgA** and **IgM** have tail peptides (T_s) 20 amino acids long, not found in **IgG** or **IgE**. The membrane forms of IgM and IgG have predominantly hydrophobic tail peptides (T_m) different from the secreted form. The T_m of the μ_m chain is 41 amino acids long, that of the γ_m chain is approximately 70 amino acids long. It is probable that all membrane-bound **immunoglobulins** have C-terminal tail peptides.

Takatsy technique. A method for producing **doubling dilutions** with the aid of small spiral loops (like a cage) on the end of a stiff wire with a handle. The loop picks up a standard volume when dipped into a liquid. Thus, by passing the loop from tube to tube (in practice, small wells in a plastic plate) and twirling it each time, a dilution series is produced. Up to 8 loops can be used simultaneously. Used in microtechniques for **haemagglutination tests**[1,2],etc. Modern loops are of solid block form with cuts to hold the liquid (Microtitre®).

tandem immunoelectrophoresis. An analytical technique developed from **crossed immunoelectrophoresis** q.v. A gel is prepared for electrophoresis in which are cut two wells, one for the unknown mixture and one for a reference antigen. Electrophoresis is carried out in one direction, the gel is then turned through a right angle and further electrophoresis carried out so that the separated antigens enter an adjacent gel containing antibodies to all of the antigens. Precipitin bands, of the type seen in the **Laurell rocket test** q.v., appear, one of which shows a **reaction of identity** with the reference antigen.

tanned red cell test. A very sensitive **passive agglutination test** for the detection and measurement of antibody (originated by S. Boyden). Treatment of erythrocytes with tannic acid (1 in 2500) increases their agglutinability and facilitates the attachment ('coating') to them of soluble proteins.

T-antigens. A group of surface **antigens** defining subpopulations of human **T lymphocytes.** Many of these have now been defined using monoclonal antibodies, cf. the **Lyt 1, 2, 3** antigens on mouse T lymphocytes, and the surface antigens of rat T lymphocytes

Some T lymphocyte surface antigens defined by monoclonal antibodies.

Species	Antigen	T-lymphocyte class
Mouse	Thy 1	All T-lymphocytes.
	Lyt 1	Helper/inducer, DTH effector (see T_{DTH}),
	Lyt 2/3	Suppressor/cytotoxic.
Rat	W 3/13	All peripheral T lymphocytes.
	W 3/25	Helper, T_{DTH} effector.
	MRC OX8	Suppressor-cytotoxic.
Human	T1	All T lymphocytes.
	T3	All mature T lymphocytes.
	T4	Helper/inducer.
	T5/T8	Suppressor/cytotoxic.
	T6	Thymocytes.

tapioca adjuvant. The original **adjuvant** described by Gaston Ramon in 1925. It consists of pure starch granules into which the antigen solution is absorbed, so constituting a **depot forming adjuvant.**

target cell. (1) **Antigen**[1] bearing cell which is the target of attack by **primed lymphocytes** or by specific **antibody.** (2) Abnormally shaped and unusually thin red cell with central stained area seen in blood especially in certain disorders of haemoglobin formation; of no immunological significance.

T-B cell cooperation

T-B cell cooperation. *See* **T lymphocyte-B lymphocyte cooperation.**

T-cell. *See* **T lymphocyte.**

T-cell antigen-specific helper factor. *See* **antigen-specific T-cell helper factor.**

T-cell antigen-specific suppressor factor. *See* **antigen-specific T-cell suppressor factor.**

T-cell factor. Soluble product of a **T lymphocyte.**

T-cell growth factor (TCGF). *See* **interleukin-2.**

T-cell leukaemia viruses. A group of retroviruses which infect **T lymphocytes** and cause feline leukaemia, human T cell leukaemia (HTLV-1) and the **acquired immuno-deficiency syndrome** (HTLV-3).

T-cell non-antigen-specific helper factor. *See* **non-specific T-cell helper factor.**

T-cell non-antigen-specific suppressor factor. *See* **non-specific T-cell suppressor factor.**

T-cell receptor. *See* **T lymphocyte antigen receptor.**

T-cell replacing factor (TRF). **Helper T lymphocyte**-derived soluble factor which allows antibody production by **B-lymphocytes** in the absence of intact **T lymphocytes.** Synonymous with **B cell differentiation factors.** *See* also **BSF.**

T-cell subset. *See* **T lymphocyte subset.**

Tc lymphocyte. *See* **cytotoxic T lymphocyte.**

TCGF (T-cell growth factor). *See* **interleukin-2.**

TD antigen. *See* **thymus dependent antigen.**

T dependent antigen. *See* **thymus dependent antigen.**

TdT. *See* **terminal deoxynucleotidyl transferase.**

T$_{DTH}$ lymphocyte. Effector **T lymphocyte** in **delayed hypersensitivity.** Putatively a separate subset from **helper, suppressor** and **cytotoxic T lymphocytes.**

template theory. (*Hist*) An **instructive theory of antibody produc-**
tion in which it was supposed that antigen taken into a cell acted
directly as a template which determined the shape of the combining
site of the antibody produced by that cell. Originally proposed by
Haurowitz, Mudd and Alexander. *See also* **indirect template**
hypothesis.

terminal deoxynucleotidyl transferase (TdT). An enzyme
found in **pre T** and **pre B lymphocytes** and cortical **thymocytes** but
absent from their progeny. Hence used as a marker for these cells.

tertiary response. The **immune response** to a third dose of antigen.
Essentially similar to the **secondary immune response**.

test dosing. A technique used to detect **immediate hypersensitivity**
to drugs or antisera before a therapeutic dose is given. Ideally, doses
that increase by tenfold steps are given daily until a reaction occurs
or a therapeutic level is reached, the starting point being at the
microgram level for orally administered materials, and at nanogram
level for those given parenterally. N.B. **skin testing** is usually
preferable but even this is dangerous. Corticosteroid cover is often
required in these procedures.

tetanus antitoxin. Antibody to tetanus toxin, usually presented as
serum from horses that have been **hyperimmunized** against the
exotoxin of *Clostridium tetani*. Used for the prevention and
treatment of tetanus in man and animals following possible
contamination of wounds. Repeat inoculations may be dangerous if
the patient has become **primed** by horse proteins and **anaphylactic**
shock or **serum sickness** may follow. To reduce this possibility, for
use in man, the serum is usually **despecified.** However, high titre
human **antisera** against tetanus toxin are now available in some
countries and these are quite safe to use.

tetanus toxin. The toxin (an **exotoxin**) produced by *Clostridium*
tetani. A neurotoxin that blocks synaptic inhibition in the spinal cord
and also blocks neuromuscular transmission. Tetanus toxin binds to
a sialidase-labile disialosyl ganglioside, a glycolipid constituent of
cell membranes that is particularly rich in the membranes of nerve
cells (cf. **cholera toxin**). Protection induced by immunization with
tetanus toxoid q.v. *See also* **tetanus antitoxin**.

tetanus toxoid. Formaldehyde-detoxicated **tetanus toxin.** Used in
prophylactic immunization against tetanus in normal individuals or
in those at risk of tetanus following a dirty wound. Given by repeated
subcutaneous doses. Forms part of **triple vaccine**.

tetramethylrhodamine isothiocyanate. A red fluorescent dye (*see* **fluorochrome**) which combines with protein in alkaline solution. Used in **immunofluorescence** techniques.

$(CH_3)_2N$ — O — $N(CH_3)_2$

O
C=O

N=C=S

tetraparental chimera. A **chimera** (usually mouse) resulting from the artificially induced fusion of two blastocysts at the 4 or 8 cell stage. Of immunological importance as demonstrates maintenance of mutual **immunological tolerance**.

Texas red®. A reactive, sulphonyl chloride derivative of sulphorhodamine 101, particularly suited for preparing fluorescent antibodies to be used in double labelling techniques when **fluorescein** is the other label. *See also* **fluorescent antibody technique**.

(TG)AL. A synthetic **antigen** composed of short polymers of tyrosine and glutamic acid attached as side chains to a backbone of poly-L-lysine by alanine residues.

T globulin. Strong **immunoglobulin** band appearing on electrophoresis of horse serum after **hyperimmunization**. Of γ_1 mobility (*see* γ_1 **globulin**[3]), and $s_{20,w} = $ **7S**. Possibly represents an **IgG** subtype, (IgG(T).

theliolymphocyte. *See* **intraepithelial lymphocyte** (*preferred term*).

therapeutic antisera. **Antisera** used for the treatment of, or protection from, disease in contrast to antisera employed for the identification of organisms, etc. Often prepared in horses by **hyperimmunization,** and may be **despecified** for safe use in man. *See* **tetanus antitoxin,** etc.

θ **(theta) antigen**. *See* **thy 1 antigen**.

THF. *See* **thymic humoral factor(s)**.

thoracic duct drainage. Surgical technique used in man and in experimental animals whereby circulating **lymphocytes** can be withdrawn through a catheter inserted into the thoracic duct.

thy 1 antigen (previously known as theta (θ) antigen). Cell surface **isoantigen** of mice, present on **lymphocytes** in the **thymus** and on thymus derived lymphocytes in the **peripheral lymphoid tissues**. It is also present in central nervous tissue.

thymectomy. Surgical removal of the **thymus.** If carried out immediately after birth (neonatal thymectomy) in rodents a deficiency of **cell-mediated immunity** (and **humoral immunity** to some antigens, *see* **thymus dependent antigens**) follows. *See also* **wasting disease**.

thymic cortex. *See* **thymus**.

thymic epithelial cells. Epithelial cells found in the thymic cortex and medulla and derived from the third branchial pouch. They are believed to control the maturation of lymphocyte precursors by secretion of hormones: **thymosins, thymopoietin, serum thymic factor**.

thymic hormone. *See* **thymic humoral factor(s), thymopoietin** and **thymosins**.

thymic humoral factor(s).(THF) Soluble product(s) derived from the **thymus** which regulate **lymphocyte** differentiation and/or function, e.g. **thymosins, thymopoietin, serum thymic factor**.

thymic hypoplasia. Congenital **cell-mediated immunity deficiency syndrome** in human infants. In Di George's syndrome there is also parathyroid hypoplasia and the condition is characterized by a combined history of hypocalcaemic convulsions and recurrent infections (often mycotic) of the skin and upper respiratory tract; low blood calcium, high blood phosphorus, marked lymphopenia of the blood and of the **thymus dependent areas** of the **peripheral lymphoid organs** and failure to express **cell-mediated immunity** but with normal **antibody** production and normal serum **immunoglobulin** levels.

thymic medullary hyperplasia. Term used to signify the presence of **germinal centres** in the medulla of the **thymus** especially in **myasthenia gravis**. The term does not imply that thymic weight is increased. The situation has been confused by the identification of germinal centres in thymus glands of normal subjects.

thymic nurse cell. Large thymic epithelial cell with which thymocytes come into close contact. Postulated role in maturation and differentiation of **T-lymphocytes**.

thymin. A thymus hormone preparation with an activity similar to that of **thymopoietin**.

thymocyte. Any **lymphocyte** found within the **thymus**.

thymoma. Tumour of **thymus** (rare). About 50 per cent of thymic tumours are associated with **myasthenia gravis** and a smaller number with erythrocyte aplasia, **hypogammaglobulinaemia,** Cushing's syndrome, **rheumatoid arthritis** and polymyositis. Several histological types are recognized; the commonest consists of lymphoid and epithelial cells.

thymopoietin. Factor derived from the **thymus** (protein of mol. wt. 5–6000 daltons) believed to influence development of **T lymphocytes.** Induces appearance of T lymphocyte markers, e.g. **thy 1 antigen** on lymphocytes *in vivo* and *in vitro*.

thymosins (thymosines). Group of peptides derived from the thymus, including thymosin α_1, (mol. wt. 3100). *See also* **serum thymic factor**.

thymus. An organ of major importance in the ontogeny of the **immune response.** In most mammals it consists of two lobes situated in the anterior part of the thorax, ventral to the trachea and great vessels, but in some (e.g. guinea pig, foal, calf and piglet) it also extends up the neck as far as the thyroid gland. In birds, it is distributed along the neck as a series of lobes. Histologically it consists mainly of **lymphocytes** distributed into distinct cortical and medullary areas on a network of **reticular cells.** These lymphocytes ('thymocytes') are continually being produced within the gland, but after the neonatal period only 5 per cent of them appear ever to leave it. Hassall's corpuscles are present in the medulla. These consist of nests of flattened cells, concentrically arranged, of unknown function. The thymus is a relatively large organ at birth, but gets smaller with increasing age until it may be difficult to identify. During the neonatal period it plays a major role in populating the blood, lymph and **thymus dependent areas** with the **T lymphocytes** that are responsible for **cell-mediated immunity** and the regulation of the humoral immune response to **thymus dependent antigens** Hormones secreted by the thymic epithelium control the maturation of T lymphocytes (*see* **thymosin, thymopoietin, serum thymic factor**). Animals **thymectomized** at birth, or that are born without a thymus (*see* **thymic hypoplasia**) never develop the ability to give cell-mediated immune responses; animals thymectomized later in life gradually become deficient in them over an extended period of time.

thymus dependent antigen (T dependent antigen). An antigen that does not stimulate an antibody response in an animal lacking a thymus. Cooperation with **helper T lymphocytes** is required in order for **B lymphocytes** to respond to such antigens by maturation into antibody-forming cells. Most proteins and other antigens which present a diversity of **antigenic determinants** are thymus dependent. Cf. **thymus independent antigens**.

thymus dependent area. Those areas of the **peripheral lymphoid organs** that appear selectively depleted of lymphocytes in neonatally **thymectomized** animals, and in babies and animals with congenital aplasia of the **thymus** (*see* **thymic hypoplasia** and **nu nu mice**). Anatomically these areas are situated in the mid cortex (paracortical area) of **lymph nodes,** the centre of the Malpighian corpuscle of the **spleen** and in the internodular zone of **Peyer's patches.** In normal subjects they are mostly occupied by **small lymphocytes** of the circulatory pool which enter them through the walls of **high endothelial venules**. The earliest signs of the initiation of **cell-mediated immunity** are seen in the thymus dependent area in the form of **large pyroninophilic blast cells** q.v. *See* illustration on p.141.

thymus dependent cells. Population of **lymphoid cells** whose normal development depends on the presence of the **thymus** at birth, i.e. **T lymphocytes** q.v.

thymus derived cells. Lymphoid cells that have been demonstrated to be derived from the **thymus** (a) by finding labelled cells in the **peripheral lymphoid organs** following intra-thymic labelling with ^{3}H-thymidine; or (b) by finding the **T6 marker** in chromosome squashes of peripheral lymphoid organs or blood of **CBA mice** grafted with thymus from CBA/H-T6 donors; or (c) because they carry thymus specific surface antigens.

thymus independent antigen (T independent antigen). An antigen that is able to stimulate **B lymphocytes** to produce antibody without the cooperation of **T lymphocytes.** An antibody response to such antigens can be stimulated in an animal lacking a **thymus.** T independent antigens are usually repeating polymers which present an array of identical determinants to the lymphocyte. N.B. Thymus dependence and independence are terms restricted to the response of specific **humoral immunity,** not to specific **cell-mediated immunity.** Cf. **thymus dependent antigen.**

thyroid antibodies. Organ-specific **autoantibodies** found in a variety of thyroid diseases, especially **Hashimoto's thyroiditis** and **thyrotoxicosis.** The major antibodies are those against thyroglobulin, against an antigen in thyroid colloid, against a microsomal antigen of the thyroid acinar cells and against TSH-receptors which mimic the action of TSH (*see* **long acting thyroid stimulator**).

thyroiditis. Inflammatory disease of the thyroid gland. Rarely due to bacterial infection, but de Quervain's thyroiditis is probably due to mumps virus. Riedel's thyroiditis is a slow fibrous replacement of unknown cause. **Hashimoto's thyroiditis,** primary hypothyroidism (myxoedema), and chronic focal thyroiditis may result from **autoimmunity.** *See also* **thyrotoxicosis, thyroid antibodies.**

thyrotoxicosis. Disease characterized by increase in level of circulating thyroid hormones usually associated with hyperplasia or hypertrophy of the thyroid gland, either diffuse or nodular. Many cases show evidence of **autoimmune disease,** i.e. lymphocytic infiltration of the thyroid gland and the presence of circulating **autoantibodies** against thyroid antigens. The antibody known as **long acting thyroid stimulator** q.v. is characteristically found in thyrotoxicosis. It is an antibody against the receptors for thyroid stimulating hormone, and stimulates thyroid function by binding to these receptors.

T independent antigen. *See* **thymus independent antigen.**

tine test. A form of **tuberculin test,** widely used in man, in which a small amount of dried old **tuberculin** is injected intradermally to a depth of 2mm by means of a disposable applicator with four points or tines. Similar to the **Heaf test.** The **Mantoux test** is recommended in cases where the tine test gives an equivocal reaction.

tingible body (corpuscle). Pyknotic (deeply staining) nuclear debris, found within **macrophages** in the **germinal centres** of **lymphoid tissue.**

tissue specific antigen.   Cell antigen present in a given tissue and not found in other tissues, e.g. thyroglobulin is tissue specific for the thyroid. Important in classification of **autoimmune diseases** in which **autoantibodies** against either tissue specific antigens or **non-tissue-specific antigens** are found. These antigens are often not species specific (*see* **species specificity**), e.g. anti-human thyroglobulin reacts with thyroglobulin from many other species.

tissue typing.   The identification of **histocompatibility antigens.** Usually carried out by observing the cytotoxic (*see* **cytotoxicity tests**) effect of specific **antisera** or **monoclonal antibodies** on blood **leucocytes** collected from the prospective donor and recipient of organs or tissues that are to be transplanted. *See also* **mixed leucocyte reaction, HLA histocompatibility system**.

titre (*Amer.* titer).   In **serological** reactions, a measure of the amount of **antibody** in an **antiserum** per unit volume of original **serum.** The antibody is **serially diluted,** antigen is added and the **end point** is determined. If this dilution is say, 1/120, the titre of the serum can be quoted as 120 antibody units per ml. of serum. It is more frequently quoted as being the reciprocal of the **initial serum dilution** which gives the same result. If the reciprocal of the **final serum dilution** is quoted, the titre will be higher but will not correspond with the arbitrary antibody units. This measurement is arbitrary and less accurate than estimates of antibody in absolute amounts as in the **Farr test** and **quantitative precipitation test**.

T lymphocytes (T cells).   **Lymphocytes** that are derived from the **thymus**. Play a major role (a) as **antigen reactive cells** and effector cells in **cell-mediated immunity** and (b) by cooperation with **B lymphocytes,** in antibody production (**humoral immunity**) against **thymus dependent antigens.** For properties. *see* p.31-32. *See also* **cytotoxic, helper, suppressor T lymphocyte, T$_{DTH}$ lymphocyte.**

Tγ lymphocyte.   **T lymphocyte** which has surface **receptors** for and binds the **Fc** portion of **IgG.**

T$_h$ lymphocyte.   *See* **helper T lymphocyte.**

T$_k$ lymphocyte.   Killer T lymphocyte. *See* **killer cell.**

Tμ lymphocyte.   **T lymphocyte** which has surface **receptors** for and binds the **Fc** portion of **IgM.**

T$_s$ lymphocyte.   **Suppressor T lymphocyte** q.v.

T_s1, T_s2, T_s3 lymphocytes

T_s1, T_s2, T_s3 lymphocytes. Subsets of suppressor T lymphocytes.

T lymphocyte antigen receptor (T lymphocyte receptor, T-cell receptor). A molecule on the surface membrane of **T lymphocytes** capable of specifically binding **antigen** in association with MHC leading to activation of the cell (*See also* **B lymphocyte receptor**). The molecule has been isolated from cloned T lymphocyte **hybridomas** and T lymphocyte lines and consists of two polypeptide chains (α and β) of M.Wt 40-50,000, each containing a **variable** and a **constant region**. These possess homology with immunoglobulin variable and constant regions. One or more of these receptors is/are believed to be responsible for the phenomenon of **MHC restriction** (*see also* **altered-self hypothesis** and **dual recognition hypothesis**).

T lymphocyte-B lymphocyte cooperation. A process required for production of normal levels of antibody to most antigens, especially **thymus dependent antigens.** Most probably results from the release by **T lymphocytes** of specific factors which activate **B lymphocytes** either directly or through the participation of a third cell, an **accessory cell** or **macrophage**.

T lymphocyte receptor. *See* **T lymphocyte antigen receptor**.

T lymphocyte repertoire. The number of different antigenic determinants to which the **T lymphocytes** of an individual animal are capable of responding. Since the genetics of the **T lymphocyte antigen receptor** are not known in detail yet, it is not possible to define the T lymphocyte repertoire in terms of the heterogeneity of this molecule, cf. **B lymphocyte repertoire**.

T lymphocyte subset. Group of **T lymphocytes** which are characterised by a particular function and which may be identified by specific cell surface antigens (*See* **helper T lymphocyte, suppressor T lymphocyte, cytotoxic T lymphocyte, T_{DTH} lymphocyte, T-antigens** and table on p.213.

T lymphocyte-T lymphocyte cooperation. Postulated interaction between different **T lymphocyte** subsets (*see* **subset**) in control of immune reactions. *See also* **T lymphocyte-B lymphocyte cooperation**.

Tla antigen. Class I murine histocompatibility antigen(s), coded for by genes located on chromosome 17 distal to the *H-2 D/L* region. Recognised by specific alloantisera, with as many as six possible allelic products, on thymocytes. This region is closely associated with the Qa region (*see* **Qa antigens**), producing another series of **Class I** molecules. Tl antigens appear anomalously on leukaemia cells, and additional specifities may be expressed on such cells. **Leukaemic** cells exposed to Tl antisera undergo **antigenic modulation.** (q.v.)

TNP. *See* **trinitrophenyl group.**

tolerance. *See* **immunological tolerance.**

tolerogenic. Capable of inducing **immunological tolerance.**

tonsil. *See* **pharyngeal tonsils** and also **caecal tonsils.**

toxin-antitoxin floccules. Obsolete. At one time used for **diphtheria immunization. Antitoxin** was added so as to slightly underneutralize the toxin; however, reactions and accidents occurred, possibly when the **Danysz phenomenon** was ignored. Cf. **toxoid-antitoxin floccules.**

toxin neutralization test. Technique used to assay an **exotoxin** or **antitoxin** by mixing fixed quantities of one with graded dilutions of the other, inoculating these mixtures into mice (e.g. for clostridial toxins) or guinea pigs (e.g. **diphtheria toxin**), and observing which mice die, or which guinea pigs show skin reactions. *See* L_0 dose of toxin.

toxoid. Bacterial **exotoxin** (e.g. diphtheria or tetanus toxin) which has been treated, usually with formalin, so that its ability to stimulate the production of **protective immunity** remains but it is no longer toxic and can therefore safely be used for **immunization**[2].

toxoid-antitoxin floccules. Precipitate prepared by mixing **diphtheria toxoid** with **diphtheria antitoxin** in conditions of slight **antigen excess.** Used to produce **active immunity** against diphtheria, particularly in adults or older children who are likely to show reactions to **alum precipitated toxoid.** Contains horse serum and so recipient may become **primed** by horse proteins (for the dangers of this *see* **tetanus antitoxin**).

TPHA. *See* **Treponema pallidum haemagglutination assay.**

TPI. *See* **Treponema pallidum immobilization test.**

trace labelling. *See* **isotope labelling.**

traffic area

traffic area. *See* **thymus dependent area** (*syn.*).

transfer factor. A dialysable substance, extracted from **leucocytes** (including **lymphocytes**) that is believed to be able to transfer the ability to give a **delayed hypersensitivity** response.

transformation. *See* **lymphocyte transformation**.

transfusion reaction. Disease or physiological disturbance following transfusion of blood. Often due to a specific immune reaction of the recipient against antigens of the donor blood cells. The most severe and common form of such reactions in man is due to **ABO blood group system** incompatibility as recipient's serum contains **natural antibodies** against ABO antigens not present on his own cells. After repeated transfusions, antibodies against other antigens, e.g. **Rhesus,** Lewis, Duffy, Kidd, Kell **blood groups**, may be formed and cause reactions. Reactions can also result from transfusion of blood containing antibody reactive with the recipient's erythrocytes but are usually less severe.

transplantation antigen. *See* **histocompatibility antigen**.

transplantation immunology. The study of the **immune response** following transplantation of tissue from donor to recipient. Very largely, the study of **cell-mediated immunity** in this situation.

transplantation terminology.

Recent nomenclature	Older nomenclature		Relationship of donor and recipient of graft
Syngeneic (isogeneic) graft	{ Autograft	——	Same individual
	{ Homograft	——	Same species and genetically identical
Allogeneic graft	Homograft	——	Same species but not genetically identical
Xenogeneic graft	Heterograft	——	Different species

transport piece. *See* **secretory piece**.

Treponema pallidum haemagglutination assay. A **passive agglutination test** for antibodies against *Treponema pallidum* used in the diagnosis of syphilis. Formolized tanned sheep erythrocytes conjugated with *Treponema pallidum* **antigens** (see **tanned red cell test**) are mixed with the test serum. **Agglutination** indicates the presence of **antibody.** The **specificity** is similar to that of the **Treponema pallidum immobilization test** and the sensitivity is comparable with that of the **FTA–ABS test**.

Treponema pallidum immobilization test. Test used in diagnosis of syphilis. Serum under test is mixed with a suspension of motile *Treponema pallidum* in the presence of **complement.** The spirochaetes are immobilized by sera containing antibody to *T. pallidum.* Highly specific for syphilis, beyond the primary stage, more so than the **Wassermann reaction,** but infrequently performed due to difficulties in growing the organism (in rabbits, *in vivo*) and the dangers of handling it.

TRF. *See* **T-cell replacing factor**.

trinitrophenyl group (picryl group). A **hapten** which becomes attached to the –NH$_2$ groups of a protein when it is treated with trinitrochlorobenzene (picryl chloride) or trinitrobenzene sulphonic acid.

triple vaccine. A **mixed vaccine** containing **diphtheria toxoid, tetanus toxoid and pertussis vaccine.** Routinely used to produce **active immunity** against diphtheria, tetanus and whooping cough in infants. Several doses are given beginning at about the third to sixth month of life with the second dose a month after the first, the third six months later and a booster dose at school entry. Triple vaccine must not be given synchronously with **smallpox vaccination.** *See also* **Bordetella pertussis**.

trypan blue. Stain used to assess the viability of cells. Cells whose membrane permeability is normal do not take up trypan blue but when the plasma membrane is severely disrupted, it allows the dye in. Dead and dying cells therefore stain blue. *See* **cytotoxicity tests** and cf. **dye test** for toxoplasmosis.

trypanosome adhesion test. A test used to detect antibodies to trypanosomes. In the presence of specific antibody and **complement,** certain particles, e.g. some human and monkey erythrocytes, and bacteria of the family *Enterobacteriaceae,* adhere firmly to these protozoa. Cf. **immune adherence,** and **Rieckenberg reaction**.

tube agglutination test. **Agglutination** test carried out in test tubes or perspex plates, usually in **serial dilutions.** Cf. **slide agglutination test**.

tuberculin.   A protein or mixture of proteins, derived from *Mycobacterium tuberculosis,* which is employed in the **tuberculin test** as a diagnostic reagent for detecting sensitization by, or infection with, *M. tuberculosis.* Old tuberculin (OT) is a heat-concentrated filtrate from the fluid medium in which the organism has been grown. Purified protein derivative of tuberculin (tuberculin PPD) is a soluble protein fraction, precipitated by trichloroacetic acid from a synthetic medium in which *M. tuberculosis* has been grown. Tuberculins may be derived from the human, bovine or avian strains of the bacillus. That derived from a human strain is used for tuberculin tests in man and in cattle (when it is known as mammalian tuberculin). Avian tuberculin is used as a control to detect non-specific reactors when testing cattle by the **comparative single intradermal tuberculin test.** Tuberculin is a **mitogen** for **B lymphocytes** in mice acting mainly on differentiated cells to induce immunoglobulin production (also for **T lymphocytes**).

tuberculin hypersensitivity.   The state of being able to give a **delayed hypersensitivity response (type IV reaction)** to the inoculation of **tuberculin.** Exploited in the **tuberculin test** for the detection of **cell-mediated immunity** to *Mycobacterium tuberculosis* indicative of present or past infection.

tuberculin test.   Test for **delayed hypersensitivity** to **tuberculin** in man or animals. May be carried out by cutaneous, intradermal, subcutaneous, or ophthalmic application of old tuberculin or PPD. *See* **Mantoux test, comparative single intradermal tuberculin test, Moro test, Vollmer test.** Positive reactions are presumptive evidence of **cell-mediated immunity** to, and therefore of past or present exposure to, *Mycobacterium tuberculosis* but are in no sense diagnostic of active disease.

tuberculin type reaction.   A manifestation of **cell-mediated immunity** resembling a **tuberculin test (Mantoux test)** skin reaction. Evoked by an antigen other than tuberculin in a person or animal that has been **primed** by that antigen. For examples *see* e.g. **brucellin, histoplasmin test, mallein.**

tuberculosis immunization.   In man, **BCG** vaccine is most commonly used. A single intradermal injection is given and usually is followed within a few weeks by formation of a small local papule. It is given only to persons whose **tuberculin test (Mantoux test)** is negative and is offered to tuberculin-negative school children over 10 years of age, to medical students and to nurses and hospital staff. It gives a good degree of protection against tuberculosis for several years at least. Though cattle can be immunized against the disease, this is only rarely done (never in U.K.), as it complicates the detection and elimination of infected cases by the use of the tuberculin test.

tumour enhancement. *See* **immunological enhancement.**

tumour specific antigen. Antigen gained by any given tumour (*see* **antigen gain**). Tumour antigens may be (a) identical to antigens present in parent tissues (and therefore in no sense tumour specific), (b) not present in parent tissue but found in other unrelated normal tissues, (c) fetal antigens not normally expressed in the adult, e.g. **carcinoembryonic antigen,** or (d) unique to the tumour. Experimental tumours induced by any given virus all bear identical tumour-specific antigens, probably coded for by viral nuclear material incorporated into the host cell genome. However, the antigens in tumours induced by chemical carcinogens are different in each animal and even in multiple tumours in the same animal.

tumour specific transplantation antigen. *See* **tumour specific antigen.**

Tween 80®. Polyoxyethylene sorbitan monooleate. A non-ionic emulsifying agent which stabliizes **oil–in–water emulsions** (i.e. stops the oil drops from coalescing). Used in **water–in–oil–in–water emulsion adjuvants** and in culture media for mycobacteria.

two dimensional immunoelectrophoresis. *See* **crossed immunoelectrophoresis.**

type I reaction. Term used in Gell and Coombs' classification of **hypersensitivity** reactions. In the type I reaction, antigen combines with antibody which is fixed passively to the surface of cells, and causes the release of vasoactive substances. Thus synonymous with **immediate hypersensitivity, anaphylaxis.** The **cell bound antibody** involved is **reagin**[1] or **homocytotropic antibody,** usually IgE; the antigen is often known as an **allergen.**

type II reaction. Term used in Gell and Coombs' classification of **hypersensitivity** reactions. In the type II reaction, antibody reacts either with a cell surface antigen or with an antigen or **hapten** which has become attached to the cell surface. If the antibody is **complement** fixing, cell lysis occurs. *See* **cytotoxic antibody, immune cytolysis.**

type III reaction

type III reaction. Term used in Gell and Coombs' classification of **hypersensitivity** reactions. In this reaction the tissue damage is mediated by **immune complexes,** particularly **soluble complexes** formed in slight **antigen excess.** Such complexes are deposited in the vessel walls and become surrounded by **inflammatory cells,** especially **neutrophil leucocytes.** *See* **Arthus reaction, serum sickness, glomerulonephritis.**

type IV reaction. Term used in Gell and Coombs' classification of **hypersensitivity** reactions. In the type IV reaction, **primed lymphocytes** react with antigen at the site of its deposition resulting in the formation of a lymphocyte-macrophage **granuloma**[2]. Circulating antibody is not involved in this reaction. *See* **delayed hypersensitivity, cell-mediated immunity, tuberculin hypersensitivity.**

typhoid vaccination. *See* **TAB vaccine.**

typhus vaccination. **Inactivated vaccines** can be used for the prophylaxis of louse-borne typhus (Cox's, Craigie and Weigl vaccines), murine flea-borne typhus, and Rocky Mountain spotted fever. They are usually prepared in the yolk sacs or tissues of chick embryos or from the intestinal tract of infected lice (Weigl vaccine) and are inactivated by formaldehyde. In general the vaccines tend to diminish the severity of the disease rather than to afford solid immunity against infection. The avirulent strain 'E' of *Rickettsia prowazekii* is available as an **attenuated vaccine** against louse-borne typhus.

ulcerative colitis. Disease of man characterized by ulceration of the rectum and colon with diarrhoea and blood and mucus in the stools. Intermittent course, with considerable variation in the severity of symptoms and extent of colon involved. High incidence of carcinoma of the colon. Patients' **lymphocytes** show cytotoxicity for colon epithelial cells. **Cross-reacting antigens** between *E. coli* and colonic epithelium have been described and an **immune response** to such antigens has been postulated as an aetiological factor although this is still in dispute.

unitarian hypothesis. Hypothesis associated with the names of Dean (1917) and Zinnser (1921) that, following injection of antigen, a single antibody type with multiple functions (**agglutination, precipitation, complement fixation,** etc.) was produced rather than that each function was served by a different antibody. Hypothesis now rendered obsolete by studies of **immunoglobulin** structure and function.

univalent antibody. Antibody molecule with only a single **antigen binding site,** therefore reacting with only one molecule of antigen and unable to form antigen-antibody precipitates but capable of 'blocking' **precipitation** of antigen by divalent antibodies. At one time the term was used to describe non agglutinating antibodies such as those revealed by the **antiglobulin test,** but univalent antibodies are no longer believed to occur naturally. However, separated **Fab fragments** obtained by **papain hydrolysis** have only one combining site and behave like univalent antibodies. *See also* **incomplete antibody.**

universal donor. Human blood donor whose blood is compatible for transfusion into any recipient. Does not, in fact, exist. Term used misleadingly of group O donors whose blood lacks the A and B antigens and is therefore not likely to give rise to **ABO blood group system** incompatiblity. In practice, other grouping systems are also important, e.g. **Rhesus blood group system,** and group O blood must be **cross matched** before being transfused.

Unna-Pappenheim stain. *See* **methyl green pyronin stain.**

unprimed. Having never had contact with or responded to a given antigen (of animals, cells etc.).

unresponsiveness. *See* **immunological unresponsiveness.**

uropod. Elongated tail of a cell in locomotion. Term used *esp.* of **lymphocytes.** Moving small lymphocytes sometimes show a 'hand mirror' appearance in which the uropod resembles the handle of the mirror.

urticaria. *Syn.* hives. Skin rash characterized by localized, elevated erythematous, itchy weals due to local release of histamine and other vasoactive substances. Frequently associated with **immediate hypersensitivity (type I reaction)** on contact of the skin with antigens or more generalized as in **food allergy.**

V_H. The **variable region** of the **heavy chain** of immunoglobulin.

$V_\varkappa$. The **variable region** of the **kappa ($\varkappa$) chain** of immunoglobulin.

V_λ. The **variable region** of the **lambda (λ) chain** of immunoglobulin.

V_T region. **Variable region** of the **T lymphocyte antigen receptor**. (*See also* **IgT**).

vaccination. Production of **active immunity (protective immunity)** in man or animal by administration of **vaccines.** An extension,

vaccine

by Louis Pasteur, of the original use of the word by Edward Jenner to describe the use of **cowpox** to protect against smallpox (**variola**).

vaccine. A therapeutic material containing **antigens**[1,2] derived from one or more pathogenic organisms, which on administration to man or animal, will stimulate **active immunity** and protect against infection with these or related organisms. *See* **inactivated vaccine, live vaccine, attenuated vaccine, heterologous vaccine, lungworm vaccine**.

45/20 vaccine. *Vet. see* **brucella vaccines**[b].

vaccine virus immunization. *Vet.* Obsolete technique for the production of active immunity. A **vaccine** of low efficiency is given, followed a few weeks later by the virulent organism which acts as a **booster dose**.

vaccinia. Synonym for the virus (*Poxvirus officinale*) used in vaccination procedures to produce immunity to smallpox (**variola**) in man. Differs from the **cowpox** virus (*Poxvirus bovis*) and the smallpox virus (*Poxvirus variolae*) in minor antigens only, but was probably derived originally from cowpox virus. *See also* **smallpox vaccination**.

vaccinia gangrenosa. *See* **chronic progressive vaccinia**.

vaginal mucus agglutination test. A test used to detect antibodies in the vaginal mucus of cattle infected with *Trichomonas fetus, Campylobacter fetus* and *Brucella abortus*. The mucus is collected with a tampon and used directly in the same way as serum, or after filtration through an agar barrier, in **slide** or **tube agglutination tests** using the causative organism as antigen.

valency. In immunology; (a) the valency of an antibody equals the number of **antigenic determinants** with which one molecule of that antibody can combine. Most antibodies have two **antigen binding sites** and thus are divalent, i.e. those of the **IgG, IgD, IgE, immunoglobulin classes** but **IgM** has 10 combining sites and **IgA** can exist as monomer, dimer and higher polymers having valencies of two, four etc. In practice, antibodies often bind less antigen molecules than predicted by their valency due to **steric hindrance**. (b) The valency of an antigen may likewise be expressed as the number of antigen binding sites with which it can combine. Most large antigen molecules are multivalent.

van der Waals force. (London dispersion force). A very weak force of attraction which acts between all atoms, ions and molecules. It is inversely proportional to the seventh power of the distance between them and therefore is significant only when they are very close together. It may be important in the binding of **antigen** to **antibody**.

variable region. The **N terminal** half of the **light chains** (V_L) and the N terminal half of the **Fd fragment** (V_H) of the **heavy chains** of **immunoglobulin** molecules. The amino acid sequences in these regions are variable between molecules within a single **immunoglobulin class** and light chain type, cf. **constant region.** This variation determines the configuration of the **antigen binding site.** *See* illustration on p.108.

variable region group. The **variable regions** of **heavy** and **light chains** contain **framework regions,** interspersed by **hypervariable regions,** which show similarities in amino acid sequence with other variable regions. These related sequences are placed within a group. The number of groups is believed to be related (but not equal) to the number of variable region genes. Mouse $V_\varkappa$ regions have at least 50–100 groups and subgroups (*see* **variable region subgroups**).

variable region subgroup. (1). Term used synonymously with **variable region group** q.v. to describe human immunoglobulin **variable regions.** (2). Sufficient mouse $V_\varkappa$ variable region sequences have been determined to divide some of the variable region groups into subgroups, the members of which are more closely related in amino acid sequence than other members of the same group.

variola. Smallpox, *Variola major*. A disease caused by *Poxvirus variolae*. A moderately but not highly infectious disease characterized by disfiguring vesicular and later pustular skin eruptions, viraemia and profound toxaemia. Now eliminated worldwide following WHO campaign. There was a 32 per cent mortality in the unvaccinated. *Variola minor* (alastrim) is a milder variant of smallpox caused by a strain of *Poxvirus variolae* which differs from that causing *Variola major* in being unable to form pocks on the chorioallantoic membrane of the chick embryo at 38.3°C. *See also* **smallpox vaccination, cowpox.**

vascular permeability factors. Substances which increase the permeability of the walls of small vessels and thus enhance the passage of protein, cells, etc. from blood into the extra-vascular fluid. Include molecules such as **histamine, serotonin, kinins** and **leukotrienes.**

vasoactive amines. Substances containing amino groups, such as **histamine** and **serotonin,** which cause peripheral vasodilation and increase the permeability of small vessels.

VDRL test. A rapid screening test for syphilis in which the **flocculation** of a cardiolipin–cholesterol–lecithin antigen is observed if the sera being tested contain antibody.

veiled cell. A cell characterized by large veil-like processes; found in afferent lymph especially after priming with antigen. Veiled cells possess **accessory cell** function.

V-gene. Gene coding for the **variable region** of **immunoglobulin heavy** or **light chain.** It is separated from the **C-gene** in germ line DNA but in **lymphocyte** and **plasma cell** DNA one V-gene has been translocated to a position close to the 5′ end of the C-gene but still separated from it by an **intron.** *See* figure on p.117.

Vi antigen. Surface somatic **antigen**[1] present in freshly isolated strains of *Salmonella typhi* and *S. paratyphi C*. Masks **O antigen**[1] and renders organism relatively non-agglutinable by antibody against O antigen. Associated with virulence possibly because it blocks access of antibody.

virus neutralization tests. Tests used to measure antibody response to a virus or, *vice versa,* to identify the virus. Depends on the fact that specific antibody neutralizes the infectivity of viruses. They may be carried out *in vivo* in susceptible animals or chick embryos or, more usually, in tissue cultures. *See* **neutralization test, virus neutralizing capacity**.

virus neutralizing capacity. The ability of a serum to inhibit the infectivity of a virus. This may or may not be related to the antibodies in it that can be measured by, e.g. the **complement fixation test.** Neutralizing antibody is contained in **IgM, IgG** and **IgA**.

vitamin A. In immunology, has been found to act as an **adjuvant** in increasing the antibody responses of mice to soluble protein antigens. It has a similar effect whether administered orally or **parenterally**.

V-region. *See* **variable region**.

V$_H$ region. The **variable region** of the **heavy chain** of **immunoglobulins**.

V$_L$ region. The **variable region** of the **light chain** of **immunoglobulins**.

Vollmer test. *(Obs).* A **tuberculin test** of the **patch test** type, using tuberculin impregnated gauze.

Waaler–Rose test. *See* **Rose–Waaler test.** Waaler described the test before Rose but Rose–Waaler is general usage.

Waldenström's macroglobulinaemia. Disease described by Waldenström (1944) occuring mainly in elderly males, characterized by **paraproteinaemia** of **IgM** type, **lymphoid tissue** enlargement, splenomegaly, haemorrhagic tendency and depression. Lymphoid tissue infiltrated with large basophilic mononuclear cells with **PAS** positive material in cytoplasm. High serum IgM level and positive **Sia test.** The Waldenström IgM is **monoclonal** but occasionally has antibody activity, e.g. as **rheumatoid factor.** Course of disease more benign than that of **myelomatosis.**

warm antibody. Antibody that can be detected at a higher dilution at 37°C than at 20°C or at 4°C. Used especially in reference to antibodies against erythrocytes and in classification of autoimmune **haemolytic anaemias. Cf. cold agglutinin.**

Wassermann reaction. Complement fixation test used in the diagnosis of syphilis. **Cardiolipin** derived from ox heart is used as antigen because the sera of patients with syphilis regularly contain antibody which reacts with this substance. However, false positive results may be obtained (*see* **biological false positive reaction**) and confirmatory tests, e.g. the **Reiter complement fixation test,** the **FTA–ABS test** and, more rarely, the **Treponema pallidum immobilization test** may have to be carried out. In the last two, the antigen is *T. pallidum* itself and antibody to the organism is detected rather than antibody to cardiolipin.

wasting disease. Fatal disease developed by neonatally **thymecto- mized** animals and characterized by loss of weight, hunched appearance, ruffled fur and diarrhoea. Germ-free neonatally thymectomized mice do not develop wasting disease, thus suggesting that the impairment of **cell-mediated immunity** in thymectomized **conventional animals** leads to some form of fatal infection.

water–in–oil emulsion adjuvant.. An **adjuvant** in which the antigen, dissolved or suspended in water, is enclosed as tiny droplets within a continuous phase of mineral oil. The antigen solution constitutes the disperse phase. The phases are stabilized, so that they do not readily separate out, by the presence of an emulsifier such as **Arlacel A®** in the oil. *See* **incomplete Freund's adjuvant** and **complete Freund's adjuvant.**

water–in–oil–in–water emulsion adjuvant. (multiple or double emulsion adjuvant). A **water–in–oil emulsion adjuvant** which has been redispersed in a continuous saline phase with the aid of an emulsifier such as **Tween 80®**, so as to form a free-flowing liquid. Thus the continuous phase is saline, the primary disperse phase oil, and the secondary disperse phase, antigen solution.

wax D. An **adjuvant**-active extract of mycobacteria, defined as the fraction soluble in chloroform and insoluble in boiling acetone. It is a mixture of **glycolipid** and **peptidoglycolipid** of high molecular weight (up to 70 000). The peptidoglycolipid derived from human strains of *Mycobacterium tuberculosis* (but not the wax fractions of bovine strains, nor from *M. phlei*, *M. avium* or *M. smegmatis*), when injected with antigen, shows most of the adjuvant properties of whole mycobacteria; thus it produces an enhanced **antibody** response, **delayed hypersensitivity, autoimmune diseases, granuloma,** and a qualitative alteration of the type of antibody produced.

weal and flare response. Local response of skin to injury. Following minor, non-penetrating injury of any type or degree, erythema limited to the injured site appears immediately. This is followed in a minute or two by formation of a weal or oedema in the line of injury and a flare of erythema spreading out round the site. This was described by Thomas Lewis in 1927 as the 'triple response'. It is due to release of **histamine** and the lesion of **immediate hypersensitivity (type I reaction)** following histamine release is exactly as described by Lewis.

Weil–Felix reaction. **Agglutination** test used in diagnosis of rickettsial infections (typhus, etc.). Depends on carbohydrate **cross-reacting antigen** shared by *Rickettsiae* with certain strains of *Proteus*. The agglutination pattern of serum from patients with rickettsial disease against O-agglutinable strains of *Proteus* OX19, OX2 and OXK is diagnostic of the various rickettsial diseases.

western blotting. A technique for the analysis and identification of protein **antigens.** The proteins are separated by **polyacrylamide gel electrophoresis** and then transferred electrophoretically to a nitrocellulose membrane or chemically treated paper to which the proteins bind in a pattern identical to that originally in the gel (the 'blot'). Bands of antigen bound to the nitrocellulose or paper are detected by overlaying with **antibody** followed by anti-immuno-globulin or **protein A** labelled with a radioisotope, fluorescent dye or enzyme (e.g. horseradish peroxidase). The advantages of this technique are that the antigens are exposed on the surface of the membrane and are immobilised, whereas direct overlay of the gel with antibody results in lower sensitivity, due to slow penetration of the gel by antibody, and loss of resolution due to diffusion of the antigen.

wheat germ agglutinin. A lectin q.v.

white cells. The nucleated cells of the blood (i.e. **granulocytes, lymphocytes** and **monocytes**) so-called because they form a white layer over the erythrocytes when sedimented.

white graft reaction. Very rapid (faster than **second set rejection**) rejection of a skin graft in an animal that is highly **immune**[2] to the antigens of the graft. Probably brought about by an antigen-antibody reaction in the graft bed so that the normal physiological 'take' of the graft, before **homograft rejection** occurs, is inhibited.

white pulp. *See* **spleen**.

whooping cough vaccine. *See* **pertussis vaccine**.

Widal reaction (Widal test). Bacterial **agglutination** test used in the diagnosis of enteric fevers. The patient's serum is titrated by **doubling dilutions** against each of the organisms likely to cause enteric fever, i.e. *Salmonella typhi, S. paratyphi B* in Britain, and *S. paratyphi A* and *C* in areas where enteric fever is caused by these organisms. The organisms used must be motile, 'smooth', and in the specific phase. Formalinized and alcoholized suspensions are used respectively for testing H and O agglutinins. The Widal test is not likely to be positive before the 10th day of the disease. False positive reactions may occur especially in persons who have received **TAB vaccine.** For these reasons a rising **titre** on repeated testing is more significant than the result of a single test. Agglutination tests to diagnose brucellosis are often carried out at the same time as the Widal test. Historically, Widal introduced the test to identify *S.paratyphi B* infection.

Wiskott–Aldrich syndrome. Sex-linked recessive disease of infants characterized by haemorrhagic diathesis, **eczema** and recurrent infections. **Delayed hypersensitivity** reactions are absent and there is a defective antibody response to polysaccharide antigens with low serum **IgM** levels. This combined defect of **cell-mediated** and **humoral immunity** probably involves failure to recognize or process antigens. Patients die early of infection or bleeding due to increased phagocytic destruction of **platelets.** Malignant lymphoma may occur.

WO. *See* **water–in–oil emulsion adjuvant**.

WOW. *See* **water–in–oil–in–water emulsion adjuvant**.

WR. *See* **Wassermann reaction**.

X-linked lymphoproliferative syndrome. A form of **infectious mononucleosis** found in patients with X-linked **immunodeficiency.** The disease is associated with polyclonal **B lymphocyte** proliferation, **EBNA** positive lymphoid cells and the presence of **plasmablasts** in the blood. The infectious mononucleosis may progress to malignant lymphoma but in either case is usually fatal. It has been proposed that the disease is due to immune deficiency to Epstein–Barr virus.

xenogeneic (xenogenic. *syn.* heterogeneic). *Preferred term* for grafted tissue that has been derived from a species different from the recipient.*See also* **transplantation terminology**.

xenograft (*syn.* heterograft). *Preferred term* for a graft from a donor of dissimilar species.

xenotype. Structural or antigenic difference between molecules. e.g. **immunoglobulins,** cell membrane antigens, etc. derived from different species.

yellow fever vaccine. A freeze-dried **attenuated vaccine** prepared from live attenuated yellow fever virus of strain 17D grown in chick embryos. Not used in United Kingdom except for persons travelling to or through areas where yellow fever is endemic, for whom vaccination is obligatory. A single dose is given, immunity lasts for at least 10 years.

zinc sulphate turbidity test. (*Obs.*) A rapid test used to make a rough measurement of the **gamma globulin** content of serum. The degree of turbidity produced on the addition of zinc sulphate (which precipitates serum **globulins,** especially **IgG**) is measured. Used to detect **hypergammaglobulinaemia** in man, and (*vet.*) to ascertain the extent to which very young calves have absorbed antibodies from **colostrum**.

zooprophylaxis. The induction in man of immunity to a parasite by exposing him to related parasites of lower animals, e.g. some degree of resistance to human schistosomiasis is produced by continual exposure to cercariae (the infective stage) of schistosomes of animals, such cercariae only producing abortive infections. Classic example is prevention of smallpox in man by vaccination with cowpox *see* **Jennerian vaccination**.

zymosan. Cell wall fraction of yeasts (*Saccharomyces cerevisiae*) which activates the **alternative complement pathway**, and thus binds **C3b.** Frequently used for study of opsonic phagocytosis.

The editors would be very grateful if readers finding errors or omissions would fill in this page and send it to:

Professor P. C. Wilkinson,
Dept. of Bacteriology and Immunology,
Western Infirmary,
Glasgow, G11 6NT
Scotland.

1.   I have looked for definitions of the following words in the *Dictionary of Immunology*, but they have been omitted:

....

....

....

....

....

....

....

....

I suggest that they might be included in any future edition. Possible definitions are given below/attached.*

2.   The definition of...
is incorrect/incomplete* and I suggest that it be amended as follows:

....

....

....

....

....

(3rd Edition)

....
....
....
....
....
....
....
....
....
....
....
....
....
....
....
....
....
....
.... (continued on attachment*).

Name...

Address...

    ....

    ....

    ....

    ....

*delete as necessary.   Date......................